Methods
of Signal
and System
Analysis

Holt, Rinehart and Winston Series
in Electrical Engineering, Electronics, and Systems

CONSULTING EDITORS

Michael Athans, *Massachusetts Institute of Technology*
Benjamin Leon, *Purdue University*
Robert Pritchard, *Stanford University*

Methods
of
Signal
and
System
Analysis

GEORGE R. COOPER

CLARE D. McGILLEM

School of Electrical Engineering
Purdue University

HOLT, RINEHART AND WINSTON, INC.
New York Chicago San Francisco Atlanta
Dallas Montreal Toronto London

Preface

The purpose of this book is to introduce the important concepts in the analysis of signals and linear systems from a unified viewpoint and at a level that makes them accessible to junior and senior undergraduates in electrical engineering. The treatment is intended to be heuristic rather than rigorous, but at the same time it is not completely devoid of the mathematical subtleties that usually appear only in more advanced discussions. In fact, considerable attention has been devoted to introducing concepts in a manner that clearly indicates that a more advanced viewpoint is possible rather than leaving the impression that the existing discussion is the final word. It is the authors' firm conviction that the educational process is best served by repeated exposures to difficult subject matter; a dogmatic treatment, which leaves the student feeling the he "understands it all," is less useful in the long run than one that leaves the door open to further learning even at the expense of some initial confusion. Although the beginning student receives a great deal of initial satisfaction from the feeling of "understanding it all," this kind of illusion must at some time be shattered if he is to reach full technical maturity.

In line with the foregoing philosophy, this book contains numerous warnings and restrictions, which serve to call attention to those aspects of the discussion that must be explored in greater depth at some future time. The student who does not comprehend the significance of these items should not despair; they are merely guideposts to future study and not items requiring current mastery.

It should also be pointed out (to add a more positive note) that considerable attention has been devoted to explaining the *reasons* certain topics are considered and the role these topics play in professional engineering. It is hoped that these somewhat philosophical comments will serve not only to motivate the student, but also to give him a clearer perspective as to how and where these techniques may be useful in engineering analysis. It is not enough that a student have powerful analytic techniques at his disposal; he must also know when to use them and when not to. These are matters of engineering judgment that no textbook or classroom can teach, but the student must be made aware of their existence.

The mathematical background assumed for this book is that of the typical undergraduate engineer—calculus, linear differential equations, and a cursory knowledge of matrix manipulation. The assumed engineering background includes elementary circuits and electronics. Some knowledge of elementary probability would be helpful, but is not essential.

A brief discussion of some of the most significant features of this book will help set the stage for a discussion of the various ways in which it can be used. One characteristic feature of the entire book is the emphasis on *system* analysis rather than *circuit* analysis. Although circuits are often used as examples of systems, the emphasis is on the input-output relations and not on the setting up of loop and node equations. Chapter 2, in particular, discusses the mathematical representation of systems from this viewpoint and clearly emphasizes the distinction between a physical system and its mathematical model.

The concepts of *signal* analysis are elaborated on in Chapter 3. Although it is not possible to discuss system analysis without considering the mathematical representation of the signals, the treatment here goes beyond that and introduces the concept that there is a body of signal theory that is important in its own right. This concept leads to the introduction of generalized orthogonal representation at a much earlier point in the student's career than is customary. However, the treatment is simple and attempts to utilize the student's physical intuition to the greatest possible extent.

Another significant departure from custom is the introduction of convolution in Chapter 4 *before* any transform techniques have been discussed. There are several reasons for this approach. In the first place, from the standpoint of the student it is the logical point at which to consider convolution, since it is a natural combination of the concepts of signals and systems that have just been covered. The fact that there may be a simpler mathematical derivation by transform methods is meaningless to him at this point. In the second place, the approach forces the student to consider convolution on a physical basis rather than viewing it as a manipulative trick that has little physical significance. This tends to build the student's understanding of convolution and his subsequent ability to use it. Finally, the student is not yet "brainwashed" by the manipulative ease of transform methods and, hence, does not build a psychological barrier against the more tedious manipulation of convolution. Hence, he is prepared to accept it as a step forward rather than a step backward.

The discussion of Fourier transforms in Chapter 5 is distinctive because it is a much more extensive treatment than is usually found in systems books. The reason for this is the concurrent emphasis on signals, and the recognition that present-day signal theory relies more heavily on Fourier transform methods than on Laplace transform methods. As a consequence of this greater detail, it becomes possible to introduce the frequency-domain concepts of modulation and sampling in a simple and plausible fashion.

Laplace transform methods are still important in system analysis, of course, and these are introduced in Chapters 6 and 7. Perhaps the most distinctive aspect of this treatment is the discussion of the two-sided Laplace transform at this elementary level.

The state-space approach to system analysis is discussed in Chapter 8. In contrast to the usual abstract treatments of this subject, the approach is heuristic and attempts to relate the basic concepts to easily visualized block diagrams. Although the level of discourse is somewhat higher in this chapter than it is in the rest of the book, it represents the first time that state variables have been presented at all for juniors. Furthermore, the remainder of the book may be handled without reference to Chapter 8, so this material may be omitted if desired.

The discussion of random signals starts in Chapter 9 with a brief introduction to probability and random processes. Although the treatment of probability may appear skimpy, it is adequate for the work that follows. The discussion of random processes emphasizes the ensemble concept and thus paves the way for a more sophisticated study of the topic at a later date. The introduction to random processes continues in Chapters 10 and 11 with discussions of correlation and spectral density. These topics are presented in a very concise fashion and at an elementary level, but no compromise is made with the philosophy that the presentation should open doors to more advanced study rather than oversimplify for the sake of immediate expediency. Thus, both concepts are introduced from the standpoint of ensemble averages rather than the more usual time average, which is typical in elementary discussions. This feature is unique in an undergraduate text and, the authors feel, represents a major contribution.

Chapter 12 utilizes all the previous discussions to analyze linear systems with random inputs. In one sense, this is the culmination of all that has gone before and brings the student to a high level of proficiency (relatively speaking) in the analysis of linear systems and signals in all circumstances. In another sense it is anticlimactic in that it all seems so straightforward and easy now that the mystery of random processes has been stripped away. This is one illusion that we prefer to allow the student to retain.

The material in this text has been used, with the exception of Chapter 8, in a one-semester, four-credit hour course, offered in the first semester of the junior year. The pace is brisk and the students have found it challenging but interesting. There are, of course, many other ways in which the text material could be utilized. For example, a more relaxed pace could be obtained by spreading all of the material, including Chapter 8, over two semesters of three credit hours each. Another possibility is to use only the material through Chapter 8 in a one-semester, three-hour course, and omit the material on random signals altogether or use it in the introductory part of a subsequent communication theory course. A final suggestion would be a one-semester, three-hour course that omits those parts of Chapter 5 dealing with sampling and modulation, those parts of Chapters 6 and 7 dealing with the two-sided Laplace transform, all of Chapter 8, the parts of Chapters 10, 11, and 12 dealing with state variables and the part of Chapter 11 dealing with the ensemble approach to spectral density. The arrangement of material is such that this can be done readily and result in a compact course that preserves the essential flavor of the approach but omits the frills.

It is essential that the authors acknowledge the very substantial aid and encouragement that they have received from their colleagues and students. A complete list is too lengthy to include here, but it is appropriate to mention the valuable suggestions and comments that have been received from Professors D. A. Landgrebe and J. A. McFadden and Mr. James U. Kincaid, all of Purdue University.

The careful and perceptive reading of the final manuscript by Professor James L. Massey of Notre Dame University is also gratefully acknowledged. A special note of thanks is due to Mr. Dennis Murray of Purdue University, for his diligent efforts in working the problems and proofreading the manuscript. Last, but not least, we acknowledge our debt to the hundreds of students who suffered with us through the embryonic stages of the project by reading, without complaint, countless pages of hastily written and barely legible class notes.

West Lafayette, Indiana   GEORGE R. COOPER

March 1967   CLARE D. MCGILLEM

Contents

1-1 Introduction

In this age of technology it is difficult to pass a single day without seeing or hearing the words "signals" and "systems." The news media and popular press have adopted these terms, along with many others, and use them so glibly that almost everyone has some notion of what they mean. However, very few people, even among engineers, could give a concise, accurate definition of these words. Any definition proposed will certainly be considered inadequate by some group of people, and there are even those who contend that the terms are undefinable.

This confusion is both natural and not very serious. It is natural because every branch of engineering, and every field within that branch, has its own set of concepts concerning the nature of signals and systems, and these may be conflicting concepts because of differing objectives. For example, radio waves from space are signals for the radio astronomer but only noise for the engineer concerned with space communication. For the electrical engineer, a system may be something as complicated as a large digital computer or a worldwide communications network, while for the metallurgical engineer it may be as simple as a block of metal. (It may be worth noting that from the standpoint of practical engineering analysis, the simple block of metal is far more complicated than the largest computer or communication network.)

The lack of a precise definition is not serious so long as the engineer can achieve his objective with the phenomena and devices that he calls signals and systems, and can describe his results to others. In order to do this, he must be able to define precisely the *particular* signal and system that he is dealing with. The most effective way to express these specific definitions is in terms of "mathematical models," since the language of mathematics is necessarily precise and unique.

One of the primary objectives of this volume is to examine in depth some of the ways in which signals and systems can be described mathematically. Such a description is a necessary first step in carrying out any system analysis or system design. However, in a larger sense, the average engineer finds a strictly mathematical definition unsatisfactory and lacking in physical reality. For this reason, it seems desirable to offer some more general definitions and to illustrate these by means of examples. This, at least, serves the purpose of indicating to the reader the nature of the authors' concepts concerning these terms.

1-2   Systems—What They Are and What They Do

A very general definition of a system is that it consists of a group of objects that can interact with one another and are assembled in a manner intended to achieve a desired objective. Such a definition does not convey much understanding until the objects and their interconnections are described more fully. This is best done by means of specific examples.

Consider an electric power system first. The desired objective of such a system is to deliver electrical energy to the consumer in the form and amount that he requires and to do this with greatest possible efficiency. The objects that compose the system include the original energy source (such as coal, oil, or water power); the prime mover, which converts this energy to mechanical form; the generator, which converts it to electrical form; the control devices, which regulate frequency and voltage; transformers; transmission lines; switches; circuit breakers and other protective devices; secondary distribution circuits; indicating and recording instruments; and, finally, the devices used by the consumer. All of these objects must be interconnected properly in order to accomplish the desired objective. The resulting system is so complex that a complete analysis of the overall system, including all of its components, is not feasible. It becomes necessary, therefore, to subdivide the complete system into smaller parts for which reasonable mathematical models can be obtained.

This illustrates the important fact that *most* system analysis really deals with only a portion of a more complex system, and that the basic decision as to how much to include in a given analysis problem calls for much engineering experience and judgment.

As a second example, consider a radio communication system. The objects that compose this system include a message source (such as a person, a machine, or a physical quantity); a transducer, which converts the message into electrical energy; a source of radio-frequency energy; a modulator, which alters the radio-frequency energy in accordance with the message; a transmitting antenna; a transmission medium; a receiving antenna; a receiver with a demodulator to extract the message information; and a transducer to convert the electrical message into a form usable at the ultimate destination. Again, the system is very complex and may take many different forms.

Countless other examples of systems could be listed, such as radar systems, ballistic missile systems, space probes, navigation systems, control systems for all types of machines and processes, and computers. It is not at all necessary that systems be electrical in nature. For example, chemical processing systems, refrigeration systems, hydraulic control systems, pipeline distribution systems, and sewerage systems do not involve electrical quantities in any major way.

Systems may also include human beings as an essential part. For example, aircraft control systems, traffic control systems, automobile power steering, manual tracking systems, remote manipulators, and powered prosthetic devices all include one or more human beings as an essential part of the system.

It is clear from this discussion that there are a great many different types of systems in use today. The engineer is responsible for design, analysis, and production of these systems. The mathematical tools for system analysis that will be discussed in this volume are applicable to a wide range of systems problems and are not limited to electrical systems.

1-3 Signals

One may inquire as to why a discussion of signals is necessary in considering methods of system analysis. One answer, of course, is that without the signal to direct the system, it becomes a useless collection of hardware. It is the signal that forces the system to take the action necessary for accomplishing the desired objective. In addition, the response of the system to certain prescribed signals provides a very convenient way of describing the system mathematically and such a description can be used in the process of general system analysis.

The input to any system is a "force" to which the system can respond.

In an electrical system this "force" will usually be either a voltage or current, whereas in a mechanical system it may be a mechanical force or a velocity. The output signal is the response of the system to the input signal. It may be of the same form as the input signal or it may have some entirely different form. For example, the input signal may be a voltage and the output signal a velocity (as in a motor), or the input may be a mechanical force and the output an angular displacement (as in an aircraft flight control system).

In complicated systems there will usually be more than one input signal and/or output signal. There is no necessity for the number of input and output signals to be the same. For example, in a power system there may be three or four input signals (generating stations) and several thousand output signals (consumers).

A signal is almost always a function of time. It may be a function that is simple and completely known, such as a sinusoid or exponential, or it may be a very complicated and largely unknown function of time, such as a speech wave or random noise. In either case, it is necessary to be able to represent the signal mathematically.

There are a great many different ways in which signals arise in system studies. In some cases, specific waveforms are generated for special purposes — for example, in power systems, where the basic signal is a sinusoid or in cases where signals are generated for purposes of testing the response of a system. In such cases, simple signals such as step changes in the input, short pulses, or sinusoids are convenient because of the ease with which theoretical responses can be computed for comparison with experimentally observed responses. There are also situations in which specific signal waveforms are used in normal system operation. These occur, for example, in radar systems and in digital computers, both of which utilize short pulses for normal operation.

In many other types of systems, the signals are related to some physical quantity, and the way they vary with time cannot be controlled by the system designer. This is true, for example, in most types of control systems and communication systems.

1-4 System Analysis and System Design

The major problem of system analysis is that of finding the output signal or response when the system and the input signal are specified. There are many reasons why system analysis is an important aspect of system studies:

    1. It is almost always easier and cheaper to determine the response of a system to a specified input by analysis rather than by experiment.

    2. Many system studies are aimed at determining the feasibility of a particular system that is not actually in existence. In this case, analysis is the only possibility.

3. In some cases, the analysis may assume conditions that would be impossible or dangerous to create on an experimental basis. Examples might be such things as faults in power systems, unstable aircraft flight-control systems, a nuclear reactor operating near critical, or an overloaded telephone system.

4. System analysis is often an important part of system design.

The major problem of system design is that of determining the characteristics that will yield a desired response to any specified input. One part of this problem is that of determining the mathematical model for the system. Explicit techniques may not be available, and thus the determination can often be accomplished only by extending the results of analysis. Another part of the design problem is that of determining the specific hardware that will best approximate the mathematical model. This part calls for the use of good engineering judgment and careful attention to a multitude of conflicting requirements.

It is in the area of system design that the modern engineer finds some of his greatest challenges. In order to be successful in this area, he must be able to design complex systems to solve complex problems. This requirement calls for creativity, which enables him to conceive of potential methods and devices. It also calls for engineering judgment, which enables him to evaluate the effectiveness of proposed methods and to develop reasonable mathematical models. Finally, the engineer must be able to carry out experiments to test the methods, the models, and the devices which he conceives. The starting point on this long path to professional engineering is system analysis, and a thorough understanding of the methods and mathematical techniques of analysis is indispensable to the future engineer.

■ REFERENCE

1. Wilson, Warren E., *Concepts of Engineering System Design.* New York: McGraw-Hill Book Company, Inc., 1965.

   This elementary, but very interesting, book attempts to summarize the important aspects of system design and put them in their proper perspective.

■ PROBLEMS

1-1 Look up and write down a dictionary definition of the word "system." Choose the form that seems most appropriate for engineering systems (not necessarily electrical).

1-2   Make as complete a list as you can of the components that make up a telephone system.

1-3   Look up and write down a dictionary definition of the word "signal." Choose the form that seems most appropriate for electrical signals.

1-4   It was pointed out in this chapter that system analysis was often an important part of system design. In order to illustrate this point in a very simple way, consider the fire alarm system shown.

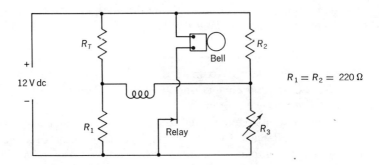

This is essentially a bridge circuit, in which three resistors (R_1, R_2, and R_3) are invariant with temperature and one resistor (R_T) has a positive temperature coefficient of 0.05 ohm per ohm per degree F. The unbalanced current passes through the coil of a relay, which has a resistance of 100 ohms, a pull-in current of 10 mA, and a release current of 8 mA. The temperature-sensitive resistor has a resistance of 220 ohms at a temperature of 60°F.

a.   Write a general expression for the current in the relay coil as a function of R_3 and R_T. This is the *preliminary analysis* part of the problem.

b.   It is desired to make R_3 adjustable so that the alarm will ring at any preset temperature between 150°F and 250°F. Find the range of resistance values over which R_3 must be adjustable in order to accomplish this. This is a *design* calculation based on the previous analysis.

c.   Assume that R_3 is set so that the alarm rings at 200°F and that the temperature has exceeded this value. To what value must the temperature drop in order for the alarm to shut off? This computation represents an analysis of performance after the design has been completed.

d.   List some other factors that would need to be considered in designing a practical version of this fire alarm.

2

System Representation and Analysis

2-1 Introduction

The purpose of this chapter is to explain some terminology and to present a preview of the material on systems and system analysis which will be treated subsequently in greater depth. In an effort to avoid the vagueness that may accompany too much generality, the discussion will be phrased in terms of electrical systems in which the input and output signals are considered to be voltages. The same terminology and methods will apply, of course, to other types of systems, and generalization of this sort will be considered later.

2-2 System Representation

An actual physical system consists of a collection of devices, such as filters, amplifiers, motors, antennas, and many others. In order to determine the response of any system to a prescribed input signal, by means of analysis rather than experiment, it is necessary to be able to represent the system mathematically. Such a representation, which becomes the *mathematical model* for the system, forms the starting point for the problem of system analysis.

The mathematical model is used so commonly to represent the system that one frequently tends to regard the model as the actual system and ignore the limitations imposed by physical considerations. Such a practice can be both dangerous and costly when complex systems are involved, and thus the competent engineer never loses sight of physical reality.

Nevertheless, in an introductory discussion of system analysis, it is neither possible nor desirable to discuss the physical considerations in detail and at the same time do justice to the mathematical techniques which are essential for analysis. To attempt to do so would place the student in the position of living in two unfamiliar worlds at the same time and trying to learn the rules of both. Hence, it seems better to concentrate first on the mathematical techniques and not dwell at length on the practical limitations. The student should be aware of their existence, however, and realize that the real world is not as simple and unambiguous as his mathematical model.

Some of the limitations of mathematical models can be discussed in general terms. In the first place, the mathematical model is *always* an approximation. Hopefully, it will be a good approximation for the range of frequencies and signal amplitudes to be encountered, but even if it is not, an analysis based on a poor approximation may be preferable to no analysis at all. The important point is for the engineer to have some understanding of the degree of confidence that can be placed in the results of his analysis, and to appreciate the problems that would arise from trying to obtain a more accurate model.

In the second place, the mathematical model always represents a compromise between the conflicting requirements of accuracy and mathematical simplicity. The nature of the physical problem dictates how this compromise should be made. As a simple illustration of this, consider a single 50 ohm resistor consisting of a thin film of metal deposited on a ceramic tube and covered with another ceramic material. At frequencies up to several megahertz and at low voltages, the mathematical model indicated in Fig. 2-1(a) is quite adequate and is as accurate as any measurements that might be made. This model is not adequate if the resistor is to be used with nanosecond pulses, and the model in Fig. 2-1(b) might be preferable. At still higher frequencies, in the microwave region, no lumped parameter model is really adequate, and therefore a distributed-parameter model, as in Fig. 2-1(c), would be necessary. The important point here is that all of these models represent the *same* physical device, but their complexity is vastly different because of the different physical situations in which they are used.

In almost all of the following discussions of system analysis, the math-

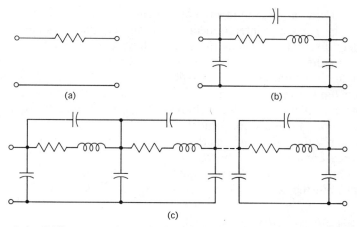

Figure 2-1 Different mathematical models for the same physical device. **(a)** Low-frequency model. **(b)** Nanosecond-pulse model. **(c)** Microwave-frequency model.

ematical model will be specified, either explicitly or by implication, and attention will be concentrated on the mathematical techniques that enable the analysis to proceed. It should be emphasized, however, that the problem of obtaining the mathematical model for a given physical system is frequently a much more difficult one — and, from an engineering standpoint, a more important one. The engineering judgment required to obtain a suitable model is the essential ingredient that distinguishes engineering analysis from applied mathematics.

2-3 The Mathematical Model

In order to avoid making this discussion too abstract, attention will be limited to systems having only one input signal and one output signal. The concepts and methods employed in this simple case can be extended easily to include more general systems with many inputs and many outputs, but this will not be done until the basic ideas are more firmly established.

Consider the diagram shown in Fig. 2-2. The system is represented by a simple block and the input signal, $x(t)$, by an arrow directed into it. The system response, or output signal $y(t)$, is another arrow directed out of the system. This *block diagram* representation of a system forms

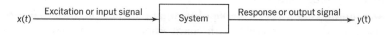

$x(t)$ —— Excitation or input signal —→ | System | —— Response or output signal —→ $y(t)$

Figure 2-2 A system and its signals.

the basis for a very common and convenient method of graphically representing the parts and interconnections of any complex system. A more complete discussion of block diagrams will be presented later.

The mathematical model for a system such as is shown in Fig. 2-2 is simply an equation, or set of equations, that specifies the mathematical relationship between $x(t)$ and $y(t)$. There are many ways in which such a relationship might be written. Although these ways must be equivalent, they are not all equally convenient.

Probably the most basic mathematical model is the differential equation representation of the system. It is beyond the scope of this discussion to prove that the following equation is applicable to almost all linear systems, but the student can verify it easily in any specific case.

$$a_n(t) \frac{d^n y(t)}{dt^n} + a_{n-1}(t) \frac{d^{n-1} y(t)}{dt^{n-1}} + \cdots + a_1(t) \frac{dy(t)}{dt} + a_0(t) y(t)$$

$$(2\text{-}1)$$

$$= b_m(t) \frac{d^m x(t)}{dt^m} + b_{m-1}(t) \frac{d^{m-1} x(t)}{dt^{m-1}} + \cdots + b_1(t) \frac{dx(t)}{dt} + b_0(t) x(t)$$

The specific form of this equation in any particular case can be used as a basis for classifying systems into various categories. This will be done in the next section.

Although (2-1) does provide a mathematical relationship between the input and output of a given system, the relationship is not unique unless one also specifies the time interval in which the response exists. For example, suppose that the input to the system, $x(t)$, is zero for all time prior to some time, t_0. It is possible to find solutions to (2-1) that are *not* zero before t_0, but such solutions cannot correspond to the response of any physical system. This is because no actual system can anticipate an excitation and begin to respond before this excitation is applied. Thus, when (2-1) is used as the mathematical model for any physical system, the further condition is imposed that if the excitation $x(t) = 0$ for all $t < t_0$, then the system response to this $x(t)$ also becomes $y(t) = 0$ for all $t < t_0$. With this assumption the mathematical model ordinarily becomes unique in the sense that any input signal results in a unique output signal.

The mathematical model specified by (2-1) expresses the behavior of the system in terms of a single nth-order differential equation. An alternative method of expressing the same information is in terms of a set of first-order differential equations. This is known as the *normal form* of the system equations. This method has an advantage of notational simplicity (since matrix notation can be employed to express the entire set of equations in a very compact form) and also is the form that is most easily extended to systems with many inputs and outputs. However,

(2-1) will be adequate for the present purpose of introducing basic system concepts so that a discussion of the normal form will be postponed until later.

2-4 Classification of Systems

There are a large number of terms which are used to classify systems, and it is essential to understand these terms before embarking on a general discussion of systems. Many of these are related to the form of the system equation (2-1) and will be introduced in that fashion.

Order of the system. The differential equation (2-1) is of nth order since this is the highest-order derivative of the *response* to appear. The corresponding system is said to be of nth order also.

Causal system, noncausal system. A *causal* (or *physical*, or *nonanticipatory*) system is one whose response does not depend upon future values of the input. As noted previously, this condition is *assumed* to apply to the system equation. A *noncausal* (or *nonphysical*, or *anticipatory*) system is one for which this condition is not assumed. Noncausal systems do not exist in the real world but can be approximated by the use of time delay.

Linear system, nonlinear system. The system equation (2-1) represents a *linear* system, since all derivatives of the excitation and response are raised to the first power only and there are no products of derivatives. One of the most important consequences of linearity is that superposition applies. In fact, this may be used as a definition of linearity. Specifically, if

$$y_1(t) = \text{system response to } x_1(t)$$
$$y_2(t) = \text{system response to } x_2(t)$$

and

$$ay_1(t) + by_2(t) = \text{system response to } ax_1(t) + bx_2(t)$$

for all a, b, $x_1(t)$, and $x_2(t)$, then the system is linear. If this is not true, then the system is not linear.

In the case of nonlinear systems, it is not possible to write a general differential equation of finite order that can be used as the mathematical model for all systems, because there are so many different ways in which nonlinearities can arise and they cannot all be described mathematically in the same form. It is also important to remember that superstition does *not* apply in nonlinear systems.

A linear system usually results if none of the components in the system changes its characteristics as a function of the *magnitude* of the excitations applied to it. In the case of an electrical system, this means that resistors, inductors, and capacitors do not change their values as the voltages across them or the currents through them change. Other electrical devices such as amplifiers, motors, or transducers would likewise not change their properties with voltage or current. In all cases, however, the concept of linearity is an approximation since any system component will change its characteristics if the forces applied to it are large enough. Hence, when we speak of a *linear system,* what we really mean is that with normal input magnitudes, the system does not change significantly; therefore, linearity will be assumed and the methods of linear system analysis will be employed. Just what changes are significant and what inputs will produce them are matters of engineering judgment.

There are many devices such as rectifiers, junction diodes, gaseous conduction tubes, and saturating magnetic devices for which the assumption of linearity is *not* valid for the normal range of excitation magnitude. Usually, if even one such device is included in the system, then the system must be treated as nonlinear.

Fixed system, time-varying system. Equation (2-1), as written, represents a *time-varying* system, since the coefficients $a_i(t)$ and $b_j(t)$ are indicated as being functions of time. The analysis of time-varying devices is very difficult, since differential equations with nonconstant coefficients cannot be solved except in special cases. The systems of greatest concern for the present discussion are characterized by a differential equation having constant coefficients. Such a system is known as *fixed,* or *time-invariant,* or *stationary.* An alternative way of defining a fixed system is to state that if excitation $x(t)$ leads to response $y(t)$, then excitation $x(t - \tau)$ leads to response $y(t - \tau)$ for any $x(t)$ and any τ. That is, the *shape* of the system response depends only upon the *shape* of the system excitation and not upon the time of application.

Fixed systems usually result when the physical components in the system, and the configuration in which they are connected, do not change with time. Most systems that are not exposed to natural environments can be considered fixed unless they have been deliberately designed to be time-varying. A time-varying system results when any of its components, or their manner of connection, do change with time. In many cases this change is a result of environmental conditions. For example, an aircraft flight control system has greatly different parameter values at sea level than it has at 40,000 feet because of differences in the air density. A long-distance telephone circuit changes from day to night as a consequence of temperature changes, and radical system changes occur in the launching of a space probe because of air density and temperature changes, fuel consumption, and the staging of the booster rockets.

There is an intermediate situation that occurs when the system changes as a consequence of switches opening or closing in negligible times. Strictly speaking, such a system is time-varying, but in most cases the system analysis can be carried out by considering the system to be fixed and replacing the switches by appropriate voltage or current sources.

Lumped-parameter system, distributed-parameter system. Equation (2-1) represents a *lumped-parameter* system by virtue of being an *ordinary* differential equation. The implication of this condition is that the physical size of the system is of no concern, since excitations propagate through the system instantaneously. This assumption is usually valid if the largest physical dimension of the system is small compared to the wavelength of the highest significant frequency considered. A *distributed-parameter* system is represented by a *partial* differential equation and generally has dimensions that are not small compared to the shortest wavelength of interest. Transmission lines, waveguides, antennas, and microwave tubes are typical examples of distributed-parameter electrical systems.

In very large and complex systems, both attributes may exist at the same time. This is true, for example, in power systems, telephone systems, and radio communication systems, in which the terminal equipment is essentially lumped-parameter but the connection between terminals is distributed-parameter. Fortunately, the analysis of the various parts of such systems can usually be handled separately.

Continuous-time system, discrete-time system. Equation (2-1) represents a *continuous-time* system by virtue of being a *differential* equation rather than a *difference* equation. That is, the inputs and outputs are defined for all values of time rather than just for discrete values of time. Since time itself is inherently continuous, all physical systems are actually continuous-time. However, there are situations (which will be discussed in a later chapter) in which one is interested solely in what happens at certain discrete instants of time. In many of these cases, the system itself is composed of a digital computer, which is performing certain specified computations and producing its answers at discrete time instants. If no changes (in input or output) take place between time instants, then system analysis is simplified by considering the system to be discrete-time and having a mathematical model that is a difference equation. Discrete-time systems can be either linear or nonlinear and either fixed or time-varying. In fact, such systems provide one of the most convenient ways to construct a system with prescribed nonlinearities or time-variation.

Instantaneous system, dynamic system. An *instantaneous* system is one in which the response at time t_1 depends only upon the excitation at time t_1 and not upon any future or past values of the excitation. This may also be called a *zero-memory* system. A typical example would be a resistance network or a nonlinear device without energy storage. If the response does depend upon past values of the excitation, then the system is said to be *dynamic* and to have *memory*. Any system that contains at least two different types of elements, one of which can store energy, is dynamic. If past inputs over a *finite* period of time only are important then the system has finite memory. The physical construction of continuous-time, finite memory systems usually requires the use of time delay of some sort, whereas discrete-time systems are almost always finite memory because of limited data-storage capacity.

Unless otherwise specified, all systems to be considered in future discussions will be assumed to be *causal, linear, fixed, lumped-parameter, continuous-time,* and *dynamic*. As such, their basic mathematical model will be an *ordinary, linear, differential* equation with *constant* coefficients.

2-5 Examples of Mathematical Models for Systems

Before attempting to formulate the mathematical model for a complete system it is desirable to review the mathematical models for some of the components of electrical systems. In the case of the basic elements of resistance, inductance and capacitance, the mathematical model is simply the volt-ampere characteristic of the element. In this case, either the voltage or the current can be considered as the excitation and the other as the response. The choice depends upon the nature of the problem and the method selected for setting up the equilibrium equations. In the case of some of the other devices, the subscript 1 refers to the input signal and the subscript 2 to the output signal.

$$\text{Resistance:} \quad v(t) = Ri(t)$$

$$i(t) = Gv(t) \qquad G = \frac{1}{R}$$

$$\text{Inductance:} \quad v(t) = L\frac{di(t)}{dt}$$

$$i(t) = \Gamma \int_{-\infty}^{t} v(\lambda)\, d\lambda \qquad \Gamma = \frac{1}{L}$$

$$\text{Capacitance: } v(t) = S \int_{-\infty}^{t} i(\lambda)\, d\lambda \qquad S = \frac{1}{C}$$

$$i(t) = C\, \frac{dv(t)}{dt}$$

$$\text{Amplifier: } \qquad v_2(t) = K\, v_1(t)$$

$$\text{Delay: } \qquad v_2(t) = v_1(t - \tau) \qquad \tau > 0$$

$$\text{Integrator: } \quad v_2(t) = \int_{-\infty}^{t} v_1(\lambda)\, d\lambda$$

As a simple example of the mathematical model for an electrical system, consider the network shown in Fig. 2-3. The input signal is $v_1(t)$

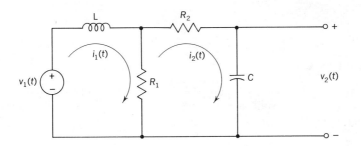

Figure 2-3 A simple electrical system.

and comes from an ideal voltage source. The output signal is $v_2(t)$. There are many ways in which the equations for this circuit might be written, but the use of loop equations is probably the most straightforward, although *not* the simplest. Thus, one may write

$$L\frac{di_1(t)}{dt} + R_1 i_1(t) - R_1 i_2(t) = v_1(t)$$

$$-R_1 i_1(t) + (R_1 + R_2) i_2(t) + \frac{1}{C}\int_{-\infty}^{t} i_2(\lambda)\, d\lambda = 0 \qquad \textbf{(2-2)}$$

$$v_2(t) = \frac{1}{C}\int_{-\infty}^{t} i_2(\lambda)\, d\lambda$$

These three equations may be used to eliminate $i_1(t)$ and $i_2(t)$ and obtain a single equation expressing the relationship between $v_1(t)$ and $v_2(t)$. The result is

$$LC \left(1 + \frac{R_2}{R_1}\right) \frac{d^2v_2(t)}{dt^2} + \left(\frac{L}{R_1} + R_2 C\right) \frac{dv_2(t)}{dt} + v_2(t) = v_1(t) \qquad \text{(2-3)}$$

which is the specific form of (2-1) that applies to this particular system. Thus, (2-3) represents the mathematical model for the physical system composed of the circuit elements shown in Fig. 2-3. The system is seen to be second-order, linear, and time-invariant.

As a second example consider the system of Fig. 2-4, which represents, in simplified form, the use of an operational amplifier as an inte-

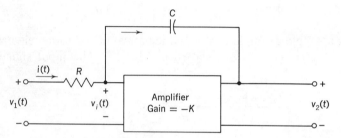

Figure 2-4   Operational amplifier used as an integrator.

grator. The amplifier is assumed to have infinite input impedance, zero output impedance, and a gain, $-K$, that is independent of frequency. It is easily seen from the diagram that

$$v_1(t) = v_2(t) + \frac{1}{C} \int_{-\infty}^{t} i(\lambda) \, d\lambda$$

$$v_i(t) = v_1(t) - Ri(t)$$

$$v_2(t) = -Kv_i(t)$$

After the elimination of $i(t)$, a single equation remains:

$$(K + 1)RC \frac{dv_2(t)}{dt} + v_2(t) = -Kv_1(t) \qquad \text{(2-4)}$$

This is the mathematical model for this system, as expressed in the form of (2-1). It may be seen that for large values of amplifier gain

$$v_1(t) \approx -RC \frac{dv_2(t)}{dt}$$

from which it is clear that the output is approximately proportional to the integral of the input.

2-6 The Normal Form of System Equations

It was noted in an earlier section that an alternative method of formulating the mathematical model for an nth-order system is by means of a set of n simultaneous first-order differential equations, known as the *normal form* of the system equations. This method will be discussed in much greater detail in a subsequent chapter, but it will be useful to take one more step in that direction at the present time in order to utilize the examples just discussed.

First of all, if there are to be n simultaneous equations, there must also be n unknown time functions to be solved for. These unknown time functions are called *state variables* and a specification of their value at some time instant is the *state* of the system at that instant. The manner in which they vary, as a function of time, in response to some excitation, provides a description of the system response. The output of the system can be represented as some combination of these state variables and the system input.

In an electrical system, the state variables may represent voltages and currents that occur at various places in the system, or they may be a set of abstract quantities that have no physical counterparts in the actual system. It should also be noted that there are many different ways in which the state variables can be selected for a given system, but that these cannot be selected completely arbitrarily if one wishes to use the smallest number of state variables.

For the general nth-order linear system, let the state variables be designated as $q_1(t)$, $q_2(t)$, $\cdots$, $q_n(t)$. If the system has only one input, $x(t)$, then a set of simultaneous, first-order, linear differential equations can be written in the form

$$\frac{dq_1(t)}{dt} = a_{11}(t)q_1(t) + a_{12}(t)q_2(t) + \cdots + a_{1n}(t)q_n(t) + b_1(t)x(t)$$

$$\frac{dq_2(t)}{dt} = a_{21}(t)q_2(t) + a_{22}(t)q_2(t) + \cdots + a_{2n}(t)q_n(t) + b_2(t)x(t) \quad \text{(2-5)}$$

$$\vdots$$

$$\frac{dq_n(t)}{dt} = a_{n1}(t)q_1(t) + a_{n2}(t)q_2(t) + \cdots + a_{nn}(t)q_n(t) + b_n(t)x(t)$$

If there is also a single output, $y(t)$, then it often can be represented as

$$y(t) = c_1(t)q_1(t) + c_2(t)q_2(t) + \cdots + c_n(t)q_n(t) \quad \text{(2-6)}$$

although this may not be adequate for some choices of state variables. Thus, (2-5) and (2-6), taken together, form a mathematical model for the general nth order, linear, *time-varying* system and are equivalent to (2-1).

If the system is *fixed,* then the coefficients $a_{ij}(t)$, $b_i(t)$, and $c_i(t)$, for $i = 1, 2, \cdots, n$, are all constants instead of being functions of time.

Since the above formulation of the mathematical model appears to be much more complicated and much more abstract than that of (2-1), the student may question why it is useful. There are several reasons why this method may be useful, and these are all related to the desire to make the mathematical model as general as possible.

Some of these reasons are:

1. By defining appropriate matrices, (2-5) and (2-6) can be written in matrix form and then applied to systems of all orders with equal ease. Thus, increasing the complexity of the system would not result in a corresponding increase in notational complexity.

2. The same general form of equations can also be applied to many types of nonlinear systems. The major differences would be that the right-hand side of (2-5) would be a nonlinear function of $x(t)$ and the $q_i(t)$ rather than a linear function.

3. In the case of time-varying systems, the solution of a set of first-order equations with nonconstant coefficients *may* be more straightforward than the solution of the corresponding nth-order equation with nonconstant coefficients. However, in either form, only certain special cases can be solved.

4. If all of the state variables are solved for, then one has a better idea of what is going on *inside* the system than would be available from a solution for the output function only. This may be important in determining whether any element within the system has such large voltages or currents associated with it that the assumption of linear behavior is of doubtful validity.

5. If either analog or digital computer methods are used to determine the system response, it is usually more convenient to work with the normal form of the equations than with the single nth-order equation.

6. The same formulation of equations applies to multiple-input/multiple-output systems when the normal form is used.

It is not intended to dwell at length on the state variable representation of systems in this chapter since it will be covered in detail later. The foregoing discussion is primarily for motivation, rather than information, and no use will be made of this material until Chapter 8. However, it is desirable to demonstrate at this time that different mathematical models can be derived for the same physical system, and the examples discussed in Section 2-5 are adequate for this purpose.

It is simplest to consider the operational amplifier of Fig. 2-4 first. From (2-3) it is clear that this is a first-order system and only one state variable is necessary. One possibility is to select $v_2(t)$ as the state variable, and this is the most natural choice. Thus, (2-4) can be written in the form of (2-5) simply by transposing one term and dividing through by the co-efficient of the derivative term. Hence,

$$\frac{dv_2(t)}{dt} = -\frac{1}{(K+1)RC}v_2(t) - \frac{K}{(K+1)RC}v_1(t) \qquad \text{(2-7)}$$

The relationship to (2-5) is made more explicit by noting that

$$n = 1$$
$$q_1(t) = v_2(t)$$
$$x(t) = v_1(t)$$

$$a_{11}(t) = -\frac{1}{(K+1)RC} \quad \text{(a constant)}$$

$$b_1(t) = -\frac{K}{(K+1)RC} \quad \text{(a constant)}$$

The corresponding output equation, analogous to (2-6), is

$$y(t) = v_2(t) \qquad \text{(2-8)}$$

where $c_1(t) = 1$, a constant. Hence, (2-7) and (2-8) represent another mathematical model for the system of Fig. 2-4.

A slightly more involved situation results from the simple electrical system of Fig. 2-3. In this case, the system is second order and two state variables will be required. Although other choices might be equally appropriate, the state variables have been selected to be

$$q_1(t) = i_1(t)$$
$$q_2(t) = v_2(t)$$

From the third equation in the set (2-2), it is seen that

$$i_2(t) = C\frac{dv_2(t)}{dt}$$

Substituting this quantity into the first two equations, and re-arranging, leads immediately to the normal equations. Thus,

$$\frac{di_1(t)}{dt} = -\frac{R_1 R_2}{L(R_1 + R_2)}i_1(t) - \frac{R_1}{L(R_1 + R_2)}v_2(t) + \frac{1}{L}v_1(t)$$
$$\qquad \text{(2-9)}$$
$$\frac{dv_2(t)}{dt} = \frac{R_1}{C(R_1 + R_2)}i_1(t) - \frac{1}{C(R_1 + R_2)}v_2(t)$$

Again the corresponding output equation is

$$y(t) = v_2(t) \qquad \text{(2-10)}$$

In order to complete the identification of (2-9) and (2-10) with (2-5) and (2-6), it should be noted that

$$n = 2$$
$$x(t) = v_1(t)$$

$$a_{11}(t) = -\frac{R_1 R_2}{L(R_1 + R_2)}$$

$$a_{12}(t) = -\frac{R_1}{L(R_1 + R_2)}$$

$$a_{21}(t) = \frac{R_1}{C(R_1 + R_2)}$$

$$a_{22}(t) = -\frac{1}{C(R_1 + R_2)}$$

$$b_1(t) = \frac{1}{L}$$

$$b_2(t) = 0$$
$$c_1(t) = 0$$
$$c_2(t) = 1$$

Hence, (2-9) and (2-10) represent another mathematical model for the system of Fig. 2-3.

In the examples just discussed the state variables were apparently selected on an *ad hoc* basis with little or no thought as to whether they would lead to equations in normal form and an appropriate output equation. In actuality, the selection was not arbitrary and there are rules for selecting state variables in an appropriate manner. Some of these will be discussed in Chapter 8. In the meantime, it would be instructive for the student to attempt to write normal equations for the system of Fig. 2-3 when the state variables are chosen to be the voltage across the resistor R_1 and the voltage across the capacitor C. This will illustrate some of the problems that arise from an arbitrary selection.

2-7   Initial Conditions

The specification of a mathematical model for a system is the first step in carrying out any problem of system analysis, but it is not sufficient. It is also necessary to specify the conditions of energy storage within the system at the time the input signal is applied. There are various ways in which these initial conditions can be established, but so far as system analysis is concerned it makes no difference: the effect of any set of initial conditions is exactly the same regardless of how they came into being. A viewpoint that is consistent with the concept that only causal systems can exist is that the initial conditions were established by previous inputs, possibly so far in the past that equilibrium conditions have been established.

There are also various ways of handling initial conditions, and it is difficult to single out any one procedure and state that it will always be the easiest one to use. The following procedures are in common use and each has certain advantages to recommend it:

1. Probably the most basic procedure is to employ the concepts of superposition and the foregoing concept of how initial conditions are established. Because of superposition, the system response to the past inputs that established the initial conditions and the system response to the desired present input can be directly added for *all time*. Therefore, the system can be analyzed by assuming that all initial conditions are zero, and then adding the response due to the initial conditions to the result. This method is particularly convenient when the system configuration is known.

2. When the mathematical model for the system is in the form of an nth-order differential equation, as in (2-1), an appropriate method of specifying initial conditions is to give the value of the output signal and $n - 1$ of its derivatives at the time the desired input signal is applied. This procedure must be used with care when the mathematical model involves *derivatives of the input signal,* but when properly applied it is probably the easiest one to use in this case.

3. When the mathematical model is given in terms of the normal equations, the appropriate procedure is to specify the values of the state variables at the time the desired signal is applied. As will be seen in Chapter 8, this form of initial conditions arises quite naturally in the solution of the normal equations.

Although the use of concrete examples might be desirable to illustrate these procedures, it is not needed to achieve the objectives of the present chapter since solutions for the mathematical models are not being sought. Hence, the present discussion will terminate with the foregoing cursory statement of concepts, and the necessary details will be supplied as the need arises.

■ REFERENCES

There are many books that discuss methods for obtaining mathematical models for linear systems. The following five represent some of those suitable for students at a junior or senior level.

1. Brown, R. G., and J. W. Nilsson, *Introduction to Linear System Analysis*. New York: John Wiley & Sons, Inc., 1962.

> Chapter 2 of this book is concerned with translating the physical problem into mathematical language. This discussion includes mechanical systems as well as electrical systems.

2. Cheng, D. K., *Analysis of Linear Systems*. Reading, Mass.: Addison-Wesley Publishing Company, Inc., 1959.

> This book has several chapters on the mathematical models for linear systems, including an extensive discussion of mechanical and electro-mechanical systems.

3. Kuo, Franklin F., *Network Analysis and Synthesis,* 2d ed. New York: John Wiley & Sons, Inc., 1966.

> This book contains a chapter on the solution of linear differential equations and another chapter on the solution of network equations. There is an excellent discussion of initial conditions.

4. Lynch, W. A., and J. G. Truxal, *Signals and Systems in Electrical Engineering*. New York: McGraw-Hill Book Company, Inc., 1963.

> This book contains an extensive discussion of systems of many types, with interesting illustrative examples. The examples are often complex systems treated in an elementary fashion, rather than just simple electrical circuits.

5. Schwarz, R. J., and B. Friedland, *Linear Systems*. New York: McGraw-Hill Book Company, Inc., 1965.

> This book is written at a somewhat higher mathematical level than the preceding one. It does contain, however, a discussion of state variables and the normal form of system equations. There is also some discussion of discrete systems.

■ PROBLEMS

2-1   A two-stage, *L-C,* low-pass filter has the following configuration:

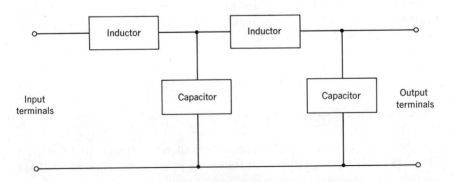

a. Sketch a circuit diagram that might form the basis for a mathematical model for this filter at frequencies well below the cutoff frequency.

b. Sketch a circuit diagram that might form the basis for a mathematical model for this filter at frequencies well above the cutoff frequency.

c. If the two inductors are close together in the same container, there may be coupling between them. How would this affect the foregoing mathematical models?

d. If the inductors have iron cores, what additional precautions would have to be observed in using the mathematical model?

2-2 A given inductor consists of 100 turns of copper wire, having a diameter of 0.01 inch, wound on a polystyrene tube 1 inch in diameter. This is mounted inside a grounded aluminum shield can 1½ inches in diameter, and 2 inches long. For each of the following frequencies, sketch without calculation a different circuit diagram that might form the basis for a mathematical model of this inductor. Assume that neither end of the winding is connected to the shield can.

a. dc

b. 100 kHz

c. 4 MHz

d. 1000 MHz

2-3 Consider the differential equation

$$\frac{dy(t)}{dt} + y(t) = x(t)$$

which represents a system whose input is $x(t)$ and whose output is $y(t)$. Show that if the input is

$$x(t) = 0 \qquad t < 0$$
$$x(t) = 10 \qquad t \geq 0$$

there are two different responses, $y(t)$, depending upon whether or not the system is assumed to be causal.

2-4 For each of the following differential equations, determine the order of the system and classify it with respect to linearity, invariance, dynamic, etc. The system input is $x(t)$ and the output is $y(t)$.

a. $\dfrac{dy(t)}{dt} + 10y(t) = 5x(t) + 5$

b. $\dfrac{d^2y(t)}{dt^2} + t^2 \dfrac{dy(t)}{dt} + 5y(t) = \dfrac{dx(t)}{dt} + 10x(t)$

c. $y(t) = 10x^2(t) + 100$

d. $\dfrac{d^2y(t)}{dt^2} + 6\dfrac{dy(t)}{dt}\, y(t) = 12\, x(t)$

2-5 For each of the following engineering systems, state whether the mathematical model is *fundamentally* time-varying or whether it can be considered to be invariant under most circumstances.
a.   A home television receiver.
b.   A single telephone.
c.   A complete telephone system.
d.   An electrical network composed of resistors, inductors, capacitors, and transistors operating in the laboratory.
e.   The same network operating in a space vehicle that has just been launched.
f.   A computer-controlled milling machine.
g.   A satellite communication system.

2-6 An unknown function, $x(t)$, is observed at discrete time instants only. These time instants are $\cdots t_{-1},\, t_0,\, t_1,\, t_2,\, \cdots$ and the corresponding values of the time function are $\cdots x_{-1},\, x_0,\, x_1,\, x_2,\, \cdots$. These values are used to compute another set of numbers, which, at time t_i, are given by

$$y_i = x_i + \frac{1}{2}x_{i-1} + \frac{1}{3}x_{i-2} + \frac{1}{4}x_{i-3} \qquad -\infty < i < \infty$$

If this equation is the mathematical model for the system, classify it with respect to as many of the descriptions in Section 2-4 as you can.

2-7 a. Write a single differential equation that relates input and output for the system illustrated.

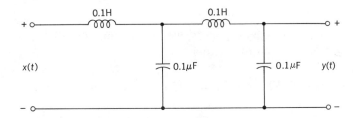

b.   What is the order of this system?

2-8 a. Write a single differential equation that relates input and output for the system shown.
b.   What is the order of this system?

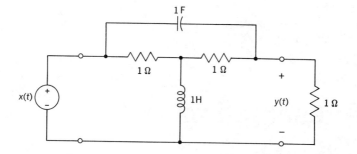

2-9 Write the differential equations that represent the system of Problem 2-7 in normal form.

2-10 Write the differential equations that represent the system of Problem 2-8 in normal form.

CHAPTER

3

Representation
of Signals

3-1 General Methods of Signal Representation

It was mentioned previously that a signal is a function of time and that a mathematical representation of this function is necessary in order to be able to carry out any type of system analysis. The most general representation is by means of an abstract symbol, such as $x(t)$, and many general analytical results can be obtained without resorting to more specific representations. For example, it was shown in Chapter 2 that the mathematical model for a linear system could be obtained by representing the input and output signals by abstract symbols. This is possible because the system characteristics do not depend in any way upon the explicit form of the signals.

It is clear, however, that such an abstract representation is not quantitative; that is, it does not specify the numerical value of the signal at any instant of time. In order to be able to specify such values, it is necessary to represent the signal in terms of one or more explicit functions of time whose numerical values are exactly defined for all instants of time.

It is important to recognize that any quantitative representation of a real signal is necessarily an approximation. The actual variation of signal amplitude with time is so complex that it can never be represented exactly by any finite number of explicit time functions. When the signal waveform is intended to have a simple form, such as an exponential or sinusoid, the approximation may be very good, but in more general cases the approximation usually leaves a significant error. The problem of deciding how good an approximation must be to obtain meaningful results in any specific application of system analysis calls for the exercise of engineering judgment.

3-2 Classification of Signals

Before some of the more useful methods for representing signals explicitly are discussed, it is desirable to consider some of the various classes of signals that will be of importance. To a considerable extent, the most useful method of signal representation for any given situation depends upon the type of signal being considered. There are many different ways in which signals can be separated into categories, and only a few of the more important ones are discussed here.

Periodic, nonperiodic.   A periodic signal is one that repeats the sequence of values exactly after a fixed length of time known as the *period*. More precisely, a signal, $x(t)$ is periodic if there is a number T such that

$$x(t) = x(t + T)$$

(3-1)

for all t. The smallest positive number T that satisfies (3-1) is the period, which defines the duration of one complete *cycle*. The *fundamental frequency* of a periodic signal is

$$f = \frac{1}{T}$$

(3-2)

A nonperiodic, or aperiodic, signal is one for which there is no value of T satisfying (3-1). This is an extremely important class of signals, which must include all *actual* signals (since they must start and stop at finite times). It will be shown later, however, that even nonperiodic signals can be represented in terms of periodic ones; thus, from the standpoint of the mathematical representation of signals, the periodic class undoubtedly has the greatest theoretical importance.

Typical examples of periodic signals are the sinusoidal signals used in power systems and for some types of system testing, and periodically repeated, nonsinusoidal signals such as the rectangular pulse sequences used in radar and the sawtooth waveform used as a time base in oscilloscopes. In almost all such cases, it is possible to write an explicit mathematical expression for the periodic signal involved.

Typical nonperiodic signals include speech waveforms, transients due to switching, and random signals arising from unpredictable disturbances of all kinds. In some cases it is possible to write explicit mathematical expressions for nonperiodic signals and in other cases it is not.

Another class of signals represents a borderline case between periodic and nonperiodic signals. These *almost-periodic* signals are actually the sum of two or more periodic signals having incommensurate periods. The resultant signal is nonperiodic, since there is no T that will satisfy (3-1), but it has many of the properties of periodic signals and can be represented by a finite (countably infinite) number of periodic signals. The almost-periodic signal arises in the analysis of many types of communication systems.

Random, nonrandom.   Another method of classifying signals is based on whether or not there is any randomness associated with them. This rather subtle point will be discussed in great detail in a later chapter. For the time being, it is sufficient to state that a random signal is one about which there is some degree of uncertainty *before* it actually occurs. This terminology is most often applied to signals that are random functions of time in the sense that their magnitude varies in an erratic and unpredictable manner. For example, the output of a radio receiver responding to atmospheric disturbances, man-made interference, and internal noise sources will have such a random behavior. If future values of the signal cannot be predicted, even after observation of past values, then it is not possible to write an explicit mathematical expression for the signal.

It is possible, however, to have random signals that have a great deal of regularity and whose future values can be predicted once the past values are observed. For example, a sinusoid, whose phase is unknown before it is observed, can be considered random if the particular phase that actually occurs is purely a matter of chance. Once it has been observed, for a sufficient period of time, the phase is known and all future values can be predicted. Random signals of this type can be represented by an explicit mathematical expression and the randomness is associated with the parameters of the representation.

A nonrandom signal is one about which there is no uncertainty before it occurs, and in almost all cases an explicit mathematical expression can be written for it. All of the signals to be discussed in the earlier chapters of this book will be considered to be nonrandom in order to avoid the subtleties that would otherwise confuse the basic concepts.

Energy signals, power signals.   For electrical systems, the signal is usually a voltage or a current. The energy dissipated by a voltage in a resistance during a given time interval, t_1 to t_2, is simply

$$E = \int_{t_1}^{t_2} \frac{e^2(t)}{R} \, dt \quad \text{watt seconds} \tag{3-3}$$

For a current, it would be

$$E = \int_{t_1}^{t_2} Ri^2(t) \, dt \quad \text{watt seconds} \tag{3-4}$$

In each case the energy is proportional to the integral of the *square* of the signal.

It is often convenient to talk about the energy "on a one-ohm basis." For this case, the R in (3-3) and (3-4) becomes unity, and the equations assume the same form. Because of this convenience, it has become customary to speak of the "energy" associated with any signal $x(t)$, regardless of units, as

$$E = \int_{t_1}^{t_2} x^2(t) \, dt \tag{3-5}$$

in spite of the fact that this does not appear to be dimensionally correct. This seldom causes confusion (except to the neophyte) because "everyone knows" that equations of this type implicitly contain a (1) with the appropriate dimensions. This convenient practice will be followed here and in subsequent chapters.

An *energy signal* is defined here to be one for which (3-5) is finite even when the time interval becomes infinite. Specifically, if $x(t)$ satisfies the condition

$$\int_{-\infty}^{\infty} x^2(t) \, dt < \infty \tag{3-6}$$

it is said to have finite energy and will be called an *energy signal*. Specific examples of energy signals are decaying exponentials and exponentially damped sinusoids (in the semi-infinite interval, $t > 0$), rectangular pulses, or any signal that is nonzero in a finite time interval only and finite within that interval.

However, there are many interesting signals that do not satisfy (3-6). Examples include all periodic signals and many aperiodic signals as well. In these cases it is often more appropriate to consider the *average power* of the signal.

The average power associated with (3-5), for example, is simply

$$P = \frac{1}{t_2 - t_1} \int_{t_1}^{t_2} x^2(t) \, dt \tag{3-7}$$

where, again, this is understood to be on a one-ohm basis. If this remains greater than zero when the time interval becomes infinite, then the signal has finite average power and will be called a *power signal.* More specifically, a power signal satisfies the condition.

$$0 < \lim_{T \to \infty} \frac{1}{2T} \int_{-T}^{T} x^2(t) \, dt < \infty \qquad \text{(3-8)}$$

Upon comparing (3-6) and (3-8), it is clear that an energy signal has zero average power, and a power signal has infinite energy. Thus, a signal may be classified as one or the other, but not both. There are, of course, some signals that may not be classified as either since both the energy and average power may be infinite. The signal

$$x(t) = \epsilon^{-\alpha t} \qquad -\infty < t < \infty$$

is an example of this.

3-3 Representation in Terms of Elementary Signals

It was noted previously that in order to have a quantitative description of a signal it is necessary to represent it in terms of explicit time functions whose numerical values are exactly defined. There are, of course, a great many different ways in which this representation might be realized, even for the same physical signal. The choice of any particular method is usually motivated by mathematical convenience or ease of visualization.

Mathematical convenience usually dictates that a signal $x(t)$ be represented as a *linear* combination of a set of elementary time functions. These elementary functions, usually called *basis functions,* are selected to have certain convenient properties that will be discussed later. The signal representation can be formulated in a very general way by use of an abstract notation for the basis functions. This general formulation can be employed to indicate desirable characteristics for the basis functions. It will then be possible to consider some specific types of basis functions within the same mathematical framework and, thus, achieve a degree of versatility that would not be possible if the specific types were considered separately and independently.

Accordingly, let the set of basis functions be designated as $\phi_0(t)$, $\phi_1(t)$, $\phi_2(t)$, $\cdots$, $\phi_N(t)$, where N may be infinity in some cases, and write the linear combination of these as

$$x(t) = \sum_{n=0}^{N} a_n \, \phi_n(t) \qquad \text{(3-9)}$$

The use of only positive integers for indexing the basis functions was an arbitrary choice. In some cases, examples of which will be shown later, both positive and negative integers are employed. The problem of selecting the best set of basis functions $\phi_n(t)$ for a given application and of determining the corresponding coefficients a_n has not been solved in general. Instead, a great many specific results are available for functions that have specific properties, and these serve as an aid in making an appropriate selection in any given case.

One property that is desired for a set of basis functions is known as *finality of coefficients*. This property allows one to determine any given coefficient without the need for knowing any other coefficient. Stated another way, more terms can be added to the representation (to obtain greater accuracy, for example) without making any changes in the earlier coefficients. In order to achieve finality of coefficients, it is necessary that the basis functions be *orthogonal* over the time interval for which the representation is to be valid.

The condition of orthogonality for real basis functions requires that

$$\int_{t_1}^{t_2} \phi_n(t)\phi_k(t)dt = 0 \qquad k \neq n$$
$$= \lambda_k \qquad k = n \tag{3-10}$$

for all k and n.[1] If $\lambda_k = 1$, for all k, the basis functions are *orthonormal*. The limits of integration in (3-10) can define either a finite interval or an infinite (or semi-infinite) interval, depending upon the nature of the problem.

In order to demonstrate how the coefficients can be determined, multiply both sides of (3-9) by $\phi_j(t)$, for any j, and integrate over the specified interval. This gives

$$\int_{t_1}^{t_2} \phi_j(t)x(t)dt = \int_{t_1}^{t_2} \phi_j(t) \left[\sum_{n=0}^{N} a_n\phi_n(t) \right] dt$$

$$= \sum_{n=0}^{N} a_n \int_{t_1}^{t_2} \phi_j(t)\phi_n(t)\,dt \tag{3-11}$$

From the orthogonality condition of (3-10), this equation may be written as

---

[1] If the basis functions are *complex* functions of time, and $\phi_k{}^*(t)$ is the complex conjugate of $\phi_k(t)$, then the condition for orthogonality is

$$\int_{t_1}^{t_2} \phi_n(t)\,\phi_k{}^*(t)dt = \begin{cases} 0 & k \neq n \\ \lambda_k & k = n \end{cases}$$

where the λ_k are real. The general discussion here will assume that the basis functions are real. An example of complex basis functions will be given in the next section.

$$\int_{t_1}^{t_2} \phi_j(t)x(t)\, dt = a_j\, \lambda_j \qquad (3\text{-}12)$$

since all of the terms on the right side of (3-11) will be zero except for $n = j$. Thus, the coefficient a_j may be expressed quite generally as

$$a_j = \frac{1}{\lambda_j} \int_{t_1}^{t_2} \phi_j(t)x(t)\, dt \qquad (3\text{-}13)$$

when the basis functions are orthogonal and real.[2]

The discussion so far has been so general as to give no clue to desirable types of functions to use as basis functions. Even the requirement of orthogonality is not very restrictive, since a great many different classes of functions can be made orthogonal over some interval by suitable definitions. To a large extent the choice depends upon the eventual use that is to be made of the signal representation. When the application is system analysis, as it will be here, the sinusoidal functions are extremely useful because they remain sinusoidal after the various mathematical operations that are needed in such an analysis are performed. Specifically, the sum or difference of two sinusoids of the same frequency is still a sinusoid, and the derivative or integral of a sinusoid is still a sinusoid. These properties, combined with the superposition properties of linear systems, imply that representing a signal as a sum of sinusoids may be a very convenient technique. This method will be used for periodic signals in the next section. A later chapter will describe how the same thing can be accomplished for aperiodic signals.

There are also some other classes of basis functions that are useful in system analysis. One of these is the class of real exponentials, which possess much the same properties as the sinusoids. Another commonly used basis function is known as the *sinc function* and the resulting expansion is known as a *cardinal function*. This class arises in connection with sampling-type representations and will be discussed in a later chapter.

Before leaving this general discussion of signal representation to consider some specific cases, it is instructive to discuss another property of orthogonal functions, one which is of great usefulness in many situations. This property has to do with the accuracy of the representation when not all of the terms needed for an exact representation can be used. In almost all cases, the value of N in (3-9) will be infinity in the exact case, but the values of a_n get successively smaller as n becomes large.

---

[2] For complex basis functions, this becomes

$$a_k = \frac{1}{\lambda_k} \int_{t_1}^{t_2} \phi_k^*(t)x(t)\, dt$$

and a_k may be complex.

Since it is not possible to use an infinite number of terms in any practical numerical example, the series must be terminated after some finite number of terms and the resulting expression is an *approximation* to $x(t)$. Thus, the approximation, $\hat{x}(t)$, may be expressed as[3]

$$\hat{x}(t) = \sum_{n=0}^{M} \hat{a}_n \, \phi_n(t) \qquad \text{(3-14)}$$

where the value of M is determined by practical computational considerations and the $\hat{a}_n$ are yet to be determined.

The practical question which now arises is how to select the coefficients $\hat{a}_n$ so that for a given, finite M the approximation $\hat{x}(t)$ is as close as possible to the true value $x(t)$. The use of (3-13) is still possible, of course, but it was derived to insure finality of coefficients and the matter of accuracy of the representation was not considered. Is it possible to find another set of coefficients, which may be more difficult to obtain, but which yield a better approximation? The answer to this question, fortunately, is "no."

In order to investigate this statement, it is necessary to have some measure of the closeness of the approximation. One measure that is frequently used is the integral of the *square* of the differences between $x(t)$ and $\hat{x}(t)$. This quantity, called the *integral squared error,* is given by

$$I = \int_{t_1}^{t_2} [x(t) - \hat{x}(t)]^2 \, dt \qquad \text{(3-15)}$$

and is zero only when $\hat{x}(t) = x(t)$. Otherwise, it is always positive, and the smaller it is, the better the approximation.

In connection with this integral squared error, it should be mentioned that it is usually applicable *only* when $x(t)$ is an energy signal or when $x(t)$ is periodic. If $x(t)$ is an energy signal, then the limits of integration may extend from $-\infty$ to $+\infty$. When $x(t)$ is periodic, then $t_2 - t_1$ is usually chosen to be equal to the period T.

The coefficients $\hat{a}_n$, whose optimum values are being sought, may be introduced into (3-15) by using (3-14). Thus, for the case of real basis functions, the integral squared error becomes

$$I = \int_{t_1}^{t_2} \left[x(t) - \sum_{n=0}^{M} \hat{a}_n \, \phi_n(t) \right]^2 \, dt \qquad \text{(3-16)}$$

---

[3] When the basis functions are complex, this approximation may be expressed as

$$\hat{x}(t) = \sum_{n=-M}^{M} \hat{a}_n \, \phi_n(t)$$

It is now desired to find the set of coefficients $\hat{a}_n$ that will make the integral have its *minimum* value.

Various methods might be employed to minimize I. A straightforward procedure would be to differentiate I with respect to each of the coefficients and set these derivatives equal to zero. It could then be shown that the resulting values of $\hat{a}_n$ do in fact lead to a minimum rather than a maximum. An alternative procedure, which will be followed here, is to rearrange the terms in (3-16) in such a way that the result becomes obvious.

If the squared term in the integrand of (3-16) is expanded, then I may be expressed as

$$I = \int_{t_1}^{t_2} \left[x^2(t) - 2x(t) \sum_{n=0}^{M} a_n \, \phi_n(t) + \sum_{n=0}^{M} \hat{a}_n \, \phi_n(t) \sum_{k=0}^{M} \hat{a}_k \, \phi_k(t) \right] dt \quad (3\text{-}17)$$

Upon interchanging the sequence of integration and summation and writing as separate integrals, this equation becomes

$$I = \int_{t_1}^{t_2} x^2(t) \, dt - 2 \sum_{n=0}^{M} \hat{a}_n \int_{t_1}^{t_2} x(t) \, \phi_n(t) \, dt$$

$$+ \sum_{n=0}^{M} \sum_{k=0}^{M} \hat{a}_n \, \hat{a}_k \int_{t_1}^{t_2} \phi_n(t) \phi_k(t) \, dt$$

$$(3\text{-}18)$$

It may be noted that the first integral does not depend upon $\hat{a}_n$ at all and hence, for purposes of minimizing I, can be replaced by a constant, say K. The second integral is, from (3-13), simply the previous coefficient, a_n, multiplied by λ_n. From the orthogonality condition (3-10), the last integral is zero when $n \neq k$ and λ_n when $n = k$. Then (3-18) may be written as

$$I = K - 2 \sum_{n=0}^{M} \hat{a}_n a_n \lambda_n + \sum_{n=0}^{M} \hat{a}_n^{\,2} \lambda_n \quad (3\text{-}19)$$

(Note that the double summation in the third term is no longer needed since only the terms for $n = k$ remain.)

Equation (3-19) can now be rewritten by adding and subtracting terms involving $\lambda_n a_n^{\,2}$. Thus,

$$I = K - \sum_{n=0}^{M} \lambda_n a_n^{\,2} + \sum_{n=0}^{M} \lambda_n (a_n - \hat{a}_n)^2 \quad (3\text{-}20)$$

It is now clear that the quantity being sought, $\hat{a}_n$, appears *only* in the term $(a_n - \hat{a}_n)^2$ and that this term can never be negative. Hence, I will have its minimum value when the term is as small as it can be, which is zero; this occurs when

$$\hat{a}_n = a_n \qquad n = 0, 1, 2, \cdots, M$$

From this result, it may be concluded that the previously defined coefficients are also the best ones from the standpoint of minimizing the approximation error when only a finite number of terms is used. Thus, the use of orthogonal basis functions is not only convenient from the standpoint of finality of coefficients but these same coefficients also minimize the integral squared error of the representation. Because of the ease of computing the coefficients, orthogonal basis functions are almost always employed whenever a series representation of the type given by (3-9) is used.

It is also of interest to note that the foregoing results can be used to determine how good an approximation $\hat{x}(t)$ is to $x(t)$. The constant K is simply the energy E of the actual signal in the time interval from t_1 to t_2. Similarly, I can be interpreted as the energy associated with the error in the approximation in the same time interval. The ratio of this energy to the signal energy can be obtained by dividing both sides of (3-20) by E. Since the last term of (3-20) is zero, this ratio becomes[4]

$$\frac{\text{Error energy}}{\text{Signal energy}} = 1 - \frac{1}{E} \sum_{n=0}^{M} \lambda_n a_n^2 \tag{3-21}$$

It is relatively easy to show that in most cases the second term of (3-21) approaches unity as M becomes large so that the ratio approaches zero. Since the maximum value of this ratio is one, its actual value gives a realistic impression of the goodness of the approximation.

Before we go on to a practical application of signal representation in terms of orthogonal basis functions, it is desirable to consider a very simple example in order to illustrate the mechanics of the procedure. For this purpose, the basis functions are arbitrarily selected to be rectangular waveforms in a time interval from 0 to 1 as shown in Fig. 3-1. These basis functions could be used for any other finite time interval if they are suitably shifted and time-scaled. It is also arbitrarily decided that the basis functions should be orthonormal so that the $\lambda_k = 1$ for all $k \geq 0$. Accordingly, let

$$\phi_0(t) = 1 \qquad 0 \leq t \leq 1$$
$$= 0 \qquad \text{elsewhere}$$

The orthonormality condition requires that the next basis function, $\phi_1(t)$, satisfy the equations

---

[4] See Problem 3-14 for the case of complex basis functions.

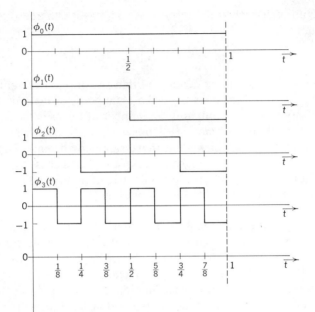

Figure 3-1 Set of rectangular basis functions.

$$\int_0^1 \phi_0(t)\phi_1(t) \, dt = 0$$

and

$$\int_0^1 \phi_1^2(t) \, dt \quad = 1$$

It is evident that this will be true if

$$\phi_1(t) = \quad 1 \qquad 0 \le t < \frac{1}{2}$$

$$= -1 \qquad \frac{1}{2} \le t < 1$$

Further thought reveals that all higher-order basis functions must change sign once in each constant interval of the next lower basis function in order to be orthogonal with respect to it. Hence,

$$\phi_2(t) = \quad 1 \qquad 0 \le t < \frac{1}{4}$$

$$= -1 \qquad \frac{1}{4} \le t < \frac{1}{2}$$

$$= \quad 1 \qquad \frac{1}{2} \le t < \frac{3}{4}$$

$$= -1 \qquad \frac{3}{4} \le t < 1$$

Several of the basis functions are sketched in Fig. 3-1.

It is now desired to represent some time function in terms of these basis functions. Suppose the desired time function is

$$x(t) = 6t \quad 0 \leq t \leq 1$$
$$= 0 \quad \text{elsewhere}$$

Since $\lambda_j = 1$ for all j, the first coefficient, a_0, is given by (3-13) as

$$a_0 = \int_0^1 (1) \, 6t \, dt$$
$$= 3$$

Similarly, the second coefficient, a_1, becomes

$$a_1 = \int_0^{1/2} (1) \, 6t \, dt + \int_{1/2}^1 (-1) \, 6t \, dt$$
$$= -\frac{3}{2}$$

In a like manner, it is easy to show that

$$a_2 = -\frac{3}{4}$$

and

$$a_3 = -\frac{3}{8}$$

The approximate mathematical representation for $x(t)$ may now be written as

$$\hat{x}(t) = 3\phi_0(t) - \frac{3}{2}\phi_1(t) - \frac{3}{4}\phi_2(t) - \frac{3}{8}\phi_3(t) - \cdots$$

The approximate representation for these four terms is shown in Fig. 3-2, and compared to the true time function.

It is also of interest to use (3-21) to compute the fractional squared error in the approximation. The energy E of the true signal is

$$E = \int_0^1 (6t)^2 \, dt = 12$$

Since $\lambda_n = 1$, for all n, and $M = 3$ in this case, (3-21) becomes

$$\frac{\text{Error energy}}{\text{Signal energy}} = 1 - \frac{1}{12} \left[(3)^2 + \left(-\frac{3}{2}\right)^2 + \left(-\frac{3}{4}\right)^2 + \left(-\frac{3}{8}\right)^2 \right]$$

$$= \frac{1}{256}$$

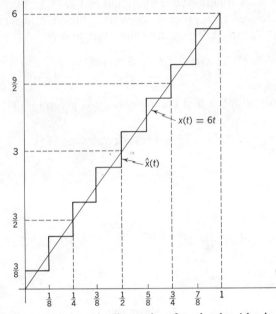

Figure 3-2   Approximation of a linear time function by 4 basis functions.

It is clear from this result that, although the approximation looks fairly crude when presented graphically, the fractional squared error is really quite small. A little thought also will reveal that one more term in the approximation will cut the maximum error in half and reduce the fractional squared error by a factor of four. Considerations of this sort may be of great value in enabling the engineer to estimate the number of terms required to obtain a desired accuracy in any signal approximation problem.

3-4   Fourier Series Representation

It was noted in the previous section that the use of sinusoidal basis functions is convenient because of the invariance of these functions with respect to summation, differentiation, and integration. Hence, this type of basis function will be used as a specific illustration of the general ideas just discussed, and the resulting representation is called a *Fourier series*.

It is certainly possible to use sines and cosines as basis functions, but this calls for the use of two summations, one for sine terms and the other for cosine terms. A more convenient method is to use complex exponentials and let the index of summation be negative as well as positive. The resulting series can be converted easily into sines and cosines, if desired, by the familiar relation

$$\epsilon^{\pm jn\omega_0 t} = \cos n\omega_0 t \pm j \sin n\omega_0 t \tag{3-22}$$

Consider the time function shown in Fig. 3-3. The Fourier series representation that will be obtained will be valid in the time interval from t_1 to t_2 for almost any time function. If, however, $x(t)$ is periodic with a period $T = t_2 - t_1$, then the representation is valid for *all* times and not just those within the interval.

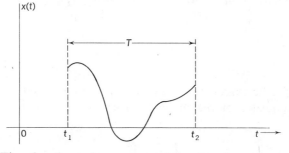

Figure 3-3   Time function to be represented by a Fourier series.

The term "almost any time function" implies that $x(t)$ must satisfy certain mathematical conditions if the resulting series is to converge to the true value of $x(t)$. These are the *Dirichlet conditions*, which require that, within the interval t_1 to t_2, $x(t)$ be single-valued, have only a finite number of maxima and minima in a finite time, have only a finite number of finite discontinuities, and satisfy the inequality

$$\int_{t_1}^{t_2} |x(t)|\, dt < \infty$$

The actual time function $x(t)$ corresponding to *any physical* signal will satisfy these conditions, although some common mathematical representations do not.

For the exponential Fourier series the basis functions may be defined as

$$\phi_n(t) = \epsilon^{jn\omega_0 t} \qquad n = 0, \pm 1, \pm 2, \cdots, \pm\infty$$

where

$$\omega_0 = \frac{2\pi}{T}$$

It is easy to show that these functions are orthogonal so that[5]

$$\int_{t_1}^{t_1+T} \epsilon^{jn\omega_0 t}\, \epsilon^{-jk\omega_0 t}\, dt = 0 \qquad n \neq k$$
$$\phantom{\int_{t_1}^{t_1+T} \epsilon^{jn\omega_0 t}\, \epsilon^{-jk\omega_0 t}\, dt} = T \qquad n = k \tag{3-23}$$

---

[5] Note that the basis functions are complex and that the complex conjugate of $\epsilon^{jk\omega_0 t}$ is $\epsilon^{-jk\omega_0 t}$. See footnote 2.

If coefficients for the Fourier series are designated as α_n then, from (3-13), they may be expressed as

$$\alpha_n = \frac{1}{T} \int_{t_1}^{t_1+T} x(t)\,\epsilon^{-jn\omega_0 t}\,dt \tag{3-24}$$

and are usually complex. In any case, however, $\alpha_{-n} = \alpha_n{}^*$. Then $x(t)$ is given by

$$x(t) = \sum_{n=-\infty}^{\infty} \alpha_n\,\epsilon^{jn\omega_0 t} \tag{3-25}$$

As a specific example of the exponential Fourier series, consider the periodic sequence of rectangular pulses shown in Fig. 3-4. The time

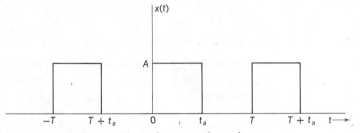

Figure 3-4   A periodic sequence of rectangular pulses.

function $x(t)$ may be defined during the time interval from 0 to T (one period) as

$$
\begin{aligned}
x(t) &= A & 0 < t < t_a \\
&= 0 & t_a < t < T
\end{aligned}
$$

Hence, the coefficients become

$$\alpha_n = \frac{1}{T} \int_0^{t_a} A\,\epsilon^{-jn\omega_0 t}\,dt$$

$$= \frac{A}{T}\left[\frac{1 - \epsilon^{-jn\omega_0 t_a}}{jn\omega_0}\right]$$

$$= \frac{A}{T}\exp\left(-jn\omega_0 t_a/2\right)\left[\frac{\exp\left(jn\omega_0 t_a/2\right) - \exp\left(-jn\omega_0 t_a/2\right)}{jn\omega_0}\right]$$

$$= \frac{At_a}{T}\left[\frac{\sin\left(n\omega_0 t_a/2\right)}{n\omega_0 t_a/2}\right]\exp\left(-jn\omega_0 t_a/2\right)$$

This may be written in slightly different form by replacing ω_0 by its equivalent, $2\pi/T$. Thus,

$$\alpha_n = \frac{At_a}{T}\left[\frac{\sin(n\pi t_a/T)}{n\pi t_a/T}\right]\exp\left[-j\frac{2\pi n}{T}\left(\frac{t_a}{2}\right)\right]$$

The complete Fourier series expression for $x(t)$ now becomes

$$x(t) = \sum_{n=-\infty}^{\infty} \frac{At_a}{T}\left[\frac{\sin(n\pi t_a/T)}{n\pi t_a/T}\right]\exp\left[j\frac{2\pi n}{T}\left(t-\frac{t_a}{2}\right)\right] \quad \textbf{(3-26)}$$

This representation of $x(t)$ is in terms of sinusoids having frequencies that are multiples of the fundamental frequency $1/T$. The coefficients α_n give the magnitude and phase of these sinusoids and, hence, are said to constitute a *frequency-domain* description of the signal. The explicit time function $x(t)$ is said to be a *time-domain* description of the signal. The properties and uses of frequency-domain descriptions will be considered in more detail in a later chapter.

3-5 Singularity Functions

There is a class of elementary signals whose members have very simple mathematical forms but are either discontinuous or have discontinuous derivatives. Because such signals do not have finite derivatives of all orders, they are usually referred to as singularity functions. Two of the most common singularity functions are the unit ramp function and the unit step function as shown in Fig. 3-5.

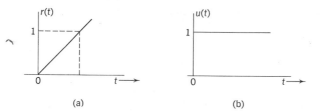

(a)   (b)

Figure 3-5 Examples of singularity functions. **(a)** Unit ramp function. **(b)** Unit step function.

Although signals such as these are mathematical idealizations and cannot really occur in any physical system, they serve several useful purposes for system analysis. In the first place, they serve as good approximations to the signals that actually do arise in systems when switching operations take place. Secondly, their simple mathematical forms make it possible to carry out system analysis much more easily than could be done with more complicated signals. Furthermore, many complicated signals can be represented as sums of these elementary ones. Finally, they can be approximated easily in the laboratory, so one can determine experimentally whether or not a given system behaves the way the mathematical analysis says it should.

The unit ramp function, designated as $r(t)$, is defined to start at $t = 0$ and have unit slope thereafter. Hence, it may be represented mathematically as

$$
\begin{aligned}
r(t) &= t & t &\geq 0 \\
&= 0 & t &< 0
\end{aligned}
\tag{3-27}
$$

If a slope other than unity is desired, it is necessary only to multiply by a constant. Thus, $br(t)$ is a ramp having a slope of b. An alternative way of changing the slope is to change the time scale of the argument. Since $r(t)$ has unit slope, its value must be unity whenever the argument is unity. Thus, $br(t)$ and $r(bt)$ both represent ramps with slopes of b.

The *unit step function,* designated as $u(t)$, is defined to be zero before zero time and unity thereafter. Thus, it may be represented mathematically as

$$
\begin{aligned}
u(t) &= 1 & t &\geq 0 \\
&= 0 & t &< 0
\end{aligned}
\tag{3-28}
$$

It may be noted that the unit ramp function is just the integral of the unit step function; that is,

$$
r(t) = \int_{-\infty}^{t} u(\lambda)\, d\lambda
\tag{3-29}
$$

It is also true that at all times except $t = 0$, where a unique derivative does not exist,

$$
u(t) = \frac{dr(t)}{dt} \qquad t \neq 0
\tag{3-30}
$$

A step change of value other than unity can be obtained by multiplying by a constant. Thus, $cu(t)$ is a step change of magnitude c. There is no time scale change that will accomplish the same result.

All of the singularity functions just discussed were assumed to start at $t = 0$. It is often necessary to consider other starting times and this can be done by translating the argument of the function in time. Thus, $u(t - a)$ is zero whenever $(t - a)$ is negative, unity when it is positive, and represents a step starting at $t = a$. Some examples of translated functions are illustrated in Fig. 3-6.

By using combinations of ramps and step functions, it is possible to represent many other types of functions. For example, a rectangular pulse of width a can be considered as the difference between a step function at the origin and one at $t = a$. This is illustrated in Fig. 3-7. Hence,

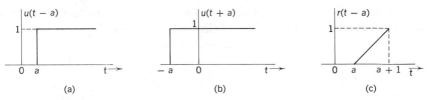

Figure 3-6   Some translated singularity functions. **(a)** Step function translated to right. **(b)** Step function translated to left. **(c)** Translated ramp functions.

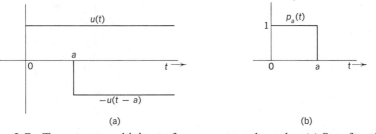

Figure 3-7   Two steps combining to form a rectangular pulse. **(a)** Step function components. **(b)** Resulting pulse function.

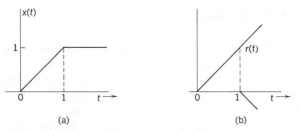

Figure 3-8   Finite ramp **(a)** and its components **(b)**.

the mathematical representation of a unit rectangular pulse, $p_a(t)$, could be written as

$$p_a(t) = u(t) - u(t - a) \tag{3-31}$$

It should also be clear that

$$cp_a(t) = c[u(t) - u(t - a)] \tag{3-32}$$

is a rectangular pulse with magnitude c and duration a.

As another example, consider the finite ramp function shown in Fig. 3-8(a). In Fig. 3-8(b) are shown the two ramps whose difference will yield the finite ramp. Thus, a mathematical representation for this finite ramp is

$$x(t) = r(t) - r(t - 1) \tag{3-33}$$

As a final example of a more complicated waveform, consider the time function shown in Fig. 3-9. It is left as an exercise for the student to show that this time function can be represented by

$$x(t) = -r(t + 1) + 2r(t) - r(t - 2) - u(t - 3) \qquad \text{(3-34)}$$

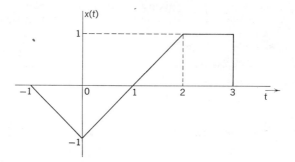

Figure 3-9   A composite waveform.

3-6   The Impulse Function

There is another singularity function, known as the impulse or delta function, which is of such great importance in system analysis that it is considered separately. This is not a well-behaved function in the sense that an explicit mathematical description can be written for it. Nevertheless, it has some well-defined properties that provide the best way of describing it. Before we discuss these properties, however, it may be helpful to discuss the impulse from an intuitive standpoint.

The intuitive interpretation of an impulse is that it is an idealization of a very narrow pulse having a finite total area. For convenience, the area is usually taken to be unity. A nonmathematical approach to this interpretation, which emphasizes its relation to the step function, can be developed by considering the finite ramp function and its derivative.[6] The particular forms of these functions that will be used for this discussion are shown in Fig. 3-10.

It is evident that the finite ramp function $f(t)$ approximates a step function when a is small. In fact, one may write

$$u(t) = \lim_{a \to 0} f(t) \qquad \text{(3-35)}$$

---

[6] As used in this section, the term "derivative" is assumed to mean the actual derivative except at those points at which a unique derivative does not exist. Hence, it corresponds to the geometrical "slope."

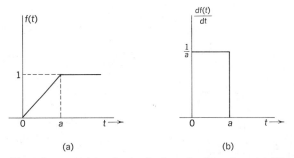

Figure 3-10   Functions used to obtain the impulse function. **(a)** The finite ramp. **(b)** Derivative of the finite ramp.

The derivative of the finite ramp is seen to be a rectangular pulse of duration a and magnitude $1/a$. As a becomes small, this pulse becomes narrower and taller, but its area remains constant at unity. Hence, the derivative of a finite ramp approaches an impulse as a approaches zero. If the impulse is designated as $\delta(t)$, then it may be expressed heuristically as

$$\delta(t) = \lim_{a \to 0} \frac{df(t)}{dt} \tag{3-36}$$

From these two relationships it is possible to write a "definition" of the impulse as

$$\delta(t) = \frac{du(t)}{dt} \tag{3-37}$$

even though the derivative of the step function does not exist in the strict mathematical sense.

The term "delta function" or "δ function" to designate the impulse function arises from the notation employed and from historical usage. It is also sometimes called a "Dirac delta function," but this terminology is more properly reserved for a special form of the impulse, which will be discussed later. The graphical representation of $\delta(t)$ is illustrated in Fig. 3-11(a); a magnitude-scaled and time-shifted version is shown in Fig. 3-11(b). It should be emphasized that the factor multiplying an impulse is really designating the *area* of the impulse and is not just scaling its magnitude. Thus, $A\delta(t - a)$ is an impulse with an area of A located at $t = a$.

The usefulness of the impulse or delta function in system analysis arises from the fact that the response of a linear system to a unit impulse at its input can be used to obtain the response of the system to *any* input signal. Thus, the *impulse response* of the system can be considered as

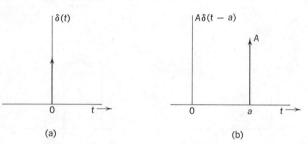

Figure 3-11 Graphical representation of the impulse function. **(a)** The unit impulse. **(b)** Time-shifted impulse with area A.

another mathematical model for the system, since it can be used to relate input and output.

It can also be shown that the impulse is a good approximation to physical pulses, of any shape, provided they are narrow compared to the time it takes the system to produce a significant response. The advantage of using the impulse rather than the actual pulse in system analysis is that the analysis is much simpler and it is only necessary to specify the *area* of the physical pulse rather than its complete time function.

Although the foregoing approach provides a convenient visualization of the delta function and some of its properties, it presents serious mathematical difficulties that cannot be resolved within the framework of the mathematical background assumed for this discussion. Hence, it seems desirable to reexamine the definition of the delta function on the basis of an axiomatic description of its properties. The following list of properties, while not complete, does provide for all of the applications of delta functions that will arise in subsequent chapters. Hence, the delta function will be defined to be a function that satisfies the following conditions:

$$(1)\ \delta(t - t_0) = 0 \qquad\qquad t \neq t_0 \tag{3-38}$$

$$(2)\ \int_{t_1}^{t_2} \delta(t - t_0)dt = 1 \qquad\qquad t_1 < t_0 < t_2 \tag{3-39}$$

$$(3)\ \int_{-\infty}^{\infty} f(t)\delta(t - t_0)dt = f(t_0) \qquad f(t) \text{ continuous at } t_0 \tag{3-40}$$

Some specific comments on these properties are in order. In the first place, conditions (1) and (2) are in complete agreement with the intuitive approach in that they define an arbitrarily narrow pulse with unit area. Condition (3) is usually referred to as the "sifting property" of the delta function[7] and is seen to be a logical consequence of the first two; that is,

---

[7] Actually, condition (3) is the only one necessary. Conditions (1) and (2) are included primarily for their heuristic value.

the integrand is zero everywhere except at $t = t_0$, where it becomes $f(t_0)\delta(t - t_0)$. Since $f(t_0)$ is a constant, and the area of $\delta(t - t_0)$ is unity, the conclusion of (3) follows. The sifting property is undoubtedly the most important one from the standpoint of using the delta function in system analysis.

It is also worth noting one property *not* included in this list: the value of $\delta(t - t_0)$ at $t = t_0$. The discussion on the delta function as the limit of a rectangular pulse with vanishing width would seem to imply that $\delta(0) = \infty$, but this same conclusion cannot be made from any of the defining conditions listed. In fact, it can be shown that $\delta(0)$ may have any value from $-\infty$ to $+\infty$, including zero. Fortunately, this lack of having a unique value is of little consequence in applications of the delta function, since it is seldom necessary to specify its value. In those cases in which it is necessary, the value of $\delta(0)$ is usually *defined* to be infinite.

Another property that is not included in the foregoing list has to do with how the area of the delta function is distributed with respect to the time t_0 at which it occurs. From Fig. 3-8(b) it would appear that for this case, all of the area occurs *after* $t = 0$. This is not always true, however, and the delta function can be defined so that any fraction of its area can occur to the right of t_0. This can be expressed mathematically by the integral

$$\int_{t_0}^{t_2} \delta(t - t_0)\, dt = K \qquad \begin{array}{c} t_2 > t_0 \\ 0 \le K \le 1 \end{array} \qquad \text{(3-41)}$$

in which K is the fraction of the area to the right of t_0. For most applications in system analysis, the value of K is taken to be unity. In a later discussion involving random time functions, it will be found necessary to define the delta function so that $K = 1/2$; that is, the delta function would be symmetrical about t_0. It may be noted here that the term Dirac delta function is properly applied *only* to the case for $K = 1/2$.

Before we leave the subject of delta functions, it is desirable to list some other properties that may be useful in some cases. These properties will be stated without proof.

   1. *Time scaling.*

$$\delta(bt) = \frac{1}{|b|} \delta(t) \qquad \text{(3-42)}$$

2. *Derivative.* It is possible to define a function that may be interpreted as the "derivative" of a delta function even though a true derivative does not exist in the usual sense. This derivative, which is usually called a *doublet,* can be defined axiomatically by specifying a set of conditions, analogous to (3-38), (3-39), and

(3-40), which it must satisfy. If the doublet is designated as $\delta'(t)$, the conditions may be written as

$$\delta'(t - t_0) = 0 \qquad t \neq t_0 \tag{3-43}$$

$$\int_{t_1}^{t_2} \delta'(t - t_0) \, dt = 0 \qquad t_1 < t_0 < t_2 \tag{3-44}$$

$$\int_{-\infty}^{\infty} f(t)\delta'(t - t_0) \, dt = -f'(t_0) \qquad \text{for } f(t) \text{ and } f'(t) \tag{3-45}$$
$$\text{continuous at } t_0.$$

3. *Multiplication by a time function.*

$$f(t)\delta(t - t_0) = f(t_0)\delta(t - t_0) \qquad f(t) \text{ continuous at } t_0 \tag{3-46}$$

$$f(t)\delta'(t - t_0) = -f'(t_0)\delta(t - t_0) + f(t_0)\,\delta'(t - t_0)$$
$$f(t) \text{ and } f'(t) \text{ continuous at } t_0 \tag{3-47}$$

4. *Integral of product of delta functions.*

$$\int_{t_1}^{t_2} \delta(\lambda - t)\delta(\lambda - t_0) \, d\lambda = \delta(t - t_0) \qquad t_1 < t_0, \, t < t_2 \tag{3-48}$$

■ **R E F E R E N C E S**

Except for Fourier series, much of the material in Chapter 3 on signal representation is available only at an advanced level. However, some aspects of this material are treated at a more appropriate level in the following books:

1. Davis, R. F., *Fourier Series and Orthogonal Functions*. Boston, Mass.: Allyn and Bacon, Inc., 1963.
   This book contains an introductory treatment of orthogonal functions and discusses some applications of them.

2. Lathi, B. P., *Signals, Systems and Communication*. New York: John Wiley & Sons, Inc., 1965.
   Lathi treats orthogonal signal representation methods at a more advanced level than the present text and uses some matrix notation in doing so. However, it should be readable by junior-level students interested in extending their knowledge.

3. Marshall, J. L., *Introduction to Signal Theory*. Scranton, Pa.: International Textbook Company, 1965.
   This book contains an expanded treatment of the topics in Chapter 3 at an elementary level.

■ **PROBLEMS**

3-1 For each of the following engineering systems, classify the signals involved with respect to periodicity, randomness, power, etc. Specify the time interval you are considering.

a. Power system
b. Telephone system
c. Radar system
d. Nuclear radiation counter
e. Aircraft flight control system
f. Digital computer

3-2 For each of the following signals, state whether it is periodic or non-periodic, and whether it is an energy signal or a power signal. If it is periodic, determine the period. Also calculate its energy or average power.

a. $x(t) = 10 \sin 20\pi t \qquad t \geq 0$
$\qquad = 0 \qquad\qquad\qquad t < 0$

b. $x(t) = 10\epsilon^{-5t} \qquad\quad t \geq 0$
$\qquad = 0 \qquad\qquad\qquad t < 0$

c. $x(t) = 10 \sin 20\pi t + 5 \cos 22\pi t \qquad -\infty < t < \infty$

d. $x(t) = 10\epsilon^{5t} \cos 20\pi t \qquad t < 0$
$\qquad = 10\epsilon^{-5t} \cos 20\pi t \qquad t \geq 0$

e. $x(t) = \cos 2\pi t + \cos 2\pi^2 t \qquad -\infty < t < \infty$

3-3 Determine whether each of the following statements is true or false.
a. The *product* of two periodic signals is also always periodic.
b. The *sum* of two periodic signals is always almost-periodic.
c. All periodic signals are also power signals.
d. All energy signals are nonperiodic.
e. All random signals are power signals.
f. The product of a random, periodic signal and a nonrandom, non-periodic signal is always random and nonperiodic.

3-4 A signal $x(t)$ is scaled in both magnitude and time to become $ax(bt)$.
a. If $x(t)$ is an energy signal with energy E over all time $(-\infty < t < \infty)$, find the energy of $ax(bt)$.
b. If $x(t)$ is a power signal with average power P, find the average power of $ax(bt)$.

3-5 An energy signal $x(t)$ has an energy, over all time, of E_x. A power signal $y(t)$ has an average power of P_y. A new signal $z(t)$ is formed from the product

$$z(t) = x(t)y(t)$$

a. Is $z(t)$ an energy signal, a power signal, or neither?
b. If $z(t)$ is an energy signal, what can you say about its energy E_z?
c. If $z(t)$ is a power signal, what can you say about its average power P_z?

3-6 Consider a set of real basis functions of the form

$$\phi_n(t) = B_n \cos 2\pi n t$$

a. Find the *smallest* time interval over which these basis functions are orthogonal for all n.
b. Find the values of B_n that will make these basis functions orthonormal.

3-7 Derive the result shown in footnote 2 for obtaining the coefficients of an orthogonal expansion when the basis functions are complex.

3-8 Let a real time function, $f(t)$, be represented by the expansion

$$f(t) = \sum_{n=-\infty}^{\infty} a_n \, \phi_n(t)$$

and another time function, $g(t)$, by the expansion

$$g(t) = \sum_{n=-\infty}^{\infty} b_n \, \phi_n(t)$$

where the basis functions are orthonormal on the time interval from t_1 to t_2.

a. Write an expression, in terms of a_n, b_n, and $\phi_n(t)$, for the value of the definite integral

$$I = \int_{t_1}^{t_2} f(t)g(t) \, dt$$

b. Using the result of part a, write an expression for energy (on a 1-ohm basis) of a signal in terms of the coefficients of its orthonormal expansion.

3-9 A set of basis functions, $\phi_n(t)$, are orthonormal on the time interval from 0 to 1. These functions are to be time-scaled to form a new set of basis functions, $\psi_n(t)$, which are orthonormal on the time interval from 0 to T. Write an explicit expression that relates $\psi_n(t)$ to $\phi_n(t)$.

3-10 a. Using the set of rectangular basis functions shown in Fig. 3-1, write an expansion for the time function shown.

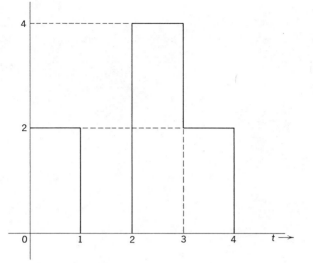

b. What is the fractional squared error for this representation?

3-11 Consider a basis function of the form

$$\phi_1(t) = \sqrt{2}\,\epsilon^{-t} \qquad t \geq 0$$
$$\qquad\quad = 0 \qquad\qquad t < 0$$

and a second one of the form

$$\phi_2(t) = A\epsilon^{-2t} + B\epsilon^{-t} \qquad t \geq 0$$
$$\qquad\quad = 0 \qquad\qquad\qquad t < 0$$

Determine the coefficients A and B such that $\phi_1(t)$ and $\phi_2(t)$ are orthonormal on the interval 0 to ∞.

3-12 a. A time function

$$x(t) = 10\epsilon^{-(3/2)t} \qquad t \geq 0$$
$$\quad\;\; = 0 \qquad\qquad\;\; t < 0$$

is to be represented in terms of the basis functions of Problem 3-11. Determine the coefficients a_1 and a_2 for this representation.
b. What is the fractional squared error for this representation?

3-13 A problem frequently arising in practical situations is that of finding a mathematical representation for experimentally observed signals. One possibility for doing this is first to select the basis functions which seem most appropriate and then to evaluate the coefficients by

approximating the integral of equation (3-13) by numerical methods
(trapezoidal rule, Simpson's rule, and so on). In order to illustrate this
procedure, consider the recorded waveform shown. It is decided to repre-

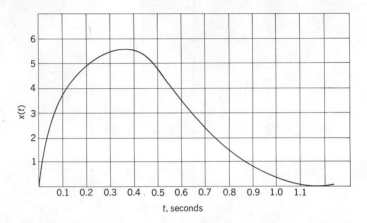

sent this waveform by means of the orthonormal exponentials introduced in Problem 3-11. Tabulated values of the first three basis functions
are as follows:

t	$\phi_1(t)$ $= \sqrt{2}\epsilon^{-t}$	$\phi_2(t) =$ $6\epsilon^{-2t} - 4\epsilon^{-t}$	$\phi_3(t) =$ $\sqrt{6}(10\epsilon^{-3t} - 12\epsilon^{-2t} + 3\epsilon^{-t})$
0.0	1.414	2.000	2.444
0.1	1.280	1.293	0.730
0.2	1.158	0.797	−0.244
0.3	1.048	0.330	−0.729
0.4	0.948	0.015	−0.904
0.5	0.858	−0.219	−0.915
0.6	0.776	−0.388	−0.840
0.7	0.702	−0.507	−0.600
0.8	0.635	−0.586	−0.410
0.9	0.604	−0.634	−0.225
1.0	0.547	−0.659	−0.055
1.1	0.471	−0.667	0.093
1.2	0.426	−0.660	0.216

a. Evaluate the coefficients a_1, a_2, and a_3.

b. Write an approximate representation for $x(t)$ in the form

$$\hat{x}(t) = c_1\epsilon^{-t} + c_2\epsilon^{-2t} + c_3\epsilon^{-3t} \qquad 0 \leq t < \infty$$

c. Approximate the energy in $x(t)$ by using the same numerical integration rule that you used in part b to approximate

$$E = \int_0^\infty x^2(t)\, dt$$

d. Using this value, determine the fractional squared error of the approximation in a and b.

3-14 When complex basis functions are used to approximate a time function, the fractional squared error may be written as

$$\frac{\text{Error energy}}{\text{Signal energy}} = 1 - \frac{1}{E} \sum_{n=-M}^{M} \lambda_n |a_n|^2$$

Prove this result under the assumption that

$$\phi_{-n}(t) = \phi_n^*(t)$$

3-15 Prove the orthogonality relation for complex exponentials as given in equation (3-23).

3-16 a. Find the exponential Fourier series representation for the time function

$$x(t) = 6t \qquad 0 \leq t < 1$$
$$= 0 \qquad \text{elsewhere}$$

b. Find the fractional squared error that results if this $x(t)$ is approximated by the terms for which $-3 \leq n \leq 3$. Compare with the example worked in Section 3-3 in which this same $x(t)$ is approximated by four rectangular basis functions.

3-17 Find the exponential Fourier series expansion for the function $x(t)$ shown.

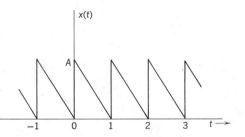

3-18 The Fourier series representation for periodic rectangular pulses was given in equation (3-26). Write this representation in its simplest form for the following special cases:

a. $t_a = \dfrac{1}{2} T$ **b.** $t_a = T$

3-19 Modify equation (3-26) so that it is applicable to each of the following functions:

a. $x(t) - \dfrac{A}{2}$ **c.** $x(10t)$

b. $x\left(t + \dfrac{1}{2}t_a\right)$ **d.** $x^2(t)$

3-20 Sketch the following functions:

a. $r(t + 2)$ **f.** $u(t + 2)$
b. $r(-t + 2)$ **g.** $u(-t + 1)$
c. $r(2t + 1)$ **h.** $u(2t + 1)$
d. $-2r(-t + 1)$ **i.** $-2u(-t + 1)$
e. $r(t) - 2r(t - 1)$ **j.** $u(t) - 2u(t - 1)$

3-21 Sketch the following functions:

a. $r(t)u(t - 1)$ **f.** $r(t) - u(t)$
b. $r(t)u(t + 1)$ **g.** $r(t - 1) - u(t)$
c. $r(-t - 1)u(t - 1)$ **h.** $\epsilon^{-\alpha t}u(t - 1)$
d. $r(t)r(t - 1)$ **i.** $\epsilon^{\alpha t}u(-t + 1)$
e. $u(t)u(-t + 1)$ **j.** $r(t) \cos \beta t$

3-22 Write a mathematical representation for each of the waveforms shown.

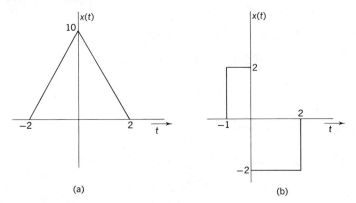

(a)

(b)

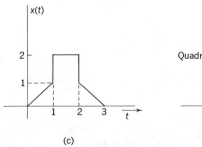

(c)

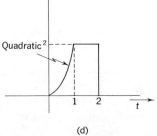

(d)

3-23 **a.** Is $r(t)$ an energy signal, a power signal, or neither?
   b. Is $u(t)$ an energy signal, a power signal, or neither?

3-24 The δ function is often "defined" in terms of a limiting operation on some continuous function. One such "definition" is

$$\delta(t) = \lim_{a \to 0} \frac{1}{\sqrt{\pi}\,a} \exp\left(-\frac{t^2}{a^2}\right)$$

a. Verify that the continuous function has unit area for all values of $a > 0$.
b. Sketch, without computation, the continuous function for several small, but nonzero, values of a in order to visualize how the δ function is approached.
c. Sketch, without computation, the derivative of the continuous function for several values of a.
d. Repeat for the second derivative.

3-25 Sketch the following functions:
a. $\epsilon^{-at}\delta(t - t_1)$ **e.** $\delta(t - 1)\delta(2t)$
b. $\delta(10t - 1)$ **f.** $(\cos t)\delta(t - \pi)$

c. $3\delta(t - 2) + 2u(t)$ **g.** $\displaystyle\int_{-\infty}^{t} \delta(3\lambda - 1)\,d\lambda$

d. $3\delta(t + 2) + 2u(t)$ **h.** $(\sin t)\delta'(t)$

3-26 Evaluate the following integrals:

a. $\displaystyle\int_{0}^{\infty} \delta(t - 2)\cos\left[\omega(t - 3)\right] dt$

b. $\displaystyle\int_{0}^{\infty} \delta(t + 3)\epsilon^{-j\omega t}\, dt$

c. $\displaystyle\int_{0}^{\infty} \delta\left(\frac{t}{2} - 1\right)(t^2 + 2)\, dt$

d. $\displaystyle\int_{0}^{\infty} \delta(3t - 1)(t^2 + 4)\, dt$

e. $\displaystyle\int_{0}^{\infty} tu(2 - t)u(t)\, dt$

f. $\displaystyle\int_{-\infty}^{\infty} \delta'\left(t - \frac{\pi}{2}\right)\cos t\, dt$

g. $\displaystyle\int_{0}^{\infty} \epsilon^{-2t}\,\delta(\lambda - t)\delta(\lambda - 2)\, d\lambda$

3-27 a. Write an expression for $v_0(t)$ in the system shown if the switch is opened at $t = 1$ second, after having been closed for a long period of time.

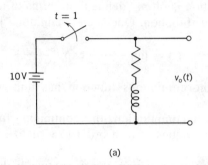

(a)

b. Write an expression for $i(t)$ in the system shown if the switch is closed at $t = 1$ second, after having been open for a long period of time.

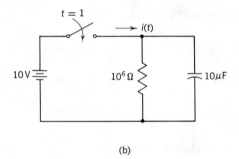

(b)

3-28 It is often convenient in system analysis to replace short pulses having complicated shapes with impulses having an equal area. For each of the following waveforms, find the equivalent δ function.

a. $\dfrac{d}{dt}\left(3 \tan^{-1} \dfrac{t}{2 \times 10^{-6}}\right)$

b. $6 \exp\left(-2 \times 10^6 |t - 3|\right)$

c. $2\left[\dfrac{\sin(\pi \times 10^6 t)}{\pi \times 10^6 t}\right]$

4
Convolution

4-1 Introduction

The central problem of system analysis is determining the response of a system to a specified input or excitation. There are a number of ways in which such a determination can be carried out, including formal solution of the differential equations characterizing the system, use of integral transformations to simplify the problem, and analysis based on the response to elementary signals and the principle of superposition. The last approach is applicable only to systems in which the principle of superposition is valid and, therefore, is limited to linear systems. The method of convolution is based on this last approach and is the one we wish to investigate in the present chapter.

Convolution can be explained on a physical basis as follows: A general signal is analyzed or resolved into a continuum of elementary signals whose sum is equal to the general signal. The response of the system to each member of the continuum of elementary signals is computed and the total response is obtained as the superposition of all of the separate responses. The elementary signals that will be used are impulses, and the expression that formally states the output in terms of the input and the system impulse response is called a convolution integral. Although the convolution integral has many interesting uses in applied mathematics, our applications will be primarily concerned with physical problems. In many cases it will be found that a graphical representation of convolution greatly simplifies interpretation of the mathematical operations involved. Besides being useful in relating the output and input in linear systems, convolution will be found valuable in evaluating Fourier and Laplace transforms and in the derivation of a number of important signal and system relationships such as the sampling theorem and the superposition integral.

4-2   Representation of Signals by a Continuum of Impulses

Consider the time function $f(t)$ shown in Fig. 4-1. This function can be approximated over the time interval $-T < t < T$ by a series of pulses as shown.

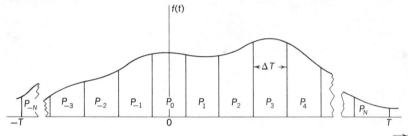

Figure 4-1   Representation of a signal by a series of pulses.

The number of pulses will be $2N + 1 = 2T/\Delta T$, where ΔT is the pulse width. The amplitude of the pulses can be taken as the amplitude of the function at the center of the pulse. Thus, the kth pulse would be

$$P_k = f(k\Delta T) \left[u\left(t - k\Delta T + \frac{\Delta T}{2} \right) - u\left(t - k\Delta T - \frac{\Delta T}{2} \right) \right] \quad \text{(4-1)}$$

The approximation to $f(t)$ is then obtained as the summation of all of the pulses.

$$f(t) \doteq \sum_{k=-N}^{N} f(k\Delta T) \left[u\left(t - k\Delta T + \frac{\Delta T}{2} \right) - u\left(t - k\Delta T - \frac{\Delta T}{2} \right) \right] \quad \text{(4-2)}$$

If we multiply and divide by ΔT we obtain

$$f(t) \doteq \sum_{k=-N}^{N} f(k\Delta T) \left[\frac{u(t - k\Delta T + \Delta T/2) - u(t - k\Delta T - \Delta T/2)}{\Delta T} \right] \Delta T$$

$$\text{(4-3)}$$

As ΔT is made smaller, the approximation becomes better. Also, as ΔT becomes smaller, the factor within the square brackets approaches more closely a δ function located at $t = k\Delta T$. In the limiting case, as $\Delta T \to 0$, N becomes infinite. However, the product $N\Delta T$ remains constant and equal to T. The product $k\Delta T$ takes on all possible values in the interval $-T < t < T$ and can be considered to be a continuous variable λ. The increment ΔT becomes the differential $d\lambda$. In this limiting case the summation becomes an integral with respect to λ over the range $-T$ to T. Accordingly, $f(t)$ can be written as

$$f(t) = \int_{-T}^{T} f(\lambda)\delta(t - \lambda)\, d\lambda \qquad -T < t < T \tag{4-4}$$

The complete time function can be obtained by letting $T \to \infty$, giving

$$f(t) = \int_{-\infty}^{\infty} f(\lambda)\delta(t - \lambda)\, d\lambda \tag{4-5}$$

The function $f(t)$ is thus represented as the summation (integral) of a continuum of impulses having strengths at any time t given by $f(t)\, dt$. The relation given in (4-5) is often used as the definition of the unit impulse. Its derivation in the foregoing manner was carried out to provide a physical basis for understanding the convolution integral to be derived in the next section.

4-3   System Impulse Response and the Convolution Integral

We have seen how a time function can be represented in terms of a continuum of impulses. By computing the response of a linear system to each member of this continuum of impulses and summing up these responses the total system response will be obtained. The validity of this approach rests on the superposition theorem, which states that the response of a linear system having a number of inputs can be computed by determining the response to each input considered separately and then summing the individual responses to obtain the total response. Superposition, as has been discussed previously, is only applicable to linear systems and in the following sections only such systems will be considered.

By the impulse response, $h(t)$, of a time-invariant system is meant the output time function which results when the input signal is a unit impulse occurring at $t = 0$. It is assumed that the output was zero before application of the impulse and would have remained zero if the impulse had not been applied. As an example, let us compute the impulse response of the R-C circuit shown in Fig. 4-2.

The desired result is most easily found by considering the response to a unit area pulse and allowing the pulse width to go to zero, leading to

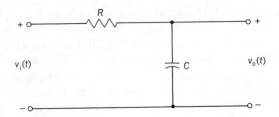

Figure 4-2   *R-C* circuit.

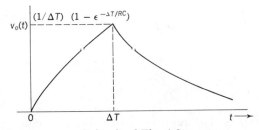

Figure 4-3   Pulse response of circuit of Fig. 4-2.

a δ function. A unit area pulse of width ΔT will have an amplitude of $1/\Delta T$. When such a pulse is applied, the output voltage exponentially increases toward a value of $1/\Delta T$. After ΔT seconds, the pulse terminates and the voltage decays toward zero from the value $1/\Delta T\,(1 - \epsilon^{-\Delta T/RC})$. This is shown in Fig. 4-3. In the limit as $\Delta T \to 0$, the initial rise occurs in zero time and reaches a value of

$$\lim_{\Delta T \to 0} \frac{1}{\Delta T}\left(1 - 1 + \frac{\Delta T}{RC} + \cdots\right) = \frac{1}{RC}$$

Therefore, the impulse response $h(t)$ is as shown in Fig. 4-4. This response can be explained physically as follows. Prior to the occurrence of the impulse the input terminals are short-circuited, since the impulse generator is assumed to be an ideal voltage source with zero internal resistance. At the instant the impulse occurs, a current flows in the circuit and charges the capacitor up to a voltage of $1/RC$. Subsequent to the impulse the input is again short-circuited and the capacitor discharges through the resistor in an exponential fashion with a time constant of RC. The voltage across the capacitor during this sequence of events is the circuit impulse response.

Simpler and more powerful methods for determining a system's impulse response will be considered later, particularly in connection with the Laplace transform. For the present, all that is necessary is to have a physical appreciation of what is meant by the impulse response of a system.

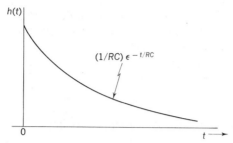

Figure 4-4 Impulse response of circuit of Fig. 4-2.

Using the concept of impulse response $h(t)$ for a linear, time-invariant system, it is now possible to determine the system output for an arbitrary input. The input $x(t)$ can be resolved into a continuum of impulses as in (4-5). Each of these impulses is of the form $x(\lambda)\delta(t - \lambda)\,d\lambda$. The response to each elementary impulse is $h(t)$ multiplied by the strength of the impulse $x(\lambda)\,d\lambda$ and is properly positioned to coincide with the time of application of the impulse. Mathematically, this is expressed as $x(\lambda)h(t - \lambda)\,d\lambda$. The total response $y(t)$ is the summation of all the elementary responses and is given by

$$y(t) = \int_{-\infty}^{\infty} x(\lambda)h(t - \lambda)\,d\lambda \qquad \text{(4-6)}$$

The integral relationship expressed in (4-6) is called the *convolution* of $x(t)$ and $h(t)$, and relates the input and output of the system by means of the system impulse response. A simple change of variable shows that convolution is commutative for time-invariant systems, and therefore an equivalent expression is

$$y(t) = \int_{-\infty}^{\infty} h(\lambda)x(t - \lambda)\,d\lambda \qquad \text{(4-7)}$$

The convolution operation is frequently denoted by a pentacle as follows[1]:

$$f_1(t) \star f_2(t) = \int_{-\infty}^{\infty} f_1(\lambda)f_2(t - \lambda)\,d\lambda \qquad \text{(4-8)}$$

The effective limits on the convolution integral will vary with the particular characteristics of the functions being convolved. As discussed in a later section, for physically realizable systems, $h(t) = 0$ for $t < 0$ and this requirement establishes the upper limit in (4-6) as t. Actually, it would not be incorrect to write the upper integration limit as ∞, since the function $h(t - \lambda)$ is zero when $\lambda > t$. Making the upper limit t just places this property more clearly in evidence. Similarly, if the time func-

---

[1] The asterisk is also frequently used to indicate convolution.

tion starts at a time t_0, the lower limit could be t_0. It is common practice to extend the lower limit to $-\infty$ to allow for input functions extending into the infinite past, such as constants and sinusoids. When this is done, the convolution integral becomes

$$y(t) = \int_{-\infty}^{t} x(\lambda)h(t - \lambda) \, d\lambda \qquad \text{(4-9)}$$

When the order of convolution is changed as in (4-7), the expression for physically realizable systems becomes

$$y(t) = \int_{0}^{\infty} h(\lambda)x(t - \lambda) \, d\lambda \qquad \text{(4-10)}$$

In (4-10) the lower limit is determined by the physical realizability constraint on $h(t)$ and the upper limit is set to include negative as well as positive time for the excitation $x(t)$.

As an example of the application of the convolution integral to a network problem, let us compute the response of the R-C circuit in Fig. 4-2 to a rectangular pulse of amplitude A and duration T. The expression for the pulse is $A[u(t) - u(t - T)]$ and the impulse response can be taken from Fig. 4-4. The output $v_0(t)$ then becomes

$$v_0(t) = \int_{-\infty}^{\infty} A\,[u(\lambda) - u(\lambda - T)] \left(\frac{1}{RC}\right) \exp\left(-\frac{t - \lambda}{RC}\right) u(t - \lambda) \, d\lambda$$

$$= \frac{A}{RC} \left\{ \int_{-\infty}^{\infty} \exp\left(-\frac{t - \lambda}{RC}\right) u(\lambda)u(t - \lambda) \, d\lambda \right.$$

$$\left. - \int_{-\infty}^{\infty} \exp\left(-\frac{t - \lambda}{RC}\right) u(\lambda - T)u(t - \lambda) \, d\lambda \right\} \qquad \text{(4-11)}$$

The limits on the integrals are determined by the regions of the λ axis over which the step functions are nonzero and can be seen by sketching out the three functions involved, as shown in Fig. 4-5. It is evident that for t less than T the product $u(\lambda)u(t - \lambda)$ is unity over the range $0 < \lambda < t$ and zero elsewhere and that the product $u(t - T)u(t - \lambda)$ is zero everywhere in the interval. Therefore, for $t < T$ the limits on the first integral become 0 and t, and the value of the second integral is zero. When $t > T$ the limits on the first integral are unchanged but the limits on the second integral now become T and t. Accordingly, we can write (4-11) as

$$v_0(t) = \frac{A}{RC} \left[\int_{0}^{t} \exp\left(-\frac{t - \lambda}{RC}\right) d\lambda \right] u(t)$$

$$- \frac{A}{RC} \left[\int_{T}^{t} \exp\left(-\frac{t - \lambda}{RC}\right) d\lambda \right] u(t - T)$$

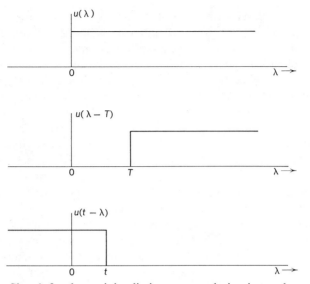

Figure 4-5 Sketch for determining limits on convolution integral.

Carrying out the integration gives

$$v_0(t) = A \left\{ \left[1 - \exp\left(-\frac{t}{RC}\right) \right] u(t) - \left[1 - \exp\left(-\frac{t-T}{RC}\right) \right] u(t-T) \right\}$$

This can be written equivalently as

$$v_0(t) = A \left[1 - \exp\left(-\frac{t}{RC}\right) \right] \qquad\qquad 0 < t \le T$$

$$= A \left[1 - \exp\left(-\frac{T}{RC}\right) \right] \exp -\frac{t-T}{RC} \qquad t > T$$

This response is of the same form as that sketched in Fig. 4-3. Much simpler methods of evaluating the convolution integral are available and will be considered next.

4-4 Evaluation and Interpretation of Convolution Integrals

Consider the convolution of the two time functions $f_1(t)$ and $f_2(t)$. Formally, the convolution operation is given by

$$f_3 = f_1 \star f_2 = \int_{-\infty}^{\infty} f_1(\lambda) f_2(t - \lambda) \, d\lambda$$

The value of f_3 for any particular time t is seen to be the area under the product of $f_1(\lambda)$ and $f_2(t - \lambda)$. In order for the convolution technique to be used efficiently, it is necessary to be able to sketch rapidly (or visualize mentally) the functions $f_1(\lambda)$ and $f_2(t - \lambda)$. In visualizing these functions, there is no difficulty with the first function $f_1(\lambda)$, since it is identical with $f_1(t)$ except for a change in independent variable from t to λ. The function $f_2(t - \lambda)$ as a function of λ requires a little more thought, however. It can be visualized most readily as a combination of reflection and translation of the original function $f_2(\lambda)$. This process, called folding, is most easily described by means of an example. In Fig. 4-6(a), an arbitrary function $f_2(\lambda)$ is shown. The function $f_2(-\lambda)$, shown in Fig. 4-6(b), is merely a reflection of $f_2(\lambda)$ about the vertical axis. In order to sketch the reflected function, it is only necessary to start at the origin with the ordinate $f_2(0)$ and sketch on the right that portion of the function which was originally on the left and sketch on the left that portion of the function which was originally on the right. The function $f_2(t - \lambda)$ can be thought of as $f_2[-(\lambda - t)]$, in which case it is clear that the variable λ has been replaced by $\lambda - t$, which corresponds to a delay (or translation to the right) by an amount t when the function is plotted along the λ axis. The function $f_2(t - \lambda)$ is shown in Fig. 4-6(c) for an arbitrary t. The amount of displacement t is measured from the position of $f_2(-\lambda)$, which corresponds to $f_2(t - \lambda)$ with $t = 0$. The convolution is then given as the area under the product of $f_1(\lambda)$ and $f_2(t - \lambda)$; it is generally a function of t, since the

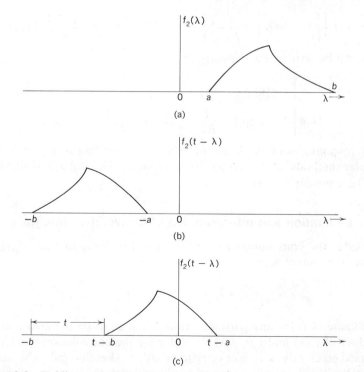

Figure 4-6 Folding and sliding the function $f_2(\lambda)$.

value of t determines the relative positions of $f_1(\lambda)$ and $f_2(t - \lambda)$. The convolution can be thought of as being obtained by folding or reflecting one function and then determining the area under the product as the folded function is slid along the horizontal axis to the right for positive time and to the left for negative time. Figures 4-7, 4-8, and 4-9 show some examples of convolution. The action of the functions f_1 and f_2 on each other can be thought of as a smoothing or weighting operation, and one

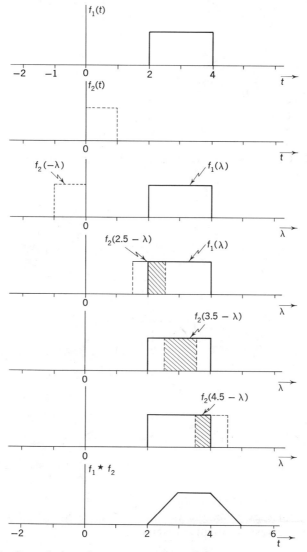

Figure 4-7   Convolution of two rectangular pulses.

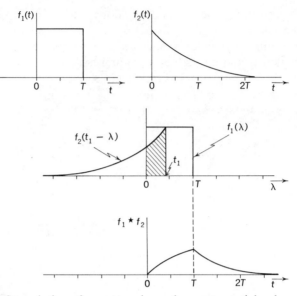

Figure 4-8 Convolution of a rectangular and an exponential pulse.

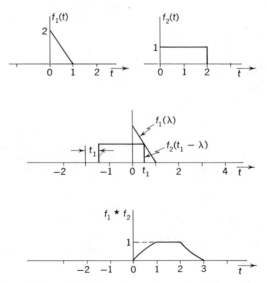

Figure 4-9 Convolution of a triangular and a rectangular pulse.

of the functions is often referred to as a weighting function. In the convolution integral describing the output of a linear system, the weighting function is the system impulse response.

Convolution can also be carried out analytically. In many cases of interest, the functions are discontinuous and thus difficulties arise in keeping the limits straight on the integrals. Consider, for example, the functions shown in Fig. 4-9. Analytically, these functions can be expressed as

$$f_1(t) = (2 - 2t)[u(t) - u(t - 1)] \tag{4-12}$$

$$f_2(t) = u(t) - u(t - 2) \tag{4-13}$$

$$f_3(t) = f_1 \star f_2 = \int_{-\infty}^{\infty} (2 - 2\lambda)[u(\lambda) - u(\lambda - 1)]$$
$$[u(t - \lambda) - u(t - 2 - \lambda)] \, d\lambda \tag{4-14}$$

From the sketch of Fig. 4-9, the following behavior of the functions can be deduced.

$t < 0$.   There is no overlap of the functions and $f_3(t)$ is, therefore, zero.

$$f_3(t) = 0 \qquad\qquad t < 0$$

$0 \leq t \leq 1$.   The folded function begins to overlap f_1 and the amount of overlap increases up to $t = 1$. The integrand in this region is the product of f_1 and the amplitude of the folded function. The integrand extends from the beginning of f_1 (that is, $\lambda = 0$) to the end of the folded function (that is, $\lambda = t$).

$$f_3(t) = \int_0^t (2 - 2\lambda) \, d\lambda$$
$$= 2t - t^2 \qquad\qquad 0 \leq t \leq 1$$

$1 \leq t \leq 2$.   As the folded function slides along f_1 in this region, there is no change in the product because of the uniformity of the folded function. The value of f_3, therefore, stays constant at the same value it had when $t = 1$.

$$f_3(t) = 1 \qquad\qquad 1 \leq t \leq 2$$

$2 \leq t \leq 3$.   During this interval the overlap is decreasing and the convolution is given by

$$f_3(t) = \int_{t-2}^1 (2 - 2\lambda) \, d\lambda$$
$$= 9 - 6t + t^2 \qquad\qquad 2 \leq t \leq 3$$

3 ≤ *t* < ∞.   There is no overlap in this region and, therefore, f_3 is zero.

$$f_3(t) = 0 \qquad\qquad 3 \le t < \infty$$

The same solution can be obtained by writing out the formal expressions for each time epoch involved and then determining the corresponding expression for the product. The integration can then be carried out and will lead to the same result as above. This procedure is usually more difficult to carry out than the preceding method, in which sketches are employed.

4-5   Numerical Convolution

Functions can be convolved numerically using the same techniques as are used for numerical integration. When a numerical convolution is computed by use of a desk calculator one convenient technique is to tabulate the values of the functions on strips of paper that can be slid along-side each other. On one strip of paper, the function $f_1(t)$ is tabulated for increments of t giving sufficient resolution for the desired accuracy. On another, the function $f_2(-t)$ is tabulated using the same increments in t. The strips of paper are then placed adjacent to each other and the area under the product curve determined by numerical integration. The strips are then moved one increment and the new area computed. In this way, the complete convolution function can be computed. Figure 4-10 shows an example of this type of convolution. The value of 370 for $t = 30$ seconds was obtained by use of the trapezoidal rule for numerical integration.

Another scheme for carrying out numerical convolution is the so-called multiplication method. Values of the two functions being convolved are obtained at equal time increments and tabulated in rows one above the other. The values in the upper row are then multiplied one at a time by the values in the lower row and tabulated below the original rows. The multiplication starts at the left and proceeds to the right, and the beginning of each row of products is started immediately below the second-row element that is multiplying the first row. The convolution is obtained by summing the column by a suitable numerical integration procedure. An example is shown in Fig. 4-11, where again the final integration is obtained by means of the trapezoidal rule for numerical integration.

Numerical convolution is also very adaptable to digital computer calculation and provides a powerful tool for the analysis of empirical data.

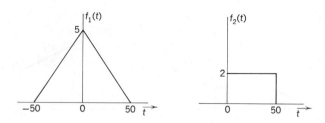

t = 0 position		f₁(λ)	λ	$f_1(\lambda) f_2(t - \lambda)$					
				t					
λ	f₂(−λ)	f₁(λ)	λ	0	10	20	30	40	50
−50	2	0	−50						
t = 30 position		1	−40						
λ	f₂(−λ)	2	−30						
−50	2	3	−20				6		
−40	2	4	−10				8		
−30	2	5	0				10		
−20	2	4	10				8		
−10	2	3	20				6		
0	2	2	30				4		
sliding strip		1	40						
		0	50						
Numerical integration to give $f_1 \star f_2$							370		

Note: The complete convolution requires t from −50 to +100

Figure 4-10 Sliding strip method of numerical convolution.

4-6 Impulse Response of a Physical System

The impulse response of a linear system is a very general and very powerful specification of system characteristics. In systems where the system parameters are varying with time it is necessary to specify the time at which the impulse is applied, because different times of application will lead to different responses. In such systems the impulse responses are written as functions of both the time of application of the impulse, ξ, and the independent variable time t. Symbolically, such an impulse response can be written as $g(t, \xi)$. An example of the impulse response of a time-varying system is

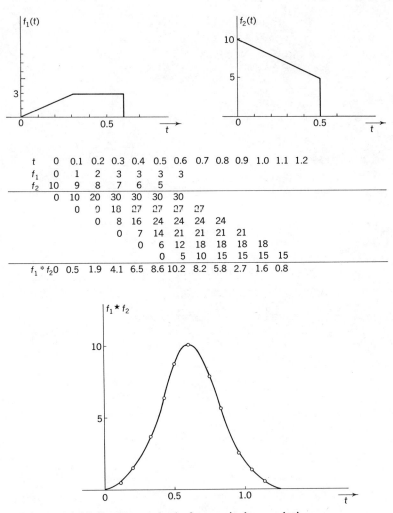

t	0	0.1	0.2	0.3	0.4	0.5	0.6	0.7	0.8	0.9	1.0	1.1	1.2
f_1	0	1	2	3	3	3	3						
f_2	10	9	8	7	6	5							
	0	10	20	30	30	30	30						
		0	9	18	27	27	27	27					
			0	8	16	24	24	24	24				
				0	7	14	21	21	21	21			
					0	6	12	18	18	18	18		
						0	5	10	15	15	15	15	
$f_1 * f_2$	0	0.5	1.9	4.1	6.5	8.6	10.2	8.2	5.8	2.7	1.6	0.8	

Figure 4-11 Multiplication method of numerical convolution.

$$g(t, \xi) = \frac{1}{10 + \cos \xi} \, \epsilon^{-(t-\xi)} u(t - \xi)$$

It is seen that the peak value of the response is dependent on the particular time ξ at which the excitation is applied. The analysis of time-varying systems is generally quite difficult and is beyond the scope of the present discussion. Accordingly, we will restrict our consideration of impulse responses to those corresponding to time-invariant systems. Such systems are characterized by the fact that if an excitation is applied at some particular time and a response $y(t)$ is observed, then an identical excitation applied t_0 seconds later will lead to the response $y(t - t_0)$, which is identical to the first response except for the time shift t_0. Another way of stating the same thing is to say that the amplitude of the response function depends only on the elapsed time since application of the excitation and not on the specific time of applying the excitation. Therefore, it may be concluded that the impulse response of a time-invariant linear system will depend only on the variable $t - \xi$, and not on t or ξ separately. Functionally, this becomes $g(t, \xi) = h(t - \xi)$. An example of such an impulse response is

$$g(t, \xi) = h(t - \xi) = \frac{1}{RC} \exp\left(-\frac{t - \xi}{RC}\right) u(t - \xi)$$

This is the response of the R-C circuit in Fig. 4-2 to an impulse applied at $t = \xi$. If the impulse were applied at $\xi = 0$, then the variable $t - \xi$ would become simply t and the impulse response would be as given previously in Fig. 4-4.

For physically realizable systems — that is, systems that are not inherently impossible to construct — it is required that[2]

$$h(t) = 0 \qquad t < 0 \tag{4-15}$$

This corresponds to the intuitively obvious requirement that the response be zero prior to application of the excitation. This relationship is known as the causality requirement and, as noted in Chapter 2, systems having this property are called causal or nonanticipatory systems.

In addition to the causality requirement, it is further generally required that $h(t) \to 0$ as $t \to \infty$ for passive physical systems. This requirement reflects the practical (but not mathematical) impossibility of having lossless elements in a system. If lossless systems or active systems (that is, systems having internal energy sources) are being considered, then it is no longer necessary that $h(t) \to 0$ as $t \to \infty$, but, to be practically useful, the system must be stable in the sense that the output must be bounded for a bounded input. A sufficient condition for this BIBO (bounded-input/bounded-output) stability is that the area under the magnitude of the system impulse response be finite. In equation form, this requirement is

$$\int_0^\infty |h(t)|\, dt \le K_2 < \infty \tag{4-16}$$

where K_2 = constant.

This relationship may be proved in the following manner. Let the input $x(t)$ be bounded by (that is, never exceed) a number K_1; in other words, let $|x(t)| < K_1$ for all t. The output, $y(t)$, may be expressed in terms of $x(t)$ as

---

[2] For the time-varying case, the requirement takes the form

$$g(t, \xi) = 0 \qquad t < \xi$$

$$y(t) = \int_0^\infty h(\lambda)x(t - \lambda) \, d\lambda$$

Using the property of integrals that the absolute value of an integral is less than or equal to the integral of the absolute value of the integrand, and making use of the boundedness of $x(t)$, we get

$$|y(t)| \leq \int_0^\infty |h(\lambda)x(t - \lambda)| \, d\lambda$$

$$\leq \int_0^\infty |h(\lambda)||x(t - \lambda)| \, d\lambda \qquad \text{(4-17)}$$

$$\leq K_1 \int_0^\infty |h(\lambda)| \, d\lambda$$

From (4-17) it follows that if (4-16) is satisfied, then the output will be bounded by $K_1 K_2$ and the system will be BIBO stable. The question of system stability will be discussed further in connection with transfer functions in Chapter 7.

The units of the impulse response vary with the input and output functions being considered. For example, if $h(t)$ is the current resulting from a voltage impulse, then the units of $h(t)$ are amperes/volt-second. The units are most easily found from the response equation. For the case just mentioned, we have

$$i_o(t) = \int_0^\infty h(\lambda)v_i(t - \lambda) \, d\lambda$$

It is seen that for the integral to have units of amperes, it is necessary that $h(t)$ have units of amperes/volt-second. For a case where the input and output are both voltages, the units of $h(t)$ are volts/volt-second or seconds^{-1}.

4-7   Convolution Algebra

The general formulation of the convolution of the functions $f_1(t)$ and $f_2(t)$ is

$$f_1(t) \star f_2(t) = \int_{-\infty}^\infty f_1(\lambda) f_2(t - \lambda) \, d\lambda \qquad \text{(4-18)}$$

where the pentacle separating the two functions on the left implies the integral on the right. This notation is widely used and allows ready handling of otherwise cumbersome expressions. Consider, for example, the convolution of one function with another function which is itself a convolution of two functions, thus

$$f_1(t) \star [f_2(t) \star f_3(t)] \tag{4-19}$$

The convolution contained in the brackets can be written as

$$f_2(t) \star f_3(t) = \int_{-\infty}^{\infty} f_2(\lambda_1)f_3(t - \lambda_1)\, d\lambda_1$$

Combining this with the first function gives

$$f_1(t) \star [f_2(t) \star f_3(t)] = \int_{-\infty}^{\infty} f_1(\lambda_2)\, d\lambda_2 \left[\int_{-\infty}^{\infty} f_2(\lambda_1)f_3(t - \lambda_1 - \lambda_2)\, d\lambda_1 \right]$$

$$= \int_{-\infty}^{\infty} d\lambda_2 \int_{-\infty}^{\infty} f_1(\lambda_2)f_2(\lambda_1)f_3(t - \lambda_1 - \lambda_2)\, d\lambda_1$$

The advantage of the pentacle notation is readily apparent.

Consider again the defining relation as given in (4-18). By making the change of variables $\lambda = t - \lambda_1$ we obtain

$$f_1 \star f_2 = \int_{\infty}^{-\infty} f_1(t - \lambda_1)f_2(\lambda_1)(-d\lambda_1)$$

$$= \int_{-\infty}^{\infty} f_2(\lambda_1)f_1(t - \lambda_1)\, d\lambda_1 \tag{4-20}$$

Therefore, $f_1 \star f_2 = f_2 \star f_1$

It therefore follows that convolution is *commutative* and the order of the functions being convolved is immaterial.

As a direct result of the superposition property of integrals (that is, the integral of a sum of terms is equivalent to the sum of the integrals of the terms taken separately), it is shown readily that convolution is *distributive*. Accordingly,

$$f_1 \star [f_2 + f_3] = f_1 \star f_2 + f_1 \star f_3 \tag{4-21}$$

When functions are reasonably well behaved, as they always are when they arise in physical problems, the order of integration can be changed and it is shown readily that convolution is also *associative*; that is,

$$f_1 \star [f_2 \star f_3] = [f_1 \star f_2] \star f_3 \tag{4-22}$$

In view of the associative property, it is unnecessary to use brackets to separate the functions being convolved, and (4-22) can be written in the equivalent forms

$$[f_1 \star f_2] \star f_3 = f_1 \star [f_2 \star f_3] = f_1 \star f_2 \star f_3 \tag{4-23}$$

Also, because of the commutative property, the order of convolution is not important. In actually carrying out the integration involved, the limits on the integrals will be different for different orders of the convolved functions, but the final result will be the same for all orders.

Some interesting and useful additional properties of convolution integrals can be obtained by considering convolution with singularity functions, particularly the unit step, unit impulse, and unit doublet. From the defining relations given in Chapter 2 it is seen readily that

$$z(t) \star \delta(t) = \int_{-\infty}^{\infty} z(\lambda) \delta(t - \lambda) \, d\lambda = z(t) \tag{4-24}$$

$$z(t) \star u(t) = \int_{-\infty}^{\infty} z(\lambda) u(t - \lambda) \, d\lambda = \int_{-\infty}^{t} z(\lambda) \, d\lambda \tag{4-25}$$

$$z(t) \star \delta'(t) = \int_{-\infty}^{\infty} z(\lambda) \delta'(t - \lambda) \, d\lambda = z'(t) \tag{4-26}$$

Therefore,

$$u(t) \star \delta'(t) = \int_{-\infty}^{\infty} u(\lambda) \delta'(t - \lambda) \, d\lambda = \delta(t) \tag{4-27}$$

Using these relations and the commutative property of convolution, the following relationships may be obtained readily. Assume that

$$z(t) = x(t) \star y(t)$$

Then
$$z(t) \star \delta'(t) = x(t) \star y(t) \star \delta'(t)$$
$$z'(t) = x(t) \star y'(t) \tag{4-28}$$
$$= x'(t) \star y(t) \tag{4-29}$$

and

$$z(t) \star \delta(t) = x(t) \star y(t) \star \delta'(t) \star u(t) \tag{4-30}$$

$$z(t) = [x(t) \star \delta'(t)] \star y(t) \star u(t) = x'(t) \star \int_{-\infty}^{t} y(\lambda) \, d\lambda$$

$$= y'(t) \star \int_{-\infty}^{t} x(\lambda) \, d\lambda \tag{4-31}$$

These relationships are particularly useful in the computation of Fourier transforms of the products of functions and will be discussed in that connection in the next chapter.

4-8   Superposition Integral

A relationship between the input and output of a system can also be obtained by using the step response of the system instead of the impulse response. The basic relationship could be obtained by a procedure analogous to that used in developing the convolution integral. However, a more direct derivation can be made using convolution algebra. The step response $w(t)$ of a system is related to the impulse response as follows:

$$w(t) = u(t) \star h(t) = \int_0^t h(t - \lambda) \, d\lambda$$

$$= \int_0^t h(\lambda) \, d\lambda \qquad \text{(4-32)}$$

From (4-32) it follows that

$$w'(t) = \frac{d}{dt} \int_0^t h(\lambda) \, d\lambda = h(t) \qquad \text{(4-33)}$$

Consider now the convolution of the derivative of the input, $x'(t)$, and the system step response $w(t)$:

$$x'(t) \star w(t)$$

Using (4-28) and (4-29) we obtain

$$\begin{aligned}
x'(t) \star w(t) &= x(t) \star w'(t) \\
&= x(t) \star h(t) \\
&= y(t)
\end{aligned}$$

$$y(t) = x'(t) \star w(t) = \int_{-\infty}^t x'(\lambda) w(t - \lambda) \, d\lambda \qquad \text{(4-34)}$$

In the most commonly encountered applications involving the step response, $x(t)$ is a causal time function $x_c(t)$ that is zero for $t < 0$. For this case we have

$$\begin{aligned}
y(t) &= \int_{-\infty}^t x_c'(\lambda) w(t - \lambda) \, d\lambda = \int_{0-}^t x_c'(\lambda) w(t - \lambda) \, d\lambda \\
&= \int_{0-}^{0+} x_c'(\lambda) w(t - \lambda) \, d\lambda + \int_{0+}^t x_c'(\lambda) w(t - \lambda) \, d\lambda \\
&= x_c(0^+) w(t) + \int_{0+}^t x_c'(\lambda) w(t - \lambda) \, d\lambda \qquad \text{(4-35)}
\end{aligned}$$

The relationship given in (4-35) is known as the superposition integral or Duhamel's integral. This terminology is not universally used and the name superposition integral is also frequently applied to the convolution integral involving the system impulse response. Little confusion is likely to result, since it is generally clear from the system characterization being used which integral is involved.

The first term in (4-35) results from the occurrence of a discontinuity at the origin. Such a discontinuity, having an amplitude of $x_c(0^+) - x_c(0^-)$ = $x_c(0^+)$, is equivalent to applying a step with the amplitude of the discontinuity and therefore leads to the step response indicated by the first term. The second term takes into account the remainder of the input waveform. Other expressions for computing system response by means of the step response can be obtained from (4-35) by carrying out various convolutional algebraic operations. Care must be taken to be sure that derivatives of discontinuous functions are properly taken into account by means of δ functions. One way to account systematically for such discontinuities is to write all causal functions as functions multiplied by step functions. Then, when derivatives are taken, the functions can be differentiated by the product rule, which will automatically lead to δ functions as derivatives of the step functions. Consider, for example, the response of a system to the causal function $x(t)u(t)$. As previously shown, this is given by $y(t) = x(t)u(t) \star w'(t)$. Interchanging the order of differentiation in the convolution gives

$$y(t) = x(t)u(t) \star w'(t) = w(t) \star \frac{d}{dt}[x(t)u(t)]$$

$$= w(t) \star [x'(t)u(t) + x(0)\delta(t)]$$
$$= w(t) \star x'(t)u(t) + x(0)w(t)$$

which is identical to (4-35) when we take by definition $x(0) = x(0^+)$. This is equivalent to assuming that $x(t)$ in $x(t)u(t)$ is continuous at $t = 0$.

4-9   Computing Impulse and Step Responses

The most commonly used method of computing system impulse and step responses is by means of the Laplace transform. This method will be discussed in detail in the chapters on transform methods. The impulse response and step response can also be found directly by solving the differential equations of the sytem using an impulse or step function as the driving function. The initial conditions at $t = 0^-$ are normally given. If the impulse occurs at $t = 0$, the applied excitation will be zero at $t = 0^+$ and the solution can be obtained by solving the homogeneous differential equation with a new set of initial conditions corresponding to $t = 0^+$. These new initial conditions are the result of application of the impulse. A general procedure for determining the impulse response can be developed, but since this method will not be used subsequently, only a specific example will be considered.

Let it be required to determine the impulse response of the circuit shown in Fig. 4-12. The initial currents in the inductors will be assumed

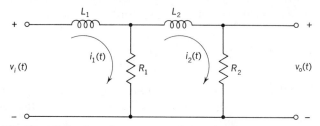

Figure 4-12 Circuit for impulse response determination.

to be zero. The differential equations of the circuit are

$$L_1 \frac{di_1}{dt} + R_1 i_1 - R_1 i_2 = v_i \tag{4-36}$$

$$-R_1 i_1 + L_2 \frac{di_2}{dt} + (R_1 + R_2)i_2 = 0 \tag{4-37}$$

$$R_2 i_2 = v_0 \tag{4-38}$$

Substituting from the second equation into the first to eliminate i_1 gives

$$\frac{L_1 L_2}{R_1} \frac{d^2 i_2}{dt^2} + \left(L_1 + \frac{R_2 L_1}{R_1} + L_2 \right) \frac{di_2}{dt} + R_2 i_2 = v_i$$

Substituting $i_2 = \dfrac{1}{R_2} v_0$ gives

$$\frac{L_1 L_2}{R_1 R_2} v_0{}'' + \left(\frac{L_1}{R_2} + \frac{L_1}{R_1} + \frac{L_2}{R_2} \right) v_0{}' + v_0 = v_i$$

In order to simplify the algebra, let us assign values to the circuit elements as follows: $L_1 = 2$, $R_1 = 1$, $L_2 = 4$, $R_2 = 2$. The equation then becomes

$$4v_0{}'' + 5v_0{}' + v_0 = v_i \tag{4-39}$$

If, now, we let $v_i = \delta(t)$, the resulting $v_0(t)$ is the impulse response. Since there is an impulse on the right-hand side of (4-39), there must also be one on the left-hand side. This impulse must occur in the highest derivative of v_0; otherwise, there would be doublets present on the left-hand side and not on the right. If $v_0{}''(t)$ contains an impulse, then $v_0{}'(t)$ will have a step and $v_0(t)$ will be continuous at the origin. Accordingly, by integrating both sides of (4-39) from $t = 0^-$ to $t = 0^+$, the value of $v_0{}'(0^+)$ can be found as follows:

$$4 \int_{0^-}^{0^+} v_o{}'' \, dt + 5 \int_{0^-}^{0^+} v_o{}' \, dt + \int_{0^-}^{0^+} v_o \, dt = \int_{0^-}^{0^+} \delta(t) \, dt$$

Only the first integral on the left can have a value different from zero since the other two integrals represent continuous functions, $v_o(t)$ and $\int v_o(t) \, dt$, as discussed previously. Therefore, we have

$$4v_o{}'(0^+) = 1$$
$$v_o{}'(0^+) = \frac{1}{4} \tag{4-40}$$

The other initial condition can be found by substituting into (4-39) for $t = 0^+$, and noting that, because it is a continuous function, $v_o(0^+) = v_o(0^-) = 0$. Accordingly,

$$4v_o{}''(0^+) + 5\left(\frac{1}{4}\right) = 0 \tag{4-41}$$

$$v_o{}''(0^+) = -\frac{5}{16}$$

With the initial conditions given in (4-40) and (4-41), it is now possible to solve (4-39) with $v_i = 0$ to give the impulse response. The solution is readily obtained by assuming the form of solution and then evaluating the constants from the initial conditions. Assume a solution of the form

$$v_o(t) = A \, \epsilon^{-p_1 t}$$

Substituting into (4-39),

$$4Ap_1{}^2\epsilon^{-p_1 t} - 5Ap_1\epsilon^{-p_1 t} + A\epsilon^{-p_1 t} = 0$$
$$4p_1{}^2 - 5p_1 + 1 = 0$$
$$p_1 = \frac{5 \pm \sqrt{25 - 16}}{8} = \frac{1}{4}, 1$$

Therefore, let $v_o(t) = A_1\epsilon^{-t/4} + A_2\epsilon^{-t}$. The constants can be evaluated from the initial conditions as

$$v_o(0^+) = 0 = A_1 + A_2$$

$$v_o{}'(0^+) = \frac{1}{4} = -\frac{1}{4}A_1 - A_2$$

$$A_1 = \frac{1}{3}$$

$$A_2 = -\frac{1}{3}$$

$$v_o(t) = h(t) = \frac{1}{3}\left[\epsilon^{-t/4} - \epsilon^{-t}\right]u(t)$$

A similar, although somewhat simpler, procedure can be employed to determine the step response. For circuit and systems problems, it is usually much easier to use transform methods for determination of impulse and step responses.

■ REFERENCES

Most textbooks on system analysis derive the convolution integral in connection with transform methods of analysis. This technique may lead to some difficulty in following the discussion if students are unfamiliar with the Laplace and Fourier transforms. The first three books listed below provide extensive discussions of convolution based on time-domain methods before tying in the ideas of frequency-domain analysis, and are recommended for further study of this technique.

1. Bracewell, R. N., *The Fourier Integral and Its Applications.* New York: McGraw-Hill Book Company, Inc., 1965.

   Although written at a more advanced level than the present text, Bracewell's book contains a wealth of useful material on convolution and related topics that can be readily understood by an average student who is willing to put forth a little extra effort.

2. Mason, S. J., and H. J. Zimmerman, *Electronic Circuits, Signals, and Systems.* New York: John Wiley & Sons, Inc., 1960.

   This book is written at about the same level as the present text and contains a good discussion of convolution, along with some interesting applications of flow graphs to the solution of convolution equations.

3. Guillemin, E. A., *Theory of Linear Physical Systems.* New York: John Wiley & Sons, Inc., 1963.

   Although this is a graduate-level text, it contains many interesting physical interpretations of mathematical operations including convolution and is recommended as a source of new perspectives for some of the items discussed in Chapter 4.

4. Kuo, F. F., *Network Analysis and Synthesis,* 2d ed. New York: John Wiley & Sons, Inc., 1966.

   Written at about the same level as the present text, this book contains a short but clear discussion of convolution and superposition. In addition, there is good coverage of a variety of circuit analysis and synthesis techniques.

■ PROBLEMS

4-1 Using the definition of linearity given in Section 2-4, show that convolution is a linear operation.

4-2 A system has an impulse response of the form $h(t) = 5\delta(t)$ $- 5\epsilon^{-5t}u(t)$. By evaluating the convolution integral, determine and sketch the output of this system when the input is a delayed step $2u(t - 1)$.

4-3 Sketch the function which results from convolving each pair of the following functions. Label the significant time and amplitude values.

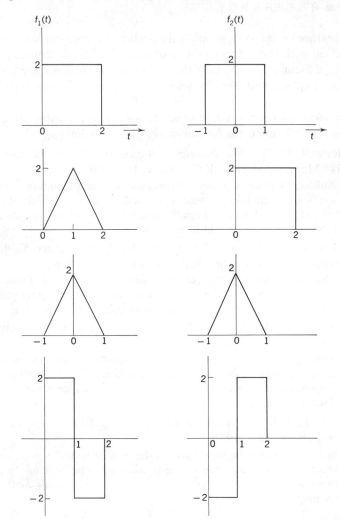

4-4 In mechanics the impulse of a force is the time integral of the force. This concept is particularly useful when the duration is short for then the response of the mechanical system can be determined from the relation that the change in linear (angular) momentum of a mass equals the impulse of the force acting on the body for an infinitesimal time. Using this principle, find the distance (neglecting the air resistance) a 1.5-

ounce golf ball would travel in flight if struck at an impact angle of $+20°$ to the horizontal by a golf club that experiences the force time curve shown in the accompanying figure. Assume $A = 1600$ newtons.

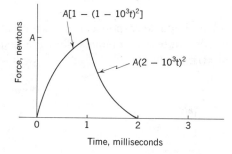

Time, milliseconds

4-5 The $R\text{-}C$ circuit shown has a time constant of one second. Compute and sketch the responses for each of the three input signals shown. Do these results agree with the premise that for a sufficiently short pulse the output of a system is proportional to the system impulse response? What are the primary factors determining how short the testing pulse must be to give a good representation of the impulse response? State qualitatively a relationship between the energy-time distribution in the testing pulse and the characteristics of the impulse response curve that will lead to a useful approximation of $h(t)$. If you were testing with several pulse lengths, how could you tell from the measurement when the testing pulse was short enough to give a good estimate of the impulse response?

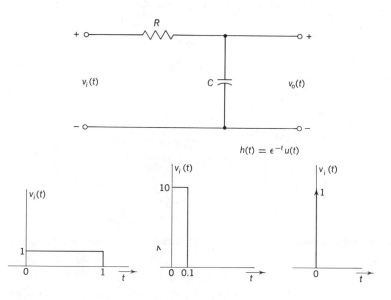

4-6 In testing systems to measure their impulse response it is often necessary to use pulse shapes that are not rectangular. How can you convert from the response of a system to a narrow pulse of arbitrary shape to the system impulse response?

4-7 A system with an impulse response as shown is called a "finite time integrator." Using convolution techniques, find the response $y(t)$ of the system to an input $x(t)$, as shown, if

a. $k = T/10$
b. $k = T$
c. $k = 10T$

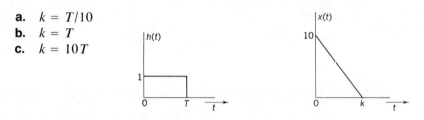

Why is this system called a finite time integrator?

4-8 A system is excited by a 1-ms pulse having a peak value of 10 volts, with a response as shown. Without carrying out any detailed mathematical computations what can you say about the response of this system to the following inputs?

a. $v_i(t) = 5[u(t) - u(t - 0.001)]$

b. $v_i(t) = 10 \sin 2\pi(1000)t \qquad 0 < t < \dfrac{1}{1000}$

$\qquad\qquad = 0 \qquad\qquad\qquad\qquad \text{elsewhere}$

c. $v_i(t) = u(t)$

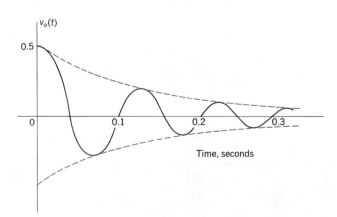

4-9 Using numerical methods, compute the convolution of the two time functions shown. Sketch the result.

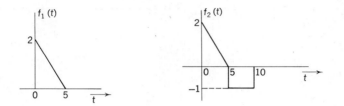

4-10 For a system having an input $x(t)$ and an impulse response $h(t)$, as shown, compute the system response at $t = 3$ and $t = 10$ seconds.

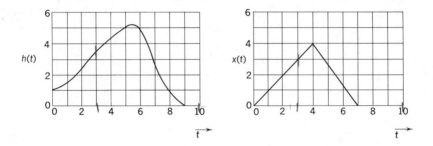

4-11 It is often convenient to use a step function as a test signal when studying system response. Such signals are easy to generate (for example, by a switch) and lead to a response whose derivative is the system impulse response. For the circuit shown in (a) compute the step response and impulse response. For the response to a unit step input voltage shown in (b) find the impulse response and sketch a system having such a response for a voltage impulse input and a system having such a response for a current impulse input.

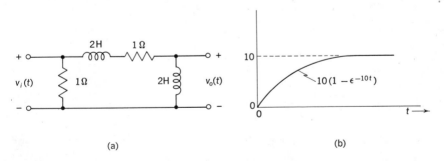

(a)   (b)

4-12 In the network shown in (a), the switch is opened at $t = 0$ and closed at $t = 2$ seconds, after which time it remains closed. This circuit can be represented as in (b). Write an expression for $i_i(t)$. Determine

$h(t)$ as the derivative of the step response of the network, $w(t)$. Sketch the output $v_o(t)$ using graphical convolution.

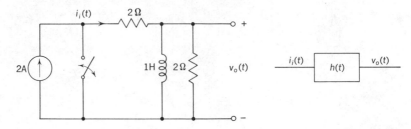

4-13 A recorder has a response to a unit step input signal as shown in the accompanying figure. On the basis of this response what duration rectangular pulse could be accurately reproduced by the recorder? What would be the appearance of the recorded signal for pulses having a much shorter duration? Compute the mean-square error present in the recording of isosceles triangular pulses having durations of 1 second and 5 seconds. (Hint: Calculate the recorded signals first, then the error.)

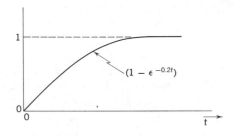

4-14 Sketch a system having a step response of the form shown. What would be the output of this system if the input were $5 \sin (2\pi t) \, u(t)$?

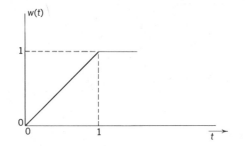

4-15 Derive the following alternate expression for the superposition integral:

$$y(t) = x_c(0)w'(t) + \int_{0^+}^{\infty} x_c(\lambda)w'(t - \lambda) \, d\lambda$$

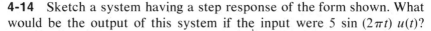

4-16 When signals are transmitted through a system their waveshapes are often distorted. In certain cases, when the characteristics of the distorting function are known, it is possible to perform operations on the distorted waveform that will recover the original signal. An example of this situation is a magnetic tape recorder, in which the recorded signal at any point on the tape is essentially an average of the signal that occurred while the tape passed under the finite width of the gap in the recording head. Such a "running average" can be expressed mathematically by the integral

$$y(t) = \frac{1}{a} \int_{t-(a/2)}^{t+(a/2)} x(\lambda) \, d\lambda$$

where $y(t)$ is the recorded signal, a is the width of the gap and $x(t)$ is the original signal. By a suitable change of variable, show that the expression can be rewritten as a convolution integral. Using convolution algebra show how to recover $x(t)$ from $y(t)$. Sketch a system capable of continuously carrying out the required operations.

CHAPTER

5
Fourier Transforms

5-1 Introduction

Determining the response of a system to a particular excitation can become a very difficult and involved process if the system contains a number of interconnected energy storage units and if the signal is at all complicated. Sometimes our interest is in modification of the signal that occurs as a result of transmitting it through the system and sometimes our interest is in the effect on the system itself. In either case the calculations can become quite involved if we attempt to solve the differential equations by classical methods when the driving function is anything but a simple function of time.

If the system impulse response is available to us, it is possible to analyze the excitation function into a continuum of impulses, and then superimpose the responses corresponding to each member of this continuum to obtain the over-all response. This leads to the convolution integral, which was discussed in the previous chapter. This method of analysis is very powerful and is particularly useful in theoretical and empirical studies. One difficulty in utilizing this method is the problem of obtaining the system impulse response. Another difficulty is that for certain types of problems, such as filtering of signals, only a limited insight into the problem is gained.

A different insight into the interaction of signals and systems can be obtained by considering an approach similar to convolution, but employing a different elementary signal. In essence, the convolution method amounts to breaking up the signal into a number of elementary signals (in this case, a continuum of impulses), computing the response to each elementary signal separately, and then computing the total response as the superposition or summation of the responses to the elementary signals. It is an inherent property of linear systems that the superposition principle is valid. There is nothing sacred about the decomposition of the excitation function into impulses; it could be done just as well using step functions or another signal capable of properly representing the excitation function over the time interval during which it exists. However, in order to use elementary signals other than impulses it would be necessary to know the system response to such signals. The problem becomes one of selecting the most convenient set of elementary signals both in terms of decomposition of the excitation and in terms of calculating the system response to the elementary signals. A signal that is attractive on both counts is the sinusoid, $\cos(\omega_0 t + \phi)$. It will be found that periodic signals can be decomposed readily into a sum of sinusoids which are harmonically related, and aperiodic signals can be decomposed into a continuum of sinusoids of infinitesimal amplitudes.

The response of linear systems to sinusoids is relatively easy to calculate (or measure); in fact, such responses are obtained by steady-state ac circuit analysis using impedance and admittance. By considering an elementary signal that is complex, namely $\epsilon^{j\omega t}$, we will find that great simplifications in computation can be made.

In addition to real and complex sinusoids, there is an infinite number of other elementary signals that could be used. Most of them, however, provide no advantage over sinusoids either because the system response to the elementary signals cannot be easily obtained or because the elementary signals are not simple to work with. There is one, however, that is related to the sinusoid; it will be considered more fully in connection with the Laplace transform. This elementary signal is the complex exponential. Just as it will be found that the complex sinusoid $\epsilon^{j\omega t}$ provides computational advantages over the real sinusoid, it will be found that the complex exponential ϵ^{st}, where s is a complex number ($s = \sigma + j\omega$), provides further simplification for certain problems, such as computation of the transient response of systems.

Before we examine the details of analyzing signals into elementary complex sinusoidal components, it is instructive to illustrate qualitatively how such a representation is possible.

5-2   Representation of Signals by Elementary Sinusoids

Suppose we have two sinusoidal signals of frequencies 100 and 104 hertz. When these signals are combined, the resultant will be

$$x_2(t) = \cos 2\pi(100)t + \cos 2\pi(104)t$$
$$= 2 \cos [2\pi(2)t] \cos [2\pi(102)t]$$

(5-1)

The waveform in (5-1) can be thought of as a 102-Hz sinusoid whose amplitude is varying sinusoidally at a frequency of 2 Hz. The frequency of the amplitude variation, called the beat frequency, is seen to occur at one half the difference between the frequencies of the two individual signals. This beat phenomenon can also be thought of as an interference pattern between the two waveforms present in x_2. When the waves add in phase, the interference is constructive and leads to a maximum in the envelope function. When the waves are out of phase, a destructive interference results, giving a minimum in the envelope. If another frequency component, say 102 Hz, is added, we have

$$x_3(t) = \cos 2\pi(100)t + \cos 2\pi(102)t + \cos 2\pi(104)t$$

(5-2)

This expression can be simplified by use of appropriate trigonometric identities to give

$$x_3(t) = [1 + 2 \cos 2\pi(2)t] \cos 2\pi(102)t$$

(5-3)

Again the beat phenomenon is present. In this case it is seen that the 102-Hz signal is modulated by the function $1 + 2 \cos 2\pi(2)t$. The signal $x_3(t)$ is shown plotted in Fig. 5-1.

Figure 5-1   Plot of the signal $x_3(t)$.

The signal $x_3(t)$ is seen from (5-2) to be periodic, with a fundamental frequency of 2 Hz, since this is the highest common factor present in the frequencies of the three components. Thus, $x_3(t)$ contains the 50th, 51st, and 52nd harmonics of a 2-Hz fundamental. The repetition period of the interference pattern is the reciprocal of the beat frequency, or 1/2 second. If now another component were added at a frequency of 103 Hz, the highest common factor would be 1 Hz and the repetition period of the interference pattern would be 1 second. As more and more components are added between 100 and 104 Hz it is seen that the repetition period of the interference pattern becomes larger and larger. For example, if there were components at 0.10-Hz intervals from 100 to 104 Hz, the interference pattern repetition period would be found to be 10 seconds. In the present example, all of the cosine terms are in phase and so the signal has a maximum at $t = 0$ and at all multiples of the fundamental period. If the summation is divided by the number of components present, we would have

$$y_N(t) = \frac{1}{N} \sum_{k=0}^{N-1} \cos 2\pi \left(f + k \frac{W}{N-1} \right) t \tag{5-4}$$

where W is the width of the frequency band in hertz. The amplitude at the origin would now be unity, and as N becomes large the magnitude of each component becomes small. Also, as W, the separation between frequencies of the components, becomes small the repetition period of the interference pattern becomes large. In the limit as $N \to \infty$, it is evident that constructive interference will occur at the origin but will be

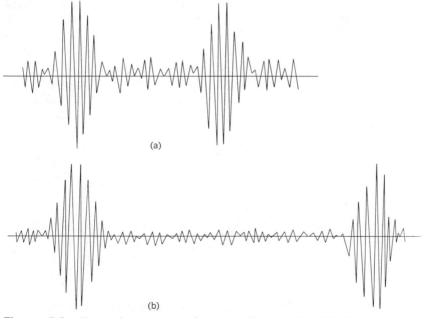

(a)

(b)

Figure 5-2. Beat phenomena, with **(a)** 1-Hz and **(b)** 0.5-Hz component separation.

aperiodic; that is, the pattern at the origin will not be repeated. Two examples of the above interference phenomenon are shown in Fig. 5-2. In both cases the band of frequencies present extends from 100 to 104 Hz. In Fig. 5-1(a) the separation of components is 1 Hz and in 5-1(b) it is 0.5 Hz.

In the interference phenomenon discussed so far, the components have all had equal amplitudes and zero phase angles. By varying these two parameters among the components, it is possible to obtain representation of an infinite variety of time signals. The determination of amplitudes and phases is essentially the problem of determining the Fourier transform of a signal and is the subject to be considered next.

5-3 Fourier Transform

There are several ways to obtain the analytical expression whereby a time function can be represented in terms of a continuum of elementary sinusoids. The method that will be used here is essentially the formal mathematical procedure corresponding to the qualitative picture given in the previous section. To this end consider a time function $f(t)$, which is to be represented in terms of complex sinusoids. This time function can be precisely represented over the interval $-T/2 < t < T/2$ by means of a Fourier series having a period of T. As the period T is increased, more and more of the time function will be included in the series representation. In the limit as $T \to \infty$, the entire function $f(t)$ will be included, at least formally, in the expansion. The validity of the resulting expression will be determined by the nature of the original time function $f(t)$ and is dependent on whether the mathematical operations are allowable or not. This will be discussed later. Consider now the representation of $f(t)$ as a complex Fourier series over the interval of $-T/2 < t < T/2$.

$$f(t) = \sum_{n=-\infty}^{\infty} \alpha_n \exp\left(j\frac{2\pi nt}{T}\right) \tag{5-5}$$

where

$$\alpha_n = \frac{1}{T} \int_{-T/2}^{T/2} f(t) \exp\left(-j\frac{2\pi nt}{T}\right) \tag{5-6}$$

The fundamental angular frequency is $\omega_0 = 2\pi/T$. In addition to being the lowest frequency component, ω_0 is also the spacing between harmonics. Using this expression for ω_0 and substituting (5-6) into (5-5) gives

$$f(t) = \sum_{n=-\infty}^{\infty} \exp\left(j\frac{2\pi nt}{T}\right)\left[\frac{\omega_0}{2\pi}\int_{-T/2}^{T/2} f(t) \exp\left(-jn\omega_0\right) dt\right] \tag{5-7}$$

If we now let $T \to \infty$, the spacing between harmonics will become a differential, that is, $\omega_0 = 2\pi/T \to d\omega$; the number of components becomes infinite, that is, $n \to \infty$; the angular frequency of any particular component is given by $n\omega_0$; and the summation formally passes into an integral. Equation (5-7) may then be written in the following form:

$$ f(t) = \int_{-\infty}^{\infty} \epsilon^{j\omega t} \left[\frac{d\omega}{2\pi} \int_{-\infty}^{\infty} f(t) \epsilon^{-j\omega t} \, dt \right] \tag{5-8} $$

Rearranging terms gives

$$ f(t) = \frac{1}{2\pi} \int_{-\infty}^{\infty} \left[\int_{-\infty}^{\infty} f(t) \epsilon^{-j\omega t} \, dt \right] \epsilon^{j\omega t} \, d\omega \tag{5-9} $$

This is the Fourier integral relation. Its significance becomes apparent when we separate the inner and outer integrals. It is evident that the inner integral is only a function of the angular frequency, since the time is integrated out. This inner integral is called the Fourier transform of $f(t)$ and is designated as

$$ \mathscr{F}[f(t)] = F(j\omega) = \int_{-\infty}^{\infty} f(t) \epsilon^{-j\omega t} \, dt \tag{5-10} $$

The relationship in (5-9) may then be considered as establishing the connection between $F(j\omega)$ and $f(t)$. This is called the inverse Fourier transform of $F(j\omega)$ and is written as follows:

$$ \mathscr{F}^{-1}[F(j\omega)] = f(t) = \frac{1}{2\pi} \int_{-\infty}^{\infty} F(j\omega) \epsilon^{j\omega t} \, d\omega \tag{5-11} $$

The functions $f(t)$ and $F(j\omega)$ are called Fourier transform pairs. The general practice of using lowercase letters for time functions and capital letters for the transform will be followed. Thus, the Fourier transform of $q(t)$ would be $Q(j\omega)$ and that of $r(t)$ would be $R(j\omega)$.

The factor $1/2\pi$ contained in the inverse transform, (5-11), could have been assigned to the direct transform, or the factor $1/\sqrt{2\pi}$ could have been included in each of the two expressions. All of these conventions have been followed by various authors; however, the relationships given in (5-10) and (5-11) are the ones most commonly used and are the ones which will be used throughout this book. In addition to their wide usage in technical literature, the defining relations used here have the further very important advantage of providing a direct extension to the Laplace transform and allow for the interchanging of tabulated transforms between tables of Laplace and Fourier transforms. This also is the reason for writing the transform of $F(j\omega)$ instead of $F(\omega)$. If the functional form is given as $F(j\omega)$, then a direct substitution of $s = j\omega$ leads to the Laplace transform $F(s)$ for a large class of functions.

Using the analogy between the Fourier series and the Fourier transform it may be concluded that the function $F(j\omega)$ analyzes $f(t)$ into a continuum of complex sinusoids having amplitudes of $(1/2\pi)F(j\omega)d\omega$. If $F(j\omega)$ is finite, as it is unless there are discrete frequencies present, then these amplitudes are infinitesimal. This can be interpreted as the distribution of the signal throughout a frequency band. Such a distribution is called a frequency spectrum and, in the case of the Fourier transform, $(1/2\pi)|F(j\omega)|d\omega$ can be thought of as the amplitude of the signal lying in the angular frequency band of ω to $\omega + d\omega$. Noting that $\omega = 2\pi f$, it is also clear that $|F(j2\pi f)|df$ equals the signal amplitude in the frequency band of f to $f + df$ hertz. The Fourier transform can be expressed more clearly in terms of frequency spectra by writing it as

$$F(j\omega) = A(\omega)\epsilon^{j\theta(\omega)}$$

where
$$A(\omega) = |F(j\omega)|$$

and
$$\theta(\omega) = \tan^{-1}\left[\frac{\text{Im } F(j\omega)}{\text{Re } F(j\omega)}\right]$$

$A(\omega)$ is then the *amplitude spectrum* (often called the frequency spectrum) and $\theta(\omega)$ is the *phase spectrum* corresponding to the phase (at $t = 0$) of the elementary sinusoid at the angular frequency ω.

Not all time functions can be represented by the Fourier integral. However, when such a representation is possible there is a unique one-to-one correspondence between a function and its Fourier transform. This means that there is only a single Fourier transform corresponding to a given time function and only a single time function corresponding to a given Fourier transform. The determining factor in the Fourier representation is whether or not the integrals are convergent. One set of conditions that assures convergence is the Dirichlet conditions, which may be stated as follows:

1. $f(t)$ must be absolutely integrable; that is,

$$\int_{-\infty}^{\infty} |f(t)| \, dt < \infty$$

2. $f(t)$ must have a finite number of maxima and minima in any finite interval.

3. $f(t)$ must have a finite number of finite discontinuities in any finite interval.

These conditions are sufficient to include virtually all useful finite-energy signals. However, they exclude a number of important signals, such as periodic waveforms and the unit step function, that are not absolutely integrable. By allowing the Fourier transform to include delta functions, it will be found that signals of this type can be handled using essentially the same methods as for finite energy signals.

5-4 Calculation of Simple Transforms

Rectangular pulse. As an example of transform computation, consider the rectangular pulse shown in Fig. 5-3. This pulse may be expressed analytically as

$$p_T(t) = 1 \qquad 0 < t < T$$
$$\quad\ = 0 \qquad \text{elsewhere} \tag{5-12}$$

The Fourier transform is found by application of (5-10)

$$P_T(j\omega) = \int_{-\infty}^{\infty} p_T(t)\epsilon^{-j\omega t}\, dt$$

$$= \int_{0}^{T} \epsilon^{-j\omega t}\, dt = \frac{\epsilon^{-j\omega t}}{-j\omega}\bigg|_{0}^{T}$$

$$= \frac{1 - \epsilon^{-j\omega T}}{j\omega} \tag{5-13}$$

The transform $P_T(j\omega)$ can be simplified by partially converting to trigonometric function as follows

$$P_T(j\omega) = \frac{\epsilon^{-j\omega T/2}}{\omega/2}\left[\frac{\epsilon^{j\omega T/2} - \epsilon^{-j\omega T/2}}{2j}\right]$$

$$= T\epsilon^{-j\omega T/2}\frac{\sin \omega T/2}{\omega T/2} \tag{5-14}$$

The reason for putting $P_T(j\omega)$ into the form of (5-14) is to make use of the function sin $(x)/x$, which is very easy to visualize. This function occurs

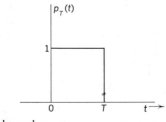

Figure 5-3 Rectangular pulse.

so frequently in Fourier analysis that it is convenient to give it a special symbol. Accordingly, we will define[1]

$$\text{sinc } (x) = \frac{\sin \pi x}{\pi x} \tag{5-15}$$

The function sinc(x) is shown plotted in Fig. 5-4 to sufficient accuracy that values can be read off the curves if required. Also a short table of sinc(x) is given in the Appendix. It is seen from Fig. 5-4 that sinc(x) is an even function of x, having a maximum of unity occurring at the origin with a damped oscillatory amplitude away from the origin. The zeros occur at all integral values of x and correspond to the zeros of sin πx in the numerator of sinc (x).

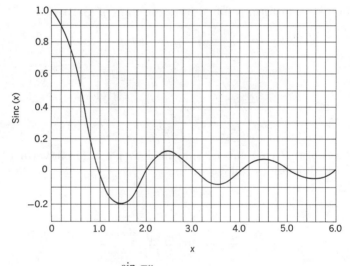

Figure 5-4 Plot of sinc $x = \dfrac{\sin \pi x}{\pi x}$.

Returning now to (5-14), we see that $P_T(j\omega)$ is a complex function of angular frequency ω having an amplitude spectrum $A(\omega)$ = $|T \text{ sinc}(\omega T/2\pi)|$. Figure 5-5 shows a plot of the amplitude and phase spectra.

In addition to the details of the spectrum of a specific pulse shape shown in Fig. 5-5, there is also illustrated a very general property of transform pairs. Note that the spectrum is concentrated over a band of frequencies in the vicinity of the origin with the first null of the major lobe of the spectrum occurring at a frequency $f = 1/T$. As the pulse width is

---

[1] The reason for including the π in the argument of sinc (x) becomes evident when the Fourier transform is expressed in terms of the frequency f instead of the angular frequency ω. This is discussed in Section 5-5.

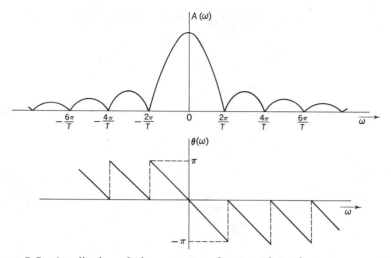

Figure 5-5 Amplitude and phase spectra of rectangular pulse.

decreased, this first null moves to a higher and higher frequency. Conversely, as the pulse width is increased, the first null moves in closer and closer to the origin. The relative amplitudes of the various portions of the spectrum are unchanged by changes in T. It is evident that for this pulse shape there is an inverse relationship between the time duration of the signal and the frequency spread of the spectrum. This is a general property of all signals: *the more compact the signal in time, the more spread out it will be in frequency and vice versa*. One consequence of this property is that there is a minimum value of time duration-bandwidth product that can be obtained with any signal. It is readily shown from the defining equations of the Fourier transform, (5-10) and (5-11), that

$$\int_{-\infty}^{\infty} f(t)dt = F(0) \quad \text{and} \quad \frac{1}{2\pi} \int_{-\infty}^{\infty} F(j\omega)d\omega = f(0)$$

Multiplying these equations together and rearranging factors leads to the following relationship

$$\frac{\int_{-\infty}^{\infty} f(t)dt}{f(0)} \cdot \frac{\int_{-\infty}^{\infty} F(j\omega)d\omega}{F(0)} = 2\pi$$

The two factors can be thought of as the equivalent duration and equivalent bandwidth of the signals respectively. In each case it is seen that the equivalent width is the area of the function divided by the ordinate at the origin. This formulation is most useful when the origin is also the centroid of the time signal. If the centroid is at t_0 rather than at the origin, the signal can be translated and the spectrum modified by methods to be discussed in a later section to give

$$\frac{\displaystyle\int_{-\infty}^{\infty} f(t)\, dt}{f(t_0)} \cdot \frac{\displaystyle\int_{-\infty}^{\infty} F(j\omega)\, \epsilon^{j\omega t_0}\, d\omega}{F(0)} = 2\pi$$

It is seen from these relationships that when the required equivalent widths exist, that is,

$$f(t_0) \neq 0 \neq F(0)$$

their product is a constant and an increase in one must therefore always result in a compensating decrease in the other. As an example, consider the rectangular pulse, $Ap_T(t)$. The centroid of the pulse is at $t = T/2$, and the equivalent duration T_{eq} and equivalent bandwidth B_{eq} are

$$T_{eq} = \frac{A\displaystyle\int_{-\infty}^{\infty} p_T(t)dt}{Ap_T(T/2)} = \int_0^T dt = T$$

$$B_{eq} = \frac{A\displaystyle\int_{-\infty}^{\infty} P_T(j\omega)\epsilon^{j\omega T/2}\, d\omega}{AP_T(0)} = \frac{T\displaystyle\int_{-\infty}^{\infty} \text{sinc}\,(\omega T/2\pi)\, d\omega}{T} = \frac{2\pi}{T}$$

The product $T_{eq} \cdot B_{eq} = 2\pi$. When the functions do not have central ordinates, as in the case of bandpass signals, a different formulation is required. In this case the duration and bandwidth are taken as the radii of gyration of the signal and spectrum measured relative to their centroids, and the required relationship states that the duration-bandwidth product must be greater than or equal to 1/2.

One-sided exponential pulse.   Because of its frequent occurrence in the solution of linear differential equations, the exponential pulse is of great importance in system analysis. Such a pulse is shown in Fig. 5-6. The

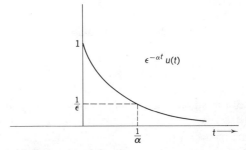

Figure 5-6   One-sided exponential pulse.

mathematical expression for this pulse is

$$f(t) = \epsilon^{-\alpha t} u(t) \tag{5-16}$$

The Fourier transform is obtained by direct application of the defining relation

$$F(j\omega) = \int_{-\infty}^{\infty} \epsilon^{-\alpha t} u(t) \epsilon^{-j\omega t} \, dt$$

$$= \int_{0}^{\infty} \epsilon^{-\alpha t} \epsilon^{-j\omega t} dt = \left. \frac{\epsilon^{-(\alpha + j\omega)t}}{-(\alpha + j\omega)} \right|_{0}^{\infty}$$

$$= \frac{1}{j\omega + \alpha} \tag{5-17}$$

The amplitude and phase spectra are given in (5-18) and (5-19) and are illustrated in Fig. 5-7.

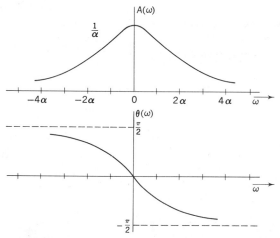

Figure 5-7   Amplitude and phase spectra of one-sided exponential pulse.

$$A(\omega) = \left[\frac{1}{\omega^2 + \alpha^2} \right]^{1/2} \tag{5-18}$$

$$\theta(\omega) = -\tan^{-1}\left(\frac{\omega}{\alpha}\right) \tag{5-19}$$

Two-sided exponential pulse.   The two-sided exponential pulse provides a means of introducing a very important concept into the discussion of Fourier transforms. The transform can be calculated by direct application of the defining integral. Referring to Fig. 5-8, we have

$$F(j\omega) = \int_{-\infty}^{0} \epsilon^{\alpha t} \epsilon^{-j\omega t} \, dt + \int_{0}^{\infty} \epsilon^{-\alpha t} \epsilon^{-j\omega t} \, dt$$

$$= \frac{1}{\alpha - j\omega} + \frac{1}{\alpha + j\omega} \qquad (5\text{-}20)$$

$$= \frac{2\alpha}{\omega^2 + \alpha^2} \qquad (5\text{-}21)$$

The important concept exhibited here concerns the relationship of the pole location in $F(j\omega)$ and the nature of the time function $f(t)$. By poles are meant the values of ω for which $F(j\omega)$ goes to infinity. In (5-21) these poles are the roots of the denominator and are seen from (5-20), which is the partial fraction expansion of (5-21), to be $\omega = \pm j\alpha$. The portion of the time function corresponding to $t < 0$ gave rise to the pole at $\omega = -j\alpha$ and the portion of the time function corresponding to $t > 0$ gave rise to the pole at $\omega = +j\alpha$. This is a general property of the Fourier transform; that is, *poles at negative imaginary frequencies correspond to negative time functions and poles at positive imaginary frequencies correspond to positive time functions*. This property can be used to break the transform up into portions corresponding to positive and negative time functions and it can be used to determine whether a given transform corresponds to a time function existing only for positive or negative time.

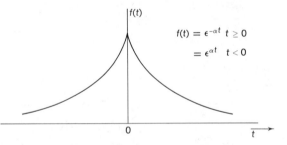

Figure 5-8 Two-sided exponential pulse.

Derivative of a time function.   The Fourier transform of the derivative of a time function can be expressed in terms of the transform of the original function. The relationship can be derived in a number of ways, but a particularly simple method is the following, which starts from the definition of the inverse transform.

$$f(t) = \frac{1}{2\pi} \int_{-\infty}^{\infty} F(j\omega)\epsilon^{j\omega t}\, d\omega$$

$$\frac{df(t)}{dt} = \frac{d}{dt}\left[\frac{1}{2\pi} \int_{-\infty}^{\infty} F(j\omega)\epsilon^{j\omega t}\, d\omega \right]$$

$$= \frac{1}{2\pi} \int_{-\infty}^{\infty} j\omega F(j\omega)\epsilon^{j\omega t}\, d\omega \qquad (5\text{-}22)$$

Now since there is a unique one-to-one correspondence between a Fourier transform and its inverse, and the right-hand side of (5-22) is the inverse Fourier transform of $j\omega F(j\omega)$, it immediately follows that

$$\mathscr{F}^{-1}\left\{j\omega\, F(j\omega)\right\} = \frac{df(t)}{dt} \tag{5-23}$$

and, conversely,

$$\mathscr{F}\left\{\frac{df(t)}{dt}\right\} = j\omega F(j\omega) \tag{5-24}$$

Thus, it is seen that the transform of a derivative is just $j\omega$ times the transform of the original function.

Circuit analysis.   As an example of the use of the Fourier transform in circuit analysis consider the *R-L* circuit shown in Fig. 5-9, in which an

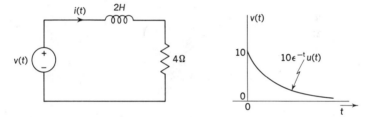

Figure 5-9   *R-L* circuit excited by an exponential pulse.

exponential pulse is applied and it is desired to determine the resulting current. Using Kirchhoff's voltage law, the differential equation for the circuit is found to be

$$2\,\frac{di(t)}{dt} + 4i(t) = v(t) \tag{5-25}$$

If we designate the $I(j\omega)$ as the Fourier transform of $i(t)$ and use (5-24) and (5-17), we obtain the Fourier transform of both sides of (5-25) as

$$j2\omega I(j\omega) + 4I(j\omega) = \frac{10}{j\omega + 1} \tag{5-26}$$

Solving for $I(j\omega)$ gives

$$I(j\omega) = \frac{5}{(j\omega + 1)(j\omega + 2)} \tag{5-27}$$

The right-hand side of (5-27) can be written as the sum of two terms, as follows[2]:

---

[2] The expansion of a rational function, such as the right-hand side of (5-27), into the sum of elementary fractions is called a partial fraction expansion; it is discussed in detail in Chapter 7.

$$I(j\omega) = \frac{5}{j\omega + 1} - \frac{5}{j\omega + 2} \tag{5-28}$$

The current is then obtained by taking the inverse transform.

$$i(t) = \mathscr{F}^{-1}\{I(j\omega)\} = \mathscr{F}^{-1}\left\{\frac{5}{j\omega + 1} - \frac{5}{j\omega + 2}\right\} \tag{5-29}$$

$$= \mathscr{F}^{-1}\left\{\frac{5}{j\omega + 1}\right\} - \mathscr{F}^{-1}\left\{\frac{5}{j\omega + 2}\right\} \tag{5-30}$$

$$= \begin{cases} 5\epsilon^{-t} - 5\epsilon^{-2t} & t \geq 0 \\ 0 & t < 0 \end{cases} \tag{5-31}$$

The last step follows directly from the transform relationship of (5-17). The shape of the current pulse is sketched in Fig. 5-10.

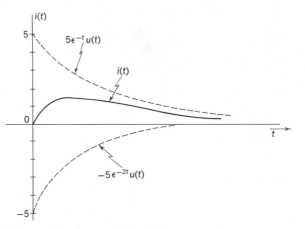

Figure 5-10   Current in circuit of Fig. 5-9.

A little study of the process just carried out in obtaining the solution will reveal that it closely resembled ac steady-state analysis. The Fourier transform of the differential equations leads to terms that are identical to impedances in steady-state ac analysis. In the case just discussed, these impedances were $j\omega L$ and R. The principal difference is that instead of a sinusoidal driving function we use the Fourier transform of the actual driving function. It will be recalled however, that the Fourier transform can be considered a method of representing a time function as a continuum of sinusoidal functions. Also, instead of the angular frequency ω being a constant, it is variable over the range of frequencies present in the driving function. The analysis could be carried out readily by replacing the circuit elements by the appropriate expressions for their impedances (or admittances) and replacing the driving functions by their Fourier transforms. The circuit is then solved, as in the case of steady-state ac circuit analysis, for the unknown response in the frequency domain. The response in the time domain is obtained by taking the inverse Fourier transform. This technique is very powerful and is widely applicable. The concept of the Fourier transform approach to circuit analysis is of the utmost importance and will be used frequently in later discussions. In actually carrying out computation of circuit response, it will be found that the closely related Laplace transform leads to somewhat simpler algebraic expressions and is, therefore, generally preferred. Although the Laplace transform is of great utility in obtaining time-domain solutions, there is also much that can be learned about systems and signals by considering their frequency-domain characteristics. This requires use of the Fourier transform or interpretation of the Laplace transform as a Fourier transform. Because of this, it is important to have a good understanding of the physical significance of the Fourier transform and to be able to manipulate and interpret such transforms.

5-5   Elementary Properties of the Fourier Transform

Before considering application of the Fourier transform to some specific problems, it is worthwhile examining some properties inherent in the transform itself.

Symmetry of $f(t)$ about the time origin.   The real and imaginary parts of the Fourier transform are dependent on the oddness and evenness of the corresponding time function. This relationship can be examined in detail by making use of the fact that any signal can be considered as being made up of an even part and an odd part, with the evenness and oddness being measured relative to the time origin. Thus, if $f(t)$ is a given time function and $f_e(t)$ is the even part and $f_o(t)$ is the odd part, we have

$$f(t) = f_e(t) + f_o(t) \tag{5-32}$$

The even function $f_e(t)$ has the property that $f_e(-t) = f_e(t)$ and the odd function $f_o(t)$ has the property that $f_o(-t) = -f_o(t)$. Substituting $t = -t$ into (5-32) and using these properties gives the following expressions for $f_e(t)$ and $f_o(t)$:

$$f_e(t) = \frac{f(t) + f(-t)}{2} \tag{5-33}$$

$$f_o(t) = \frac{f(t) - f(-t)}{2} \tag{5-34}$$

An example of a function and its odd and even parts is shown in Fig. 5-11.

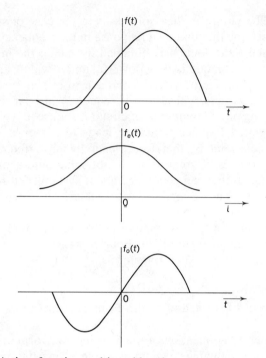

Figure 5-11 A time function and its odd and even parts.

By use of these relationships, the Fourier transform of a general time function can be found as follows:

$$F(j\omega) = \int_{-\infty}^{\infty} f(t)\epsilon^{-j\omega t}\, dt$$

$$= \int_{-\infty}^{\infty} [f_e(t) + f_o(t)][\cos \omega t - j \sin \omega t]\, dt$$

$$= \int_{-\infty}^{\infty} [f_e(t) \cos \omega t - jf_e(t) \sin \omega t + f_o(t) \cos \omega t - jf_o(t) \sin \omega t]\, dt$$

(5-35)

Since the second and third terms in the integrand are odd functions of t, their integrals over symmetrical limits will be zero. Therefore,

$$F(j\omega) = \int_{-\infty}^{\infty} f_e(t) \cos \omega t\, dt - j\int_{-\infty}^{\infty} f_o(t) \sin \omega t\, dt \qquad \textbf{(5-36)}$$

This expression for $F(j\omega)$ can also be written as

$$F(j\omega) = 2\int_{0}^{\infty} f_e(t) \cos \omega t\, dt - j2\int_{0}^{\infty} f_o(t) \sin \omega t\, dt$$
$$\text{(Real)} \qquad\qquad\qquad \text{(Imaginary)}$$

(5-37)

From (5-36), the following properties may be deduced for *real time* functions:

1. Even time functions lead to pure real transforms.
2. Odd time functions lead to pure imaginary transforms.
3. The real part of $F(j\omega)$ is an even function of ω.
4. The imaginary part of $F(j\omega)$ is an odd function of ω.
5. The amplitude spectrum $|F(j\omega)|$ is an even function of ω. This follows from:

$$|F(j\omega)| = \sqrt{\{\text{Re } [F(j\omega)]\}^2 + \{\text{Im } [F(j\omega)]\}^2}$$

in which all of the terms under the radical are even because the square of an odd or even function is even.

6. The phase spectrum $\theta(\omega)$ is an odd function of ω.

These properties are useful in sketching transforms, in checking mathematical operations, and in deducing properties of time functions from their spectra and vice versa. From (5-36) we can write $F(j\omega)$ in terms of an odd and an even part, as follows:

$$F(j\omega) = F_e(j\omega) + F_0(j\omega) \tag{5-38}$$

$$F_e(j\omega) = \int_{-\infty}^{\infty} f_e(t) \cos \omega t \, dt \tag{5-39}$$

$$F_0(j\omega) = -j \int_{-\infty}^{\infty} f_0(t) \sin \omega t \, dt \tag{5-40}$$

Symmetry of $F(j\omega)$ about the frequency origin.   Just as in the case of symmetrical time functions there are also special properties associated with symmetry in the frequency domain. Expressing $F(j\omega)$ as the sum of an odd and an even part, we have

$$f(t) = \frac{1}{2\pi} \int_{-\infty}^{\infty} [F_e(j\omega) + F_0(j\omega)] \epsilon^{j\omega t} \, d\omega \tag{5-41}$$

Expanding $\epsilon^{j\omega t}$ in terms of $\cos \omega t$ and $\sin \omega t$ and using the oddness and evenness of the resulting integrands gives

$$f(t) = \frac{1}{2\pi} \int_{-\infty}^{\infty} F_e(j\omega) \cos \omega t \, d\omega + j \frac{1}{2\pi} \int_{-\infty}^{\infty} F_0(j\omega) \sin \omega t \, d\omega \tag{5-42}$$

Note that there can be no imaginary part to $f(t)$ since we are restricting consideration to real time functions. The even and odd parts of the time function associated with a given transform are, from (5-42),

$$f_e(t) = \frac{1}{2\pi} \int_{-\infty}^{\infty} F_e(j\omega) \cos \omega t \, d\omega = \frac{1}{2\pi} \int_{-\infty}^{\infty} \text{Re } F(j\omega) \cos \omega t \, d\omega \tag{5-43}$$

$$f_0(t) = j \frac{1}{2\pi} \int_{-\infty}^{\infty} F_0(j\omega) \sin \omega t \, d\omega = -\frac{1}{2\pi} \int_{-\infty}^{\infty} \text{Im } F(j\omega) \sin \omega t \, d\omega \tag{5-44}$$

These relations could also have been found directly from (5-39) and (5-40) because of the uniqueness between transform pairs.

Causal time functions. Time functions that are identically zero prior to some specified time are called causal time functions. Unless otherwise specified, it is assumed that a causal time function is zero for $t < 0$, since a simple translation of the time scale can always be applied to the time function to make its occurrence correspond to $t = 0$. Causal time functions have great importance in system analysis since all impulse responses of physical systems have this characteristic. The Fourier transform of a causal function has the important property whereby either its real or its imaginary part is sufficient to specify the time function completely. Consider the causal function $f(t)$, which has the property that $f(t) = 0$ for $t < 0$. The even and odd parts of $f(t)$ are, for $t > 0$,

$$f_e(t) = \frac{f(t) + f(-t)}{2} = \frac{1}{2} f(t) \tag{5-45}$$

$$f_o(t) = \frac{f(t) - f(-t)}{2} = \frac{1}{2} f(t) \tag{5-46}$$

therefore,
$$f(t) = 2f_e(t) = 2f_o(t) \tag{5-47}$$

Now since $f_e(t)$ can be found from $F_e(j\omega)$ and $f_o(t)$ can be found from $F_o(j\omega)$, it follows that $f(t)$ can be found either from the real part, $F_e(j\omega)$, or from the imaginary part, $-jF_o(j\omega)$, of $F(j\omega)$. The required equations are

$$f(t) = \frac{1}{\pi} \int_{-\infty}^{\infty} F_e(j\omega) \cos \omega t \, d\omega = \frac{1}{\pi} \int_{-\infty}^{\infty} \text{Re } F(j\omega) \cos \omega t \, d\omega \tag{5-48}$$

$$= j\frac{1}{\pi} \int_{-\infty}^{\infty} F_o(j\omega) \sin \omega t \, d\omega = -\frac{1}{\pi} \int_{-\infty}^{\infty} \text{Im } F(j\omega) \sin \omega t \, d\omega \tag{5-49}$$

It must be remembered that (5-49) and (5-48) are only applicable to time functions that are zero for negative values of time.

Causality has another important consequence so far as the Fourier transform is concerned. If we are given an amplitude spectrum $A(\omega)$, we may consider that this corresponds to a causal time function if we are able to associate with it a phase spectrum $\theta(\omega)$ such that the combined function, $F(j\omega) = A(\omega)\epsilon^{j\theta(\omega)}$ has an inverse transform that is zero for $t < 0$. Now, since $A(\omega)$ and $\theta(\omega)$ are directly related to each other for causal time functions, it is reasonable to expect that only certain forms of $A(\omega)$ will lead to a nonanticipatory transient response. This is indeed the case. The specific requirement that $A(\omega)$ must meet to correspond to a causal time function is known as the Paley-Wiener criterion[3] and may be stated as follows:

---

[3] R. Paley and N. Wiener, "Fourier Transforms in the Complex Domain," *Am. Math. Soc. Colloq. Rule* **19**, 1934. Also see G. Valley and N. Wallman, *Vacuum Tube Amplifiers*, McGraw-Hill Book Company, Inc., New York, 1948, pp. 721–727.

$$\int_{-\infty}^{\infty} \frac{|\ln A(\omega)|}{1 + \omega^2} \, d\omega < \infty \qquad \text{(5-50)}$$

Two requirements on $A(\omega)$ are immediately evident from (5-50). First, $A(\omega)$ cannot go to zero over any band of frequencies, for then $|\ln A(\omega)|$ would become infinite and the integral would also become infinite. Second, the amplitude spectrum cannot fall off to zero more rapidly than exponential order or again the integral will become infinite. These results are of great significance in relation to the physical realizability of systems that are specified in terms of the Fourier transform of their impulse response, a subject that is discussed in the next section.

5-6 System Function

Consider the general linear system shown schematically in Fig. 5-12. For

Figure 5-12 General linear system.

zero initial energy storage, the relationship between the input $x(t)$ and output $y(t)$ is given by the convolution of the input signal and the impulse response as follows:

$$y(t) = \int_{-\infty}^{\infty} h(\lambda)x(t - \lambda) \, d\lambda \qquad \text{(5-51)}$$

Taking the Fourier transform of both sides of (5-51) gives

$$Y(j\omega) = \int_{-\infty}^{\infty} \left[\int_{-\infty}^{\infty} h(\lambda)x(t - \lambda) \, d\lambda \right] \epsilon^{-j\omega t} \, dt$$

Inverting the order of integration on the right-hand side, changing the variable of integration and carrying out the indicated operation leads to the following:

$$
\begin{aligned}
Y(j\omega) &= \int_{-\infty}^{\infty} h(\lambda) \left[\int_{-\infty}^{\infty} x(t - \lambda)\epsilon^{-j\omega t} dt \right] d\lambda \\
&= \int_{-\infty}^{\infty} h(\lambda) \left[\int_{-\infty}^{\infty} x(\xi)\epsilon^{-j\omega(\xi + \lambda)} d\xi \right] d\lambda \\
&= \int_{-\infty}^{\infty} h(\lambda) \, \epsilon^{-j\omega\lambda} X(j\omega) \, d\lambda \qquad \text{(5-52)} \\
&= X(j\omega) \int_{-\infty}^{\infty} h(\lambda)\epsilon^{-j\omega\lambda} \, d\lambda \\
&= X(j\omega)H(j\omega)
\end{aligned}
$$

There are two important results implied in (5-52). First, the Fourier transform of the convolution of two functions is equal to the product of the Fourier transforms of the functions taken separately. Symbolically this may be stated as

$$\mathscr{F}\{f_1(t) \star f_2(t)\} = F_1(j\omega)F_2(j\omega) \qquad (5\text{-}53)$$

Second, the Fourier transform of the output of a linear system is given by the Fourier transform of the input *multiplied* by the Fourier transform of the system impulse response. Because of its frequent use the Fourier transform of the impulse response, $H(j\omega) = \mathscr{F}\{h(t)\}$, is called the *system function*[4] or *transfer function* and represents another mathematical model for the system when there is no initial stored energy. The system function is generally found as the ratio $H(j\omega) = Y(j\omega)/X(j\omega)$ by solution of the circuit equations of the system. Use of the system function concept often greatly simplifies computation of system response and is of enormous value in the theoretical analysis of systems.

The system function $H(j\omega)$ is the ratio of the component of the output corresponding to the frequency ω to the component of the input corresponding to the same frequency. This ratio is commonly called the *frequency response* of a network or system. It should be noted that $H(j\omega)$ contains both amplitude and phase information. The value of $H(j\omega)$ at some particular frequency can be measured by applying a signal of known frequency and amplitude and measuring the output signal. The ratio of the phasors representing the input and output sinusoids gives the value of $H(j\omega)$. The physical explanation of why $H(j\omega)$, the Fourier transform of the system impulse response, is the frequency response of the system is readily obtained by formally carrying out the computation of the response of a system in the frequency domain when a unit impulse is applied. The output will be the product of $H(j\omega)$ and the Fourier transform of the unit impulse. The Fourier transform of the unit impulse is

$$\mathscr{F}\{\delta(t)\} = \int_{-\infty}^{\infty} \delta(t)\,\epsilon^{-j\omega t}\,dt = 1 \qquad (5\text{-}54)[5]$$

$$\delta(t) \Longleftrightarrow 1$$

From (5-54) it is seen that the spectrum of the unit impulse is uniform; that is, all frequency components are present with equal amplitudes and zero initial phase. When a signal having these characteristics is applied to a system, the output is a direct measure of the transmission of each

---

[4] The function $H(j\omega)$ will generally be called the system function when the Fourier transform variable $j\omega$ is used and the transfer function when the Laplace transform variable is used. This notation will sometimes be interchanged for convenience or clarity.

[5] The double arrow is a shorthand notation relating a function and its transform. The same representation will also be used in connection with the Laplace transform.

frequency component and this in turn is just the frequency response of the system. The uniform spectrum exhibited by the unit impulse is the primary characteristic which makes it such a valuable test signal. Unfortunately, an impulse is not a physically realizable signal because of its infinite amplitude and infinite frequency extent; however, by using signals having uniform spectra over the transmission band of a system, it is possible to obtain system responses that, for all practical purposes, are indistinguishable from the true impulse response. Thus, pulses make suitable test signals provided they are sufficiently narrow.

As an example of a system function consider the simple *R-C* circuit shown in Fig. 5-13. As discussed previously, this circuit can be analyzed

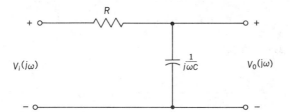

Figure 5-13 Simple *R-C* circuit.

by replacing the circuit elements with their equivalent impedances at the variable frequency ω and then proceeding in the same manner as in steady-state analysis using the Fourier transforms of the input and output signals. The circuit obtained using this procedure is shown in Fig. 5-14.

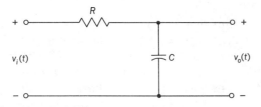

Figure 5-14 Transformed circuit of Fig. 5-13.

The system function can now be written down by inspection as

$$H(j\omega) = \frac{V_o(j\omega)}{V_i(j\omega)} = \frac{1/j\omega C}{R + 1/j\omega C} = \frac{1/RC}{j\omega + 1/RC} \tag{5-55}$$

This system function is shown plotted in Fig. 5-15. It is seen that the amplitude is essentially constant in the vicinity of the origin and falls off rapidly away from the origin. At the angular frequency $\omega = 1/RC$, the amplitude is down to 0.707 of its value at zero frequency and the phase angle is 45°.

An adequate graphical representation of the frequency response of a

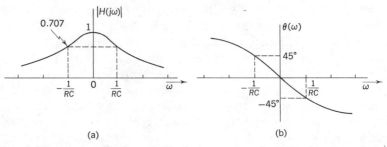

(a)   (b)

Figure 5-15 (a) Amplitude and (b) phase spectra of system function of circuit of Fig. 5-13.

system often requires that a very wide range of frequencies be included. This tends to make linear representations such as Fig. 5-15 very compressed and inconvenient to use. In order to alleviate this problem it is common practice to plot frequency response curves using a logarithmic frequency scale. The phase is plotted linearly (in degrees or radians) against the frequency scale and the amplitude is plotted logarithmically (in decibels[6]) against the frequency scale. Figure 5-16 is a plot of the mag-

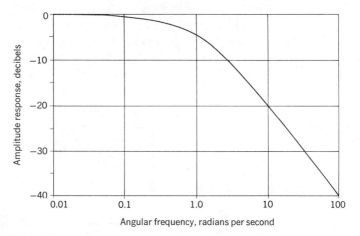

Figure 5-16 Frequency response on a logarithmic scale.

---

[6] The decibel is a logarithmic (to the base 10) measure of the ratio of the powers in two signals x_1 and x_2 and is defined as

$$\left.\frac{P_{x_1}}{P_{x_2}}\right|_{dB} = 10 \log \frac{P_{x_1}}{P_{x_2}} = 10 \log \frac{x_1^2}{x_2^2} = 20 \log \frac{x_1}{x_2}$$

The last two expressions are based on the proportionality between the power in a signal and the square of the signal amplitude.

nitude of the transfer function (5-55) for a time constant of $RC = 1$. Analytically this function may be expressed as

$$|H(j\omega)| = \left| \frac{1}{j\omega + 1} \right| = \sqrt{\frac{1}{\omega^2 + 1}}$$

In terms of logarithmic units, the amplitude spectrum of $H(j\omega)$ becomes

$$|H(j\omega)|_{dB} = 10 \log |H(j\omega)|^2 = 10 \log \left(\frac{1}{1 + \omega^2} \right) = -10 \log (1 + \omega^2)$$

(5-56)

For high frequencies, ω^2 is much greater than 1 and (5-56) can be written as

$$|H(j\omega)|_{dB} \approx -20 \log \omega$$

(5-57)

From (5-57) it is seen that each time the frequency doubles $|H(j\omega)|_{dB}$ is decreased by $20 \log 2 = 6$ dB, and each time the frequency increases by a factor of 10 the amplitude spectrum decreases by 20 dB. Such a response curve is said to be falling off at a rate of 6 dB per octave or 20 dB per decade and is characteristic of a circuit containing a single energy-storage element. Data of this general type are often called Bode diagrams, after H. W. Bode who employed them extensively in analyzing feedback systems. They find wide application in analysis of automatic control systems and much information about system characteristics can be deduced from such plots. For further information on Bode plots, the references at the end of the chapter may be consulted.

Examination of Fig. 5-15 or 5-16 shows that the *attenuation* of signals transmitted through the circuit of Fig. 5-14 is small at low frequencies and large at high frequencies. A circuit having this type of transmission characteristic is called a low-pass filter. There are many other kinds of filters, including bandpass, band-stop, high-pass, equalizing, and other related types. Oftentimes, it is convenient to consider certain idealized types of filters. Two frequently used idealizations are the low-pass and bandpass filters, whose system functions are sketched in Fig. 5-17. The *ideal low-*

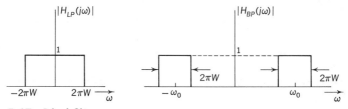

Figure 5-17   Ideal filters.

pass filter is characterized by a system function whose magnitude is constant over the angular frequency band, $-2\pi W \leq \omega \leq 2\pi W$, where W is the bandwidth of the filter measured in hertz and $2\pi W$ is the bandwidth of the filter measured in radians per second. The amplitude of the system function is referred to as the *gain* of the system and is unity for the ideal filter shown.

The *ideal bandpass filter* is characterized by unity gain over a band of frequencies of width $2\pi W$ radians per second symmetrically located about the center angular frequencies $\pm\omega_0$ as shown.

Both the ideal low-pass and ideal bandpass filters have the property of passing all frequency components lying within their passbands and completely attenuating all other frequency components. It is worth noting that systems having characteristics like the ideal filters discussed are not physically realizable. That this is the case may be seen readily by applying the Paley-Wiener criterion to $H(j\omega)$. Inserting $H(j\omega)$ into (5-50) gives the requirement

$$\int_{-\infty}^{\infty} \frac{|\ln|H(j\omega)||}{1 + \omega^2}\, d\omega < \infty$$

Since all of the ideal filters have frequency bands over which $|H(j\omega)|$ is zero, the logarithm is infinite and the criterion is not met. In a later section the theoretical responses of ideal filters to various input signals are considered, and it is shown that for such systems there is an output prior to application of the input. As a practical matter, a given amplitude spectrum can be approximated arbitrarily closely over any finite band of frequencies with a real filter provided sufficient time delay (that is, phase lag) is permitted. If the Paley-Wiener criterion is satisfied, an exact synthesis can be accomplished (theoretically) with a finite time delay. If the Paley-Wiener criterion is not satisfied, an exact synthesis requires an infinite time delay, but an approximation can be obtained with finite time delay.

5-7 Fourier Transform as a Function of *f*

For purposes of describing filter characteristics and, in fact, Fourier transforms in general, it is often convenient to talk in terms of frequency *f*, measured in hertz, rather than angular frequency ω, measured in radians per second. This can be accomplished readily merely by substituting $2\pi f$ for ω in the Fourier transforms being considered. For example, consider the system function of the simple *R-C* low-pass filter shown in Fig. 5-13. We can write this in equivalent forms as:

$$H(j\omega) = \frac{1/RC}{j\omega + (1/RC)} \qquad \text{(5-58)}$$

$$H(f) = \frac{1/RC}{j2\pi f + (1/RC)} = \frac{1/2\pi RC}{jf + (1/2\pi RC)} \qquad \text{(5-59)}$$

Here we have used a somewhat simplified notation. To be correct mathematically, the left-hand side of (5-59) should be $H(j2\pi f)$, since we obtained (5-59) from (5-58) by substituting $\omega = 2\pi f$. However, for the sake of convenience and simplified notation, we suppress the factor $j2\pi$ in the argument of the symbolic form of the Fourier transform when using f as the variable. This should not result in confusion once it is realized what is being done; in fact, this type of representation is commonly encountered in the technical literature. When computations are carried out, there will be no possibility of confusion if either $F(j\omega)$ or $F(f)$ is used consistently. If it is necessary to change from one variable to the other, then all that is required is to make the substitution $f = \omega/2\pi$ into the algebraic expression of $F(f)$ to get $F(j\omega)$ or to make the substitution $\omega = 2\pi f$ into the algebraic expression for $F(j\omega)$ to get $F(f)$.

Using this notation, the ideal low-pass and bandpass filters corresponding to Fig. 5-17 can be specified in terms of frequency f as shown in Fig. 5-18. Further examples of this notation are given in later sections.

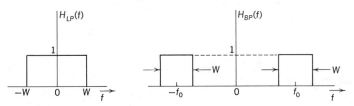

Figure 5-18 Ideal filter characteristic as functions of f.

5-8 Energy Spectrum

In developing the Fourier transform concept we have discussed the idea of amplitude and phase spectra which relate to the relative magnitudes and phases of the infinitesimal signals making up a continuum of complex sinusoids representing the original signal. The idea of signal spectra can be put on a more intuitively satisfying basis by considering the distribution of signal energy as a function of frequency. The required relationship is found by expressing the energy in the time domain and then writing an equivalent expression using inverse transforms of the frequency-domain representation of the time function. As discussed in Chapter 3, the instantaneous power in a signal is generally taken as the square of the signal amplitude. Thus, for the signal, $f(t)$, the instantaneous signal power is

$[f(t)]^2$. Actually, this is only a true power for certain situations. For example, if the signal were a voltage across a resistance R, the true instantaneous power would be $(1/R)[f(t)]^2$. If $R = 1 \ \Omega$, then $[f(t)]^2$ is the true power. However, if R is something different from one ohm, then $[f(t)]^2$ is only proportional to true power, with the constant of proportionality being $1/R$. A similar situation occurs for the case in which $f(t)$ is a current. The power is always proportional to the square of the signal amplitude, but the constant of proportionality varies with the particular resistance level in the circuit. In order to avoid carrying extra constants along in computation, it is customary in signal analysis to consider that the units of power are the square of the amplitude of the signals involved. For a signal voltage the power is therefore measured in volts² and energy measured in volts²-second. This is equivalent to assuming that the signal voltage is measured across a one-ohm resistance. A similar relationship is used for signals measured in other units. Little confusion results if the units are included, and a great simplification in talking about power is possible when this convention is employed.

Using this convention, the energy in a signal $f(t)$ is given as

$$E = \int_{-\infty}^{\infty} [f(t)]^2 \, dt \qquad \text{(5-60)}$$

Letting $F(j\omega)$ be the Fourier transform of $f(t)$, (5-60) can be written as

$$\int_{-\infty}^{\infty} [f(t)]^2 \, dt = \int_{-\infty}^{\infty} f(t) \left[\frac{1}{2\pi} \int_{-\infty}^{\infty} F(j\omega) \epsilon^{j\omega t} \, d\omega \right] dt \qquad \text{(5-61)}$$

Interchanging the order of integration on the right-hand side of (5-61) and rearranging gives

$$\int_{-\infty}^{\infty} [f(t)]^2 \, dt = \frac{1}{2\pi} \int_{-\infty}^{\infty} F(j\omega) \left[\int_{-\infty}^{\infty} f(t) \, \epsilon^{j\omega t} \, dt \right] d\omega \qquad \text{(5-62)}$$

The factor in this integrand that is enclosed in brackets is seen to be $F(-j\omega)$. Therefore, (5-62) can be written as

$$\int_{-\infty}^{\infty} [f(t)]^2 \, dt = \frac{1}{2\pi} \int_{-\infty}^{\infty} F(j\omega) F(-j\omega) \, d\omega \qquad \text{(5-63)}$$

This can be put into a somewhat simpler form by noting from the definition of the Fourier transform that if $f(t)$ is real (that is, it has no imaginary part), then $F(-j\omega) = F^*(j\omega)$, the complex conjugate of $F(j\omega)$. Using this relationship, (5-63) can then be written as

$$\int_{-\infty}^{\infty} [f(t)]^2 \, dt = \frac{1}{2\pi} \int_{-\infty}^{\infty} F(j\omega) F^*(j\omega) \, d\omega \qquad \text{(5-64)}$$

$$= \frac{1}{2\pi} \int_{-\infty}^{\infty} |F(j\omega)|^2 \, d\omega \qquad \text{(5-65)}$$

The relationship in (5-63), which is a fundamental property of Fourier transforms, is called *Parseval's theorem*. In words, Parseval's theorem states that the energy in the signal $f(t)$ is equal to $1/2\pi$ times the area under the square of the magnitude of the Fourier transform of $f(t)$. The quantity $|F(j\omega)|^2$ is called the *energy spectrum*, or *energy density spectrum*, of $f(t)$ since, from (5-65), it can be interpreted as the distribution of energy with frequency.[7] The units of $|F(j\omega)|^2$ are dependent on the units of $f(t)$; for example, if $f(t)$ were a voltage, then $|F(j\omega)|^2$ would have units of volts²-seconds per hertz.

In order to appreciate the full significance of the energy spectrum, it is necessary to understand how the system function of a linear system affects this spectrum for a signal transmitted through the system. It was previously shown that for the case of a simple system, having a system function $H(j\omega)$, the output and input are related by

$$Y(j\omega) = H(j\omega)X(j\omega)$$

The energy spectrum of the output is then found to be

$$\begin{aligned}
|Y(j\omega)|^2 &= Y(j\omega)Y^*(j\omega) \\
&= [H(j\omega)X(j\omega)][H^*(j\omega)X^*(j\omega)] \\
&= |H(j\omega)|^2|X(j\omega)|^2
\end{aligned}$$
(5-66)

From (5-66) it is seen that the output signal energy spectrum is related to the input signal energy spectrum by the quantity $|H(j\omega)|^2$. Because of this relationship, $|H(j\omega)|^2$ is sometimes called the *energy transfer function* of the system.

Using the energy transfer function concept, it is possible to obtain a better appreciation of the physical significance of the energy spectrum. Suppose that a signal having an arbitrary energy spectrum is passed through an ideal bandpass filter having a narrow passband centered at a frequency f_1. The energy transfer function of the filter will be unity for those components lying in the filter passband and will be zero for all other components. The energy spectrum of the output will therefore be just that portion of the energy spectrum of the input corresponding to the frequencies in the filter passband. Figure 5-19 shows a typical example of such an arrangement. The total energy of the output will be given by

$$E_o = \int_{-\infty}^{\infty} |V_o(f)|^2 \, df = 2\int_{f_1 - W/2}^{f_1 + W/2} |V_i(f)|^2 \, df$$
(5-67)

where in (5-67) the factor $1/2\pi$ was absorbed into the variable of integration. For a sufficiently narrow filter bandpass (narrow enough so that

---

[7] More precisely, $|F(j\omega)|^2(d\omega/2\pi)$ is the signal energy contained in the differential frequency band from ω to $\omega + d\omega$.

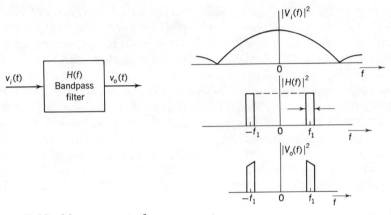

Figure 5-19   Measurement of energy spectrum.

Solving for $V_i(f_1)$ gives

$$|V_i(f_1)|^2 = \frac{E_o}{2W}$$

From this expression it is evident that $|V_i(f)|^2$ can be interpreted as the energy per unit bandwidth.

As an example of the energy spectrum of a signal consider the pulse signal, $p_T(t)$, which was discussed earlier. From (5-14) we have

$$|P_T(j\omega)|^2 = T^2 \left[\frac{\sin \omega T/2}{\omega T/2} \right]^2 \tag{5-68}$$

Changing from ω to $f = \omega/2\pi$ gives the energy spectrum as

$$|P_T(f)|^2 = T^2 \left[\frac{\sin \pi Tf}{\pi Tf} \right]^2 = T^2 \operatorname{sinc}^2 (fT) \tag{5-69}$$

The energy spectrum $|P_T(f)|^2$, of the rectangular pulse, is shown in Fig. 5-20. It is seen that the energy is concentrated in the low-frequency

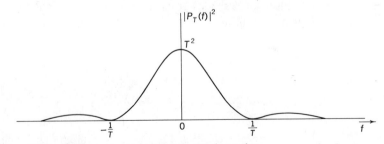

Figure 5-20   Energy spectrum of rectangular pulse.

portion of the spectrum. The extent of this concentration can be found by computing the energy in the first loop (that is, for $|f| < 1/T$) and comparing this to the total energy. The ratio, found by graphical integration, is 0.902. Thus, 90.2 percent of the energy in a rectangular pulse is contained in the band of frequencies below a frequency equal to reciprocal of the pulse length. As a useful rule of thumb, it is often assumed that a pulse transmission system having a bandwidth equal to the reciprocal of the pulse width will perform satisfactorily. Actually, if high-fidelity reproduction of the pulse shape is required, a much greater bandwidth will be necessary. However, it can be seen that a system with this bandwidth will transmit most of the pulse energy.

5-9   Fourier Transforms Corresponding to Mathematical Operations

Certain mathematical operations performed on time functions give rise to modified functions whose Fourier transforms can be obtained by performing suitable mathematical operations on the Fourier transform of the original function. By studying some of the more frequently occurring operations and establishing the corresponding operations in the domain of the image function, great flexibility and power are added to the Fourier transform technique. An example that has already been considered is differentiation in the time domain, which was found to correspond to multiplication by $j\omega$ in the frequency domain. A number of additional operations will now be considered. In all cases it is assumed that $F(j\omega)$ is the Fourier transform of the unmodified function $f(t)$.

Scaling.   By scaling is meant multiplication of the variable in the time function by a constant. This has the effect of expanding or contracting the time scale depending on whether the magnitude of the constant is less than or greater than unity. If the constant is negative the time scale is reversed. The Fourier transform of a scaled time function can be obtained as follows:

$$\mathcal{F}\{f(at)\} = \int_{-\infty}^{\infty} f(at)e^{-j\omega t} dt$$

We must consider the case of positive and negative a separately. Consider first the positive a and change the variable of integration to $\lambda = at$.

$$\mathcal{F}\{f(at)\} = \frac{1}{a}\int_{-\infty}^{\infty} f(\lambda)\epsilon^{-j\omega\lambda/a} d\lambda$$

$$= \frac{1}{a} F\left(\frac{j\omega}{a}\right) \qquad a > 0 \tag{5-70}$$

When a is negative, the limits on the integral will be reversed when the variable of integration is changed; the final result is

$$\mathscr{F}\{f(at)\} = -\frac{1}{a} F\left(\frac{j\omega}{a}\right) \qquad a < 0 \tag{5-71}$$

These two results can be combined to give

$$f(at) \Longleftrightarrow \frac{1}{|a|} F\left(\frac{j\omega}{a}\right) \tag{5-72}$$

This relationship is useful in extending a table of transforms of normalized functions to cover more general cases. It also illustrates once more the property that as we expand the time scale of a function, its frequency spectrum is contracted. In addition, it is seen that the amplitude of the spectrum also changes. This latter effect is necessary to maintain an energy balance between the two domains.

Delay.   When a new variable $t - t_0$ is substituted for the original variable t in a time function, the resulting function is an exact replica of the original function delayed by an amount t_0. The Fourier transform of the modified function is

$$\mathscr{F}\{f(t - t_0)\} = \int_{-\infty}^{\infty} f(t - t_0)\epsilon^{-j\omega t}\, dt$$

Changing the variable of integration and carrying out the indicated operations gives

$$\mathscr{F}\{f(t - t_0)\} = \int_{-\infty}^{\infty} f(\lambda)\epsilon^{-j\omega(\lambda + t_0)}\, d\lambda$$

$$= \epsilon^{-j\omega t_0} \int_{-\infty}^{\infty} f(\lambda)\epsilon^{-j\omega\lambda}\, d\lambda \tag{5-73}$$

$$= \epsilon^{-j\omega t_0} F(j\omega)$$

$$f(t - t_0) \Longleftrightarrow \epsilon^{-j\omega t_0} F(j\omega)$$

Delay in the time domain is thus seen to correspond to introduction of a phase shift in the frequency domain that varies linearly with frequency. As an example of the use of (5-73), consider the rectangular pulse shown in Fig. 5-21. This signal is identical to the pulse signal, $p_T(t)$, previously

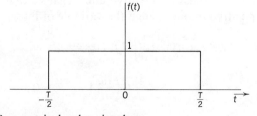

Figure 5-21   Symmetrical pulse signal.

considered, except that it is advanced by an amount $T/2$. Therefore, $f(t) = p_T(t + T/2)$.

The corresponding transform is then found from (5-73) and (5-14) to be

$$F(j\omega) = \epsilon^{j\omega T/2} p_T(j\omega)$$

$$= T\epsilon^{j\omega T/2}\epsilon^{-j\omega T/2}\frac{\sin \omega T/2}{\omega T/2} \tag{5-74}$$

$$= T\frac{\sin \omega T/2}{\omega T/2}$$

Expressed in terms of the frequency f, this can be stated as

$$F(f) = T\frac{\sin \pi Tf}{\pi Tf} = T \text{ sinc } (Tf) \tag{5-75}$$

Modulation.   Multiplication of a time function by the complex sinusoid $\epsilon^{j\omega_0 t}$ causes a translation in the frequency domain. Thus,

$$\mathscr{F}\{\epsilon^{j\omega_0 t} f(t)\} = \int_{-\infty}^{\infty} f(t)\, \epsilon^{-j(\omega - \omega_0)t}\, dt$$

$$= F[j(\omega - \omega_0)] \tag{5-76}$$

$$\epsilon^{j\omega_0 t} f(t) \Longleftrightarrow F[j(\omega - \omega_0)] \quad \text{or} \quad F(f - f_0)$$

The relationship in (5-76) can be thought of as a process in which the complex sinusoid is modulated by the time function, $f(t)$. If instead of $\epsilon^{j\omega_0 t}$, we consider the real function, $\cos \omega_0 t$, we obtain the following relationship:

$$\mathscr{F}\{f(t) \cos \omega_0 t\} = \int_{-\infty}^{\infty} f(t)\frac{\epsilon^{j\omega_0 t} + \epsilon^{-j\omega_0 t}}{2}\epsilon^{-j\omega t}\, dt$$

$$f(t) \cos \omega_0 t \Longleftrightarrow \frac{1}{2}F[j(\omega - \omega_0)] + \frac{1}{2}F[j(\omega + \omega_0)]$$

$$\tag{5-77}$$

$$\Longleftrightarrow \frac{1}{2}F(f - f_0) + \frac{1}{2}F(f + f_0)$$

Thus, modulation of a cosine wave by a time function $f(t)$ leads to a new function having a spectrum consisting of half the original spectrum translated along the positive frequency axis by an amount f_0 and half the original spectrum translated along the negative frequency axis by the amount $-f_0$. An example of this process is shown in Fig. 5-22.

Reversal.   When a time function is reflected about the origin, the corresponding spectrum is also reflected about the origin. In equation form this is

$$f(-t) \Longleftrightarrow F(-j\omega) \tag{5-78}$$

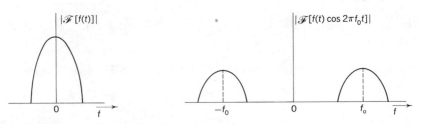

Figure 5-22 Spectrum of modulated cosine wave.

This relationship follows immediately from the expression derived for scaling, where the scale factor is -1. As an example of (5-78), consider the exponential pulse $f_1(t)$, shown in Fig. 5-23(a). This pulse can be

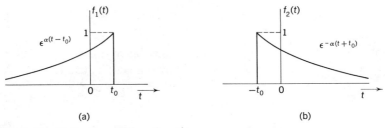

(a)   (b)

Figure 5-23 Reflection of time functions.

thought of as the reflection of the exponential pulse in Fig. 5-23(b). The transform of the pulse in Fig. 5-23(b) is simply $\epsilon^{j\omega t_0}$ times the transform of a unit amplitude exponential pulse at the origin which is given in (5-17). The required transform is, therefore,

$$\mathscr{F}\{f_1(t)\} = \epsilon^{j\omega t_0} \left.\frac{1}{j\omega + \alpha}\right|_{\omega = -\omega}$$

$$= \frac{-\epsilon^{-j\omega t_0}}{j\omega - \alpha}$$

(5-79)

Symmetry. Because of the similarity between the integrals defining the Fourier transform and the inverse Fourier transform, there is a very close relationship between the transform of a particular function of t and the inverse transform of that same function of $j\omega$. The precise relationship is

$$F(jt) \Longleftrightarrow 2\pi f(-\omega)$$

(5-80)

$$\frac{1}{2\pi}F(-t) \Longleftrightarrow f(j\omega)$$

(5-81)

These relationships can be used to extend tables of transforms and also to gain further insight into corresponding time and frequency representation of signals. As an example of this relationship, consider the time function corresponding to a transform that is constant over a specified frequency band and zero elsewhere. This situation is illustrated in Fig. 5-24(a), in which the shape of the transform is assumed to be a

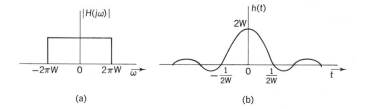

(a)   (b)

Figure 5-24 System function and impulse response of ideal low-pass filter.

rectangular pulse of width $4\pi W$ radians per second and unity amplitude. The phase function is assumed to be zero. Such a transform corresponds to the transfer function, $H(j\omega)$, of an ideal low-pass filter. Accordingly, the inverse transform will be the impulse response $h(t)$ of such a filter. The inverse transform can be found directly from (5-81) by using the previously established relationship for a pulse signal; that is,

$$p_T(t) \Longleftrightarrow T \frac{\sin \omega T/2}{\omega T/2} \epsilon^{-j\omega T/2} \tag{5-82}$$

In the present instance we can write the frequency function as

$$H(j\omega) = P_{4\pi W}(\omega + 2\pi W) \tag{5-83}$$

Therefore, the corresponding transform is

$$h(t) = \frac{1}{2\pi} \left[4\pi W \frac{\sin 4\pi W t/2}{4\pi W t/2} \right] = 2W \operatorname{sinc} (2Wt) \tag{5-84}$$

This impulse response is shown in Fig. 5-24(b). It is clear from the figure that this is not a physically realizable system because the output occurs prior to application of the input. One way of approximating the ideal filter response is to employ a system having a response of the form of Fig. 5-24(b) but delayed in time. The greater the delay the more nearly the shape of Fig. 5-24(b) can be reproduced by a physically realizable filter. The effect of the delay in the frequency domain is to produce a phase shift which varies linearly with frequency.

A collection of the most frequently used Fourier transforms of operations is given in Table 5-1. In Table 5-2 are listed a number of elementary

Table 5-1 FOURIER TRANSFORMS CORRESPONDING TO
MATHEMATICAL OPERATIONS

OPERATION	$f(t)$	$F(j\omega)$
Transformation	$f(t)$	$\displaystyle\int_{-\infty}^{\infty} f(t)\epsilon^{-j\omega t}\, dt$
Inversion	$\displaystyle\frac{1}{2\pi}\int_{-\infty}^{\infty} F(j\omega)\epsilon^{j\omega t} d\omega$	$F(j\omega)$
Superposition	$a_1 f_1(t) + a_2 f_2(t)$	$a_1 F_1(j\omega) + a_2 F_2(j\omega)$
Reversal	$f(-t)$	$F(-j\omega)$
Symmetry	$F(t)$	$2\pi f(-j\omega)$
Scaling	$f(at)$	$\displaystyle\frac{1}{\|a\|}F\left(\frac{j\omega}{a}\right)$
Delay	$f(t - t_0)$	$\epsilon^{-j\omega t_0} F(j\omega)$
Modulation	$\epsilon^{j\omega_0 t} f(t)$	$F[j(\omega - \omega_0)]$
Time differentiation	$\displaystyle\frac{d^n}{dt^n} f(t)$	$(j\omega)^n F(j\omega)$
Frequency differentiation	$t^n f(t)$	$(j)^n \dfrac{d^n}{d\omega^n} F(j\omega)$
Integration	$\displaystyle\int_0^t f_e(t)dt + \int_{-\infty}^t f_o(t)dt$	$\dfrac{1}{j\omega} F(j\omega)$
Integration	$\displaystyle\int_{-\infty}^t f(t)dt$	$\dfrac{1}{j\omega} F(j\omega) + \pi F(0)\delta(\omega)$
Convolution	$f_1 * f_2 = \displaystyle\int_{-\infty}^{\infty} f_1(\lambda)f_2(t - \lambda)d\lambda$	$F_1(j\omega)F_2(j\omega)$
Multiplication	$f_1(t)f_2(t)$	$\dfrac{1}{2\pi}\displaystyle\int_{-\infty}^{\infty} F_1(j\xi)F_2(j\omega - j\xi)d\xi$

transform pairs. Additional transform pairs are given later in the chapter
in Table 5-3 and relate to signals having nonzero average power. More
extensive tabulations of Fourier transforms are available in the references listed at the end of the chapter. A short table of Fourier transforms
using the variable f instead of the variable $j\omega$ is included in Appendix A.

Table 5-2 FOURIER TRANSFORMS OF ENERGY SIGNALS

$f(t)$		$F(j\omega)$	$\lvert F(j\omega) \rvert$
 Rectangular Pulse	$u(t + \frac{T}{2}) - u(t - \frac{T}{2})$	$T\,\dfrac{\sin(\frac{\omega T}{2})}{\frac{\omega T}{2}}$	
 Exponential	$\epsilon^{-\alpha t}\, u(t)$	$\dfrac{1}{j\omega + \alpha}$	
 Triangular	$1 - 2\,\frac{\lvert t \rvert}{T},\ \lvert t \rvert < \frac{T}{2}$ $0 \quad \text{elsewhere}$	$\dfrac{T}{2}\left[\dfrac{\sin(\frac{\omega T}{4})}{\frac{\omega T}{4}}\right]^2$	
 Gaussian	$\mathcal{A}\ \epsilon^{-\alpha^2 t^2}$	$\dfrac{\sqrt{\pi}}{\alpha}\,\epsilon^{-(\omega^2/4\alpha^2)}$	
 Double Exponential	$\epsilon^{-\alpha \lvert t \rvert}$	$\dfrac{2\alpha}{\alpha^2 + \omega^2}$	
 Damped Sine	$\epsilon^{-\alpha t}\sin(\omega_0 t)\, u(t)$	$\dfrac{\omega_0}{(\alpha + j\omega)^2 + \omega_0^2}$	
 Damped Cosine	$\epsilon^{-\alpha t}\cos(\omega_0 t)\, u(t)$	$\dfrac{\alpha + j\omega}{(\alpha + j\omega)^2 + \omega_0^2}$	
	$\dfrac{1}{\beta - a}\left[\epsilon^{-\alpha t} - \epsilon^{-\beta t}\right] u(t)$	$\dfrac{1}{(j\omega + \alpha)(j\omega + \beta)}$	
 Cosine Pulse	$\cos \omega_0 t\left[u(t + \frac{T}{2}) - u(t - \frac{T}{2})\right]$	$\dfrac{\pi T}{2}\left[\dfrac{\sin(\omega - \omega_0)T/2}{(\omega - \omega_0)T/2}\right.$ $\left. - \dfrac{\sin(\omega + \omega_0)T/2}{(\omega + \omega_0)T/2}\right]$	

5-10   Fourier Transforms of Power Signals

The ordinary Fourier transform is limited to the transformation of functions that are absolutely integrable — that is, functions that obey the inequality

$$\int_{-\infty}^{\infty} |f(t)|\,dt < \infty \tag{5-85}$$

A number of functions having great usefulness do not meet this requirement; for example, a sine wave or a step function does not satisfy (5-85). Many such functions can nevertheless be handled by allowing the Fourier transform to contain impulses, or, in some cases, higher-order singularity functions. This procedure can be put on a rigorous mathematical basis by means of the theory of generalized functions[8]; however, it will be sufficient for our purposes to justify this approach by considering the impulse as a limiting form of a proper function, and by showing that correct results are obtained when this method is used.

Consider the function sgn (t), called signum t, which is defined as

$$\begin{aligned} \text{sgn}\,(t) &= -1 & t < 0 \\ &= 0 & t = 0 \\ &= +1 & t > 0 \end{aligned} \tag{5-86}$$

This function is shown in Fig. 5-25. It is evident that it has a zero average

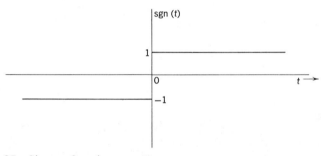

Figure 5-25   Signum function, sgn (t).

value and is not absolutely integrable. The Fourier transform of this function cannot be computed in the formal manner since it leads to a divergent integral. Consider instead a sequence of functions that approaches sgn (t) as a limit. Such a sequence can be obtained by introducing a suitable convergence factor multiplying sgn (t). A suitable function is $\epsilon^{-\alpha|t|}$ sgn (t). The transform may now be computed as

$$\mathscr{F}\{\text{sgn }(t)\} = \mathscr{F}\left\{\lim_{\alpha \to 0} \epsilon^{-\alpha|t|} \text{ sgn }(t)\right\}$$

---

[8] A. H. Zemanian, *Distribution Theory and Transform Analysis,* McGraw-Hill Book Company, Inc., New York, 1965.

Interchanging the limiting and integration operations gives[9]

$$\mathscr{F}\{\text{sgn }(t)\} = \lim_{\alpha \to 0} \int_{-\infty}^{\infty} \epsilon^{-\alpha|t|} \text{ sgn }(t) \, \epsilon^{-j\omega t} \, dt$$

$$= \lim_{\alpha \to 0} \left[\int_{-\infty}^{0} -\epsilon^{(\alpha - j\omega)t} \, dt + \int_{0}^{\infty} \epsilon^{-(\alpha + j\omega)t} \, dt \right]$$

$$= \lim_{\alpha \to 0} \left[\frac{-\epsilon^{(\alpha - j\omega)t}}{\alpha - j\omega} \Big|_{-\infty}^{0} + \frac{\epsilon^{-(\alpha + j\omega)t}}{-(\alpha + j\omega)} \Big|_{0}^{\infty} \right] \qquad \text{(5-87)}$$

$$= \lim_{\alpha \to 0} \left[\frac{-1}{\alpha - j\omega} + \frac{1}{\alpha + j\omega} \right] = \frac{2}{j\omega}$$

$$\text{sgn }(t) \Longleftrightarrow \frac{2}{j\omega}$$

The amplitude of the spectrum is shown plotted in Fig. 5-26.

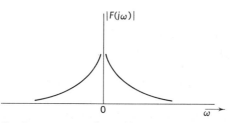

Figure 5-26   Amplitude spectrum of sgn (t).

The spectrum of a constant can be found in a similar fashion using the same type of convergence factor:

$$\mathscr{F}\{1\} = \lim_{\alpha \to 0} \int_{-\infty}^{\infty} \epsilon^{-\alpha|t|} \, \epsilon^{-j\omega t} \, dt$$

$$= \lim_{\alpha \to 0} \left[\int_{-\infty}^{0} \epsilon^{(\alpha - j\omega)t} \, dt + \int_{0}^{\infty} \epsilon^{-(\alpha + j\omega)t} \, dt \right]$$

$$= \lim_{\alpha \to 0} \left[\frac{\epsilon^{(\alpha - j\omega)t}}{\alpha - j\omega} \Big|_{-\infty}^{0} - \frac{\epsilon^{-(\alpha + j\omega)t}}{\alpha + j\omega} \Big|_{0}^{\infty} \right] \qquad \text{(5-88)}$$

$$= \lim_{\alpha \to 0} \left[\frac{1}{\alpha - j\omega} + \frac{1}{\alpha + j\omega} \right]$$

$$= \lim_{\alpha \to 0} \left[\frac{2\alpha}{\alpha^2 + \omega^2} \right]$$

[9] This interchange of operations is the source of trouble in mathematically justifying a derivation of this type. Mathematical proof of the validity of the results obtained by this method of derivation is well beyond the assumed mathematical level of the readers. The best justification that can be offered to the reader is that correct results are obtained when transforms obtained in this manner are used.

It is seen that the limit as $\alpha \to 0$ in (5-88) is zero except when $\omega = 0$, for which case an indeterminate form is obtained. The indeterminate form can be evaluated by L'Hospital's rule to give

$$\lim_{\alpha \to 0} \left[\frac{2}{2\alpha} \right] = \infty$$

The area under the function is found to be

$$\text{Area} = \int_{-\infty}^{\infty} \frac{2\alpha}{\alpha^2 + \omega^2}\, d\omega = 2 \tan^{-1} \left(\frac{\omega}{\alpha} \right) \Big|_{-\infty}^{\infty}$$

$$= 2 \left[\frac{\pi}{2} + \frac{\pi}{2} \right] = 2\pi$$

Therefore, we can write the Fourier transform of a constant of unit magnitude as

$$\mathscr{F}\{1\} = 2\pi\delta(\omega) \tag{5-89}$$

$$1 \Longleftrightarrow 2\pi\delta(\omega) \quad \text{or} \quad \delta(f) \tag{5-90}$$

This result can be extended to include sinusoidal functions in the following manner. From (5-89) we have

$$\mathscr{F}\{1\} = \int_{-\infty}^{\infty} (1)\epsilon^{-j\omega t}\, dt = 2\pi\delta(\omega) \tag{5-91}$$

By use of (5-91) and the modulation theorem of the Fourier transform, we can obtain the transform of the complex exponential as

$$\mathscr{F}\{\epsilon^{j\omega_0 t}\} = \int_{-\infty}^{\infty} \epsilon^{j\omega_0 t - j\omega t}\, dt = 2\pi\delta(\omega - \omega_0) \tag{5-92}$$

From (5-92) the transform of the sine and cosine functions are found to be

$$\mathscr{F}\{\cos \omega_0 t\} = \mathscr{F}\left\{ \frac{\epsilon^{j\omega_0 t} + \epsilon^{-j\omega_0 t}}{2} \right\} \tag{5-93}$$

$$\cos \omega_0 t \Longleftrightarrow \pi \left[\delta(\omega - \omega_0) + \delta(\omega + \omega_0) \right]$$

$$\Longleftrightarrow \frac{1}{2} \left[\delta(f - f_0) + \delta(f + f_0) \right]$$

$$\sin \omega_0 t \Longleftrightarrow -j\pi \left[\delta(\omega - \omega_0) - \delta(\omega + \omega_0) \right] \tag{5-94}$$

$$\Longleftrightarrow -j\frac{1}{2} \left[\delta(f - f_0) - \delta(f + f_0) \right]$$

From these relationships and the various transform operations, it is possible to derive formally (although not rigorously) most of the transforms needed. For example, the transform of the step function can be found using the equality $u(t) = 1/2 + 1/2 \operatorname{sgn}(t)$ as follows.

$$\mathscr{F}\{u(t)\} = \mathscr{F}\left\{\frac{1}{2} + \frac{1}{2}\,\text{sgn}\,(t)\right\} = \pi\delta(\omega) + \frac{1}{j\omega}$$

(5-95)

$$u(t) \iff \pi\delta(\omega) + \frac{1}{j\omega}$$

A useful expression for the Fourier transform of an indefinite integral can be obtained by considering the integral as the convolution of a function $f_1(t)$ and the unit step. Thus

$$f_2(t) = \int_{-\infty}^{t} f_1(\lambda)\,d\lambda = \int_{-\infty}^{\infty} f_1(\lambda)u(t - \lambda)\,d\lambda$$

$$= f_1(t) \star u(t)$$

From (5-53), which states that the transform of the convolution of two functions is equal to the product of the transforms of the functions taken separately, we have

$$F_2(j\omega) = F_1(j\omega)\left[\frac{1}{j\omega} + \pi\delta(\omega)\right]$$

Therefore,

$$\int_{-\infty}^{t} f_1(\lambda)\,d\lambda \iff \frac{1}{j\omega} F_1(j\omega) + \pi F_1(0)\delta(\omega)$$

(5-96)

$$\int_{-\infty}^{t} f_1(\lambda)\,d\lambda \iff \frac{1}{j2\pi f} F_1(f) + \frac{1}{2} F_1(0)\delta(f)$$

(5-97)

As an example of this expression, we will compute the Fourier transform of $\sin \omega_0 t$.

$$\mathscr{F}\{\sin \omega_0 t\} = \mathscr{F}\left\{\omega_0 \int_0^t \cos \omega_0\lambda\,d\lambda\right\} = \omega_0 \int_{-\infty}^{t} \cos (\omega_0\lambda)\,u(\lambda)\,d\lambda$$

$$= \omega_0 \frac{1}{j\omega}\left[\pi\delta(\omega - \omega_0) + \pi\delta(\omega + \omega_0)\right] + \pi \sin (0)\,\delta(\omega)$$

$$= \frac{\pi}{j}\left[\delta(\omega - \omega_0) - \delta(\omega + \omega_0)\right]$$

Since a periodic function can be expressed as a sum of complex exponentials and complex exponentials can be Fourier transformed, it should be possible to take the Fourier transform of a periodic function by taking the transforms of each term in the expansion. Suppose we are given a periodic function $f(t)$ with period T. We can proceed formally to obtain the Fourier transform of $f(t)$ by first writing the Fourier series for $f(t)$ as

$$f(t) = \sum_{n=-\infty}^{\infty} \alpha_n \epsilon^{jn\omega_0 t}$$

The Fourier transform then becomes

$$F(j\omega) = \mathcal{F}\left\{\sum_{n=-\infty}^{\infty} \alpha_n \epsilon^{jn\omega_0 t}\right\}$$

$$F(j\omega) = \sum_{n=-\infty}^{\infty} \alpha_n \mathcal{F}\{\epsilon^{jn\omega_0 t}\}$$

$$= 2\pi \sum_{n=-\infty}^{\infty} \alpha_n \delta(\omega - n\omega_0)$$

Now α_n can be expressed in terms of the Fourier transform of $f_T(t)$, the waveform over one period, as follows:

$$\alpha_n = \frac{1}{T}\int_{-T/2}^{T/2} f(t)\epsilon^{-jn\omega_0 t}\, dt$$

$$= \frac{1}{T}\int_{-\infty}^{\infty} f_T(t)\epsilon^{-jn\omega_0 t}\, dt$$

$$= \frac{1}{T}F_T(jn\omega_0)$$

Therefore,

$$F(j\omega) = \omega_0 \sum_{n=-\infty}^{\infty} F_T(jn\omega_0)\delta(\omega - n\omega_0) \qquad \textbf{(5-98)}$$

$$f(t) \Longleftrightarrow \frac{2\pi}{T}\sum_{n=-\infty}^{\infty} F_T\left(j\frac{2\pi n}{T}\right)\delta\left(\omega - \frac{2\pi n}{T}\right) \qquad \textbf{(5-99)}$$

Converting to the variable f instead of ω, the relationship becomes

$$F(f) = \sum_{n=-\infty}^{\infty} \alpha_n\delta(f - nf_0) \qquad \textbf{(5-100)}$$

$$f(t) \Longleftrightarrow \frac{1}{T}\sum_{n=-\infty}^{\infty} F_T\left(j\frac{2\pi n}{T}\right)\delta\left(f - \frac{n}{T}\right) \qquad \textbf{(5-101)}$$

The Fourier transform is thus seen to be a series of impulses at the harmonics of the repetition period with strengths determined by the shape of the waveform in one period.

As an example of the Fourier transform of a periodic function, consider the *sampling function* $f_s(t)$ shown in Fig. 5-27.

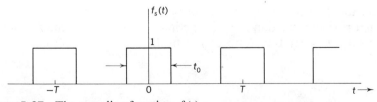

Figure 5-27 The sampling function, $f_s(t)$.

The Fourier transform of the truncated function $f_{sT}(t)$ is

$$f_{sT}(t) = f_s(t) \qquad -\frac{T}{2} < t < \frac{T}{2}$$
$$= 0 \qquad \text{elsewhere}$$

(5-102)

$$F_{sT}(j\omega) = t_0 \frac{\sin \omega t_0/2}{\omega t_0/2}$$

(5-103)

Therefore, the Fourier transform of $f_s(t)$ is

$$F_s(j\omega) = \frac{2\pi t_0}{T} \sum_{n=-\infty}^{\infty} \frac{\sin \pi n t_0/T}{\pi n t_0/T} \delta\left(\omega - \frac{2\pi n}{T}\right)$$

(5-104)

$$F_s(f) = \frac{t_0}{T} \sum_{n=-\infty}^{\infty} \frac{\sin \pi n t_0/T}{\pi n t_0/T} \delta\left(f - \frac{n}{T}\right)$$

(5-105)

The amplitude spectrum of $f_s(t)$ is shown plotted in Fig. 5-28 for $t_0/T = 1/2$.

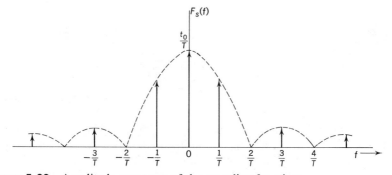

Figure 5-28   Amplitude spectrum of the sampling function.

Another important signal is the unit impulse train. Consider a function $f(t)$ composed of an infinite train of unit impulses having a repetition period T. Such a function is shown in Fig. 5-29. The Fourier transform of this function is very important in sampling theory and can be determined quite readily by first expanding $f(t)$ in a Fourier series and then taking the Fourier transform of the terms in the expansion. Following this procedure we obtain

$$f(t) = \sum_{n=-\infty}^{\infty} \delta(t - nT)$$

(5-106)

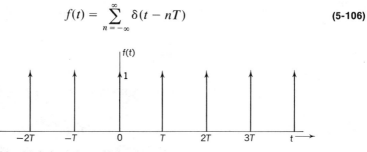

Figure 5-29   Unit impulse train.

$$= \sum_{n=-\infty}^{\infty} \alpha_n \epsilon^{jn\omega_0 t} \qquad \omega_0 = \frac{2\pi}{T} \tag{5-107}$$

The coefficient α_n is given by

$$\alpha_n = \frac{1}{T} \int_{-T/2}^{T/2} \delta(t) \, \epsilon^{-jn\omega_0 t} \, dt = \frac{1}{T} \tag{5-108}$$

Therefore, $f(t)$ can be written as

$$f(t) = \frac{1}{T} \sum_{n=-\infty}^{\infty} \epsilon^{jn\omega_0 t} \tag{5-109}$$

Taking the Fourier transform gives

$$F(j\omega) = \frac{1}{T} \sum_{n=-\infty}^{\infty} \mathscr{F}\{\epsilon^{jn\omega_0 t}\}$$

$$= \frac{2\pi}{T} \sum_{n=-\infty}^{\infty} \delta(\omega - n\omega_0) \tag{5-110}$$

$$\sum_{n=-\infty}^{\infty} \delta(t - nT) \Longleftrightarrow \frac{2\pi}{T} \sum_{n=-\infty}^{\infty} \delta\left(\omega - \frac{2\pi n}{T}\right)$$

In terms of the frequency f, (5-110) can be written as

$$\sum_{n=-\infty}^{\infty} \delta(t - nT) \Longleftrightarrow \frac{1}{T} \sum_{n=-\infty}^{\infty} \delta\left(f - \frac{n}{T}\right) \tag{5-111}$$

Thus it is seen that an impulse train in the time domain has as its Fourier transform an impulse train in the frequency domain. The amplitude spectrum is shown in Fig. 5-30.

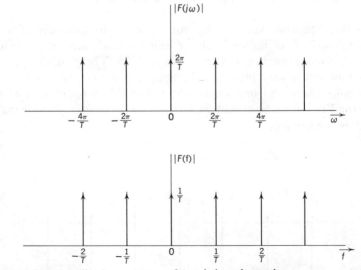

Figure 5-30 Amplitude spectrum of a unit impulse train.

Some of the more frequently used transforms of signals having non-zero average power are given in Table 5-3.

Table 5-3 FOURIER TRANSFORMS OF POWER SIGNALS

$f(t)$	$F(j\omega)$	$\lvert F(j\omega)\rvert$
Unit Impulse	$\delta(t)$	1	
Unit Step	$u(t)$	$\pi\delta(\omega) + \dfrac{1}{j\omega}$	
Signum Function	$\operatorname{sgn} t = \dfrac{t}{\lvert t\rvert}$	$\dfrac{2}{j\omega}$	
Constant	K	$2\pi K\delta(\omega)$	
Cosine Wave	$\cos \omega_0 t$	$\pi[\delta(\omega - \omega_0) + \delta(\omega + \omega_0)]$	
Sine Wave	$\sin \omega_0 t$	$-j\pi[\delta(\omega - \omega_0) - \delta(\omega + \omega_0)]$	
Periodic Wave	$\displaystyle\sum_{n=-\infty}^{\infty} \alpha_n \epsilon^{j(2\pi nt/T)}$	$\displaystyle 2\pi \sum_{n=-\infty}^{\infty} \alpha_n \delta\left(\omega - \dfrac{2\pi n}{T}\right)$	
Impulse Train	$\displaystyle\sum \delta(t - nT)$	$\dfrac{2\pi}{T} \displaystyle\sum \delta\left(\omega - \dfrac{2\pi n}{T}\right)$	
Complex Sinusoid	$\epsilon^{j\omega_0 t}$	$2\pi\,\delta(\omega - \omega_0)$	
Unit Ramp	$tu(t)$	$j\pi\delta'(\omega) - \dfrac{1}{\omega^2}$	

5-11 Convolution in the Frequency Domain

The property of the Fourier transform that convolution in the time domain corresponds to multiplication in the frequency domain also has a converse; that is, the transform of the product of two time functions is the convolution of their transforms. The exact relationship is

$$f_1(t)f_2(t) \Longleftrightarrow \frac{1}{2\pi} \int_{-\infty}^{\infty} F_1(j\xi)F_2\{j(\omega - \xi)\}\, d\xi = \frac{1}{2\pi}F_1(j\omega) \circledast F_2(j\omega)$$

$$\text{(5-112)}^{10}$$

$$f_1(t)f_2(t) \Longleftrightarrow F_1(f) \star F_2(f) \qquad \text{(5-113)}$$

These expressions can be verified by formally inverting the right-hand side.

As an example of the application of (5-112), consider the determination of the spectrum of an amplitude-modulated signal. Such a signal may be represented as follows

$$f(t) = A\left[1 + f_m(t)\right] \cos\left(\omega_0 t + \phi\right) \qquad \text{(5-114)}$$

In (5-114), the modulating function f_m must be normalized to have a maximum amplitude less than or equal to unity in order to prevent overmodulation. The function $f_m(t)$ can have either a continuous or a discrete spectrum. The spectrum of the modulated signal is given by the following convolution:

$$F(j\omega) = A\left[\mathscr{F}\{\cos(\omega_0 t + \phi)\} + \frac{1}{2\pi}\mathscr{F}\{f_m(t)\} \circledast \mathscr{F}\{\cos(\omega_0 t + \phi)\}\right]$$

$$= A\pi\left[\delta(\omega - \omega_0) + \delta(\omega + \omega_0)\right]\epsilon^{j\phi\omega/\omega_0}$$

$$\quad + \frac{A\pi}{2\pi}F_m(j\omega)\circledast\left[\delta(\omega - \omega_0) + \delta(\omega + \omega_0)\right]\epsilon^{j\phi\omega/\omega_0}$$

$$= A\pi\{\delta(\omega - \omega_0)\epsilon^{j\phi} + \delta(\omega + \omega_0)\epsilon^{-j\phi}$$

$$\quad + \frac{1}{2\pi}F_m[j(\omega - \omega_0)]\epsilon^{j\phi} + \frac{1}{2\pi}F_m[j(\omega + \omega_0)]\epsilon^{-j\phi}\}$$

It is seen that the spectrum of $F(j\omega)$ consists of a discrete component at the carrier frequency ω_0 and a reproduction of $F_m(j\omega)$ around $\pm\omega_0$. Fig. 5-31 shows the spectrum involved in a typical amplitude-modulation system.

Further examples of frequency convolution will be given in connection with the sampling theorem.

---

[10] The symbol $\circledast$, rather than $\star$, will be used to designate convolution in the frequency domain when the variable is $j\omega$, because in (5-112) the variable of integration is ξ rather than $j\xi$ as in ordinary convolution. When the variable is f, this problem is not encountered.

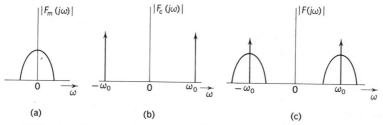

Figure 5-31 Amplitude modulation. **(a)** Modulation. **(b)** Carrier. **(c)** AM signal.

5-12 Sampling Theorem

All of the discussion so far has dealt with signals that were continuous functions of time in the sense that their amplitudes were explicitly defined for every instant of time. There is, however, another important class of signals for which the amplitude is defined only for certain discrete instants of time. Such signals, referred to as "sampled signals," in actual practice arise in pulse-modulation communication systems, in sampled data control systems, and when digital computers operate as part of an analog system. In addition, it is sometimes desirable to represent continuous signals as sampled signals simply for mathematical convenience.

In almost all cases, a sampled signal is derived from a continuous signal (either actually or mathematically) by observing its value at a set of equally spaced time instants. These sample values then become the only means of describing the original signal, and a question of considerable interest is just how good this description can be. In general, one would expect to obtain a more accurate description if the sample values were taken at more closely spaced instants of time, and that an *exact* description would require that the interval between samples approach zero. Surprisingly enough, however, there is a special class of signals, known as band-limited signals, for which an exact description can be obtained from samples taken with nonzero spacing between sampling instants.

A band-limited signal is one for which the Fourier transform (and, hence, the amplitude frequency spectrum) is identically zero everywhere except for a finite range of frequencies. If the region in which the nonzero spectrum exists includes zero frequency, then the band-limited signal is said to be low-pass. If it does not include zero frequency, the system is bandpass. In any case, however, a band-limited signal must exist for all time, although it may contain only finite energy. The concept of band-limited signals is a convenient one in practical system design as well as in theoretical calculations, even though such signals cannot exist in actuality. In almost all cases of practical interest there is some range of frequencies outside of which the spectrum is so small that it can be assumed to be zero with negligible error.

It is not at all apparent that a band-limited signal can be described exactly by a set of sample values at instants having a nonzero separation. Although this result can be proved mathematically (as will be done in a later section), there appears to be no simple physical explanation that is valid under all circumstances. The following argument, which is semi-mathematical in nature, cannot be defended rigorously either, but it does indicate the nature of the result. Later, the same result will be obtained by an application of convolution, and still later, by straightforward mathematical analysis.

Consider a low-pass, band-limited signal function whose frequency spectrum is identically zero outside of the frequency range $-W$ to W hertz. A finite portion of this signal (say T seconds in length) can be represented by means of a Fourier series expansion.

It should be noted, however, that this portion of the signal is no longer band-limited (since the discontinuities introduced at the beginning and end of the portion spread out the frequency spectrum), so the complete Fourier series contains an infinite number of terms. The number of terms that represent frequencies falling inside the original signal bandwidth ($-W$ to W) is just $2WT + 1$ (including the zero-frequency term) since the fundamental frequency is $1/T$ H$_2$. Hence, an *approximation* to the band-limited signal can be made by terminating the Fourier series at $n = \pm 2WT$. Furthermore, as T is made larger the approximation becomes better, because all of the coefficients outside the original signal bandwidth must vanish as T approaches infinity.

The coefficients in the approximate series can be obtained by using just $2WT + 1$ values of the signal function, since the coefficients appear linearly. These values can be obtained by sampling the signal every $1/2W$ seconds (including samples at both ends of the interval T), inasmuch as there are just $2WT + 1$ sample values. Hence, it can be concluded that the approximate coefficients can be determined by sampling the signal at a rate of $2W$ samples per second and that the approximation becomes exact as T approaches infinity.

The foregoing argument leads directly to a statement of the *sampling theorem* for low-pass, band-limited signals:

> A low-pass, band-limited function having no frequency components outside of the frequency interval from $-W$ to W hertz may be described uniquely and completely for all time, by a set of sample values taken at time instants separated by $1/2W$ seconds or less.

It is also possible to obtain a sampling theorem for bandpass, band-limited signals, but the procedure is somewhat more involved and will not be considered at the present time.

The physical operation of sampling is usually accomplished by means of a switch, which periodically opens and closes. The switch operation may be mechanical, but it is more likely to be electronic. If the switch is in series with the signal source, as shown in Fig. 5-32, then the interval

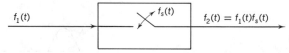

Figure 5-32 Signal samples.

during which the switch is closed is normally very short compared to its open interval. The mathematical representation of this type of sampling operation simply involves multiplying the signal function by a sampling function $f_s(t)$, which is zero whenever the switch is open and unity when the switch is closed. This is indicated in Fig. 5-32 and further

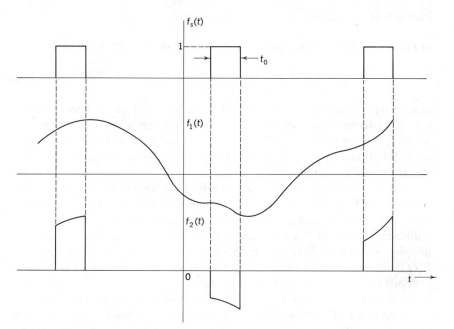

Figure 5-33 Waveforms in the sampling operation.

in Fig. 5-33, where the signal function, sampling function, and their product are shown.

It should be noted that the operation shown here is not exactly the same as that assumed in the sampling theorem because of the finite width of the sampling-function pulses. However, it would approach the ideal as the pulse width is made smaller.

Since the output of the sampler is the product of two time functions, it is now possible to use convolution in the frequency domain to show why, and under what circumstances, the sampling theorem is valid. In order to do this, let $f_1(t)$ be a low-pass, band-limited function as shown

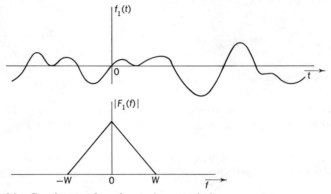

Figure 5-34   Continuous function to be sampled.

in Fig. 5-34. The sampler output, $f_2(t)$, has a Fourier transform of

$$F_2(j\omega) = \mathcal{F}\{f_1(t)f_s(t)\} = \frac{1}{2\pi}F_1(j\omega) \circledast F_s(j\omega)$$ (5-115)

Since $f_s(t)$ is a periodic function, it follows that its Fourier spectrum is a set of delta functions occurring at zero frequency, the sampling frequency, and harmonics of the sampling frequency. The strengths of these delta functions vary in accordance with the magnitude of the Fourier spectrum of the sampling pulse shape.

The two spectra and their convolution are shown in Fig. 5-35. The convolution is particularly easy to visualize in this case because one of the functions is a series of impulses, and when an impulse is convolved with another function it reproduces that function at the place where the impulse was located. In this case, it is easiest to imagine the function $F_1(f)$ sliding along the impulses and being reproduced with an amplitude proportional to the strength of each impulse.

It is necessary to insert a word of caution here about the graphical representation of convolution in the frequency domain. The quantities sketched on the graphs are the absolute magnitudes of the frequency functions being convolved, while the actual quantities entering into the convolution integral are complex. When one of the frequency functions is composed entirely of δ functions, graphical convolution will give exactly the same result as the actual integration. However, if both frequency functions have continuous parts, then graphical convolution of the magnitude does *not* yield the correct result.

The original signal can be recovered from the sampled signal by passing $f_2(t)$ through a low-pass filter of bandwidth W. This filter will pass the

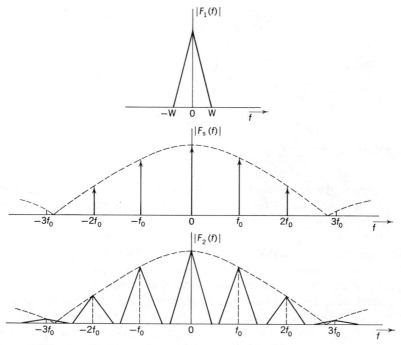

Figure 5-35   Amplitude spectrum of the sampled function.

portion of the spectrum $F_2(f)$ located at the origin; this is identical to the original signal spectrum $F_1(f)$ except for a scale factor. The mathematical relationships can be derived in the following manner. Referring to Fig. 5-36, the output signal can be related to the input by means of the spectrum of the signals.

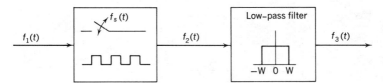

Figure 5-36   Block diagram of the signal recovery system.

$$f_2(t) = f_1(t)f_s(t)$$

$$F_2(f) = F_1(f) \star F_s(f)$$

$$= F_1(f) \star \frac{t_0}{T} \sum_{n=-\infty}^{\infty} \frac{\sin \pi n t_0/T}{\pi n t_0/T} \delta\left(f - \frac{n}{T}\right)$$

$$= \frac{t_0}{T} \sum_{n=-\infty}^{\infty} \text{sinc}\left(\frac{nt_0}{T}\right) \qquad F_1(f - \xi)\delta\left(\xi - \frac{n}{T}\right) d\xi$$

$$= \frac{t_0}{T} \sum_{n=-\infty}^{\infty} \mathrm{sinc} \left(\frac{nt_0}{T} \right) F_1 \left(f - \frac{n}{T} \right) \qquad \text{(5-116)}$$

$$F_3(f) = \mathrm{LPF} \{ F_2(f) \} = \frac{t_0}{T} F_1(f)$$

$$F_1(f) = \frac{T}{t_0} F_3(f)$$

Therefore, $f_1(t) = \dfrac{T}{t_0} f_3(t)$

The original signal can thus be recovered from the sampled signal by passing the sampled signal through an ideal low-pass filter having a gain of T/t_0.

Proper sampling requires that the samples be taken at a rate at least twice the highest frequency present in $f_1(t)$. The necessity for this may be seen by reference to Fig. 5-35. Since the spectrum of the original signal is reproduced symmetrically around each harmonic of the sampling frequency, it is necessary that the harmonics be separated by at least twice the width of the spectrum. Therefore, the first harmonic or fundamental of the sampler must be at least $f_0 = 2W$. If the signal is sampled at a rate lower than twice the bandwidth of the original signal, there will be overlapping of the spectra as shown in Fig. 5-37. When this occurs,

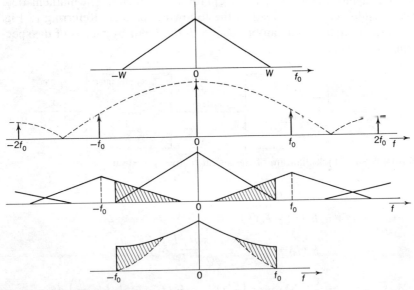

Figure 5-37   Effect of undersampling.

it is not possible to recover the original function without distortion. The amount of distortion will depend on the amount of undersampling and on the shape of the spectrum of the signal being sampled. The general effect of undersampling is to reinforce the even part of the spectrum and to diminish the odd part of the spectrum as can be seen readily by making a sketch similar to Fig. 5-37 with a spectrum having an odd symmetry. It is important to note that the duration and shape of the pulses in $f_s(t)$ do not affect the ability to recover $f_1(t)$ from its samples. As can be seen from Fig. 5-35, it is necessary only that $f_s(t)$ be periodic, with a fundamental frequency f_0 that is at least twice the highest frequency contained in $f_1(t)$.

This same operation can be carried out in the time domain by performing on the samples an operation that is equivalent to low-pass filtering. Since low-pass filtering in the frequency domain corresponds to multiplying the spectrum by the filter transfer function, it follows that the equivalent time-domain operation will be convolution of the inverse transform of the filter function with the sampled signal $f_2(t)$. The precise relationship in the time domain can be established by carrying out the indicated convolution; however, a simpler demonstration of the desired relationship can be obtained by use of the Fourier series in the following manner.

Let the time function $f(t)$ have a Fourier spectrum that is limited to the band $\pm W$ as shown in Fig. 5-34. Assume that $f(t)$ is known at discrete times $t_n = n/2W$. The value of $f(t_n)$ can be found in terms of the Fourier transform $F(j\omega)$ as follows:

$$f_n = f\left(\frac{n}{2W}\right) = \frac{1}{2\pi} \int_{-2\pi W}^{2\pi W} F(j\omega) \exp\left(j\omega \frac{n}{2W}\right) d\omega$$

This can be written as

$$f_n = 2W \left\{ \frac{1}{4\pi W} \int_{-2\pi W}^{2\pi W} F(j\omega) \exp\left[-j\left(-\frac{n\omega}{2W}\right)\right] d\omega \right\}$$

which is just $2W$ times the $-n$th coefficient of the exponential Fourier series expansion for $F(j\omega)$ over the interval $-2\pi W < \omega < 2\pi W$. In view of this, $F(j\omega)$ can be expressed in terms of f_n as

$$F(j\omega) = \sum_{n=-\infty}^{\infty} \frac{f_n}{2W} \exp\left(-j\frac{n\omega}{2W}\right)$$

Taking the inverse transform gives

$$f(t) = \frac{1}{2\pi} \int_{-2\pi W}^{2\pi W} \sum_{n=-\infty}^{\infty} \frac{f_n}{2W} \exp\left(-j\frac{n\omega}{2W}\right) \exp\left(j\omega t\right) d\omega$$

$$= \sum_{n=-\infty}^{\infty} \frac{f_n}{4\pi W} \int_{-2\pi W}^{2\pi W} \exp\left[j\omega\left(t - \frac{n}{2W}\right)\right] d\omega$$

$$= \sum_{n=-\infty}^{\infty} \frac{f_n}{4\pi W} \frac{\exp\left[j\omega\left(t - \frac{n}{2W}\right)\right]}{j\left(t - \frac{n}{2W}\right)}\Bigg|_{-2\pi W}^{2\pi W} \quad \text{(5-117)}$$

$$= \sum_{n=-\infty}^{\infty} \frac{f_n}{2\pi W} \frac{\sin 2\pi W \left(t - \frac{n}{2W}\right)}{t - \frac{n}{2W}}$$

$$= \sum_{n=-\infty}^{\infty} f\left(\frac{n}{2W}\right) \text{sinc}\, (2Wt - n)$$

From (5-117) it is seen that $f(t)$ can be recovered from f_n by summing the properly weighted values of f_n. At a particular time t_1, the value of $f(t_1)$ is obtained by multiplying each of the samples f_n by the factor sinc $(2Wt_1 - n)$ and summing the resulting terms. The influence of samples away from t_1 on the value of $f(t)$ at $t = t_1$ is determined by how rapidly sinc $(2Wt_1 - n)$ decreases with n. Depending on the sampling interval and the spectrum of the particular function being reconstructed, the number of samples required to obtain a given accuracy may vary from a few to many.

■ REFERENCES

1. Bracewell, R. M., *The Fourier Transform and Its Applications*. New York: McGraw-Hill Book Company, Inc., 1965.

    The book is written at a senior or graduate level. Although accurate and precise in its discussions, this book is written more from an engineer's than a mathematician's point of view. Much detailed information on transform methods of analysis is included and many interesting practical applications are discussed. This book is an excellent reference if you plan to carry out practical analysis employing Fourier transform methods. A number of tables are included.

2. Papoulis, A., *The Fourier Integral and Its Applications*. New York: McGraw-Hill Book Company, Inc., 1962.

    This book is written at a senior-graduate level. It provides a comprehensive treatment of the Fourier transform. More mathematical in approach than Bracewell, this book is an excellent reference if you are planning to carry out mathematical investigations using the Fourier transform.

3. Campbell, G. A., and R. M. Foster, *Fourier Integrals for Practical Applications*. Princeton, N.J.: D. Van Nostrand Company, Inc., 1948.

    This book contains an extensive table of Fourier transform pairs.

4. Erdélyi, A., W. Magnus, F. Oberhettinger, and F. G. Tricomi, *Table of Integral Transforms,* vol. 1. New York: McGraw-Hill Book Company, Inc., 1954.

> This first volume of a two-volume set of tables contains tables of Fourier, Laplace, and Mellin transforms. Recommended for persons interested in advanced work in transform techniques.

■ P R O B L E M S

5-1   State which of the following time functions are not Fourier transformable on the basis of the Dirichlet conditions, and give the reasons.

a. $f_1(t) = tu(-t)$

c. $f_3(t) = \dfrac{1}{t-1} u(t-2)u(t+2)$

b. $f_2(t) = \cos\left(\dfrac{10}{t}\right)$

d. $f_4(t) = \epsilon^{-\alpha t}$

5-2   Plot the magnitude of the Fourier transform (called a continuous spectrum) of a rectangular pulse of unit height and unit width. On the same graph plot the magnitudes of the Fourier series coefficients (called a line spectrum) for a square wave of unit height and repetition period of 2 seconds. What conclusions can you draw from comparison of the two graphs? What changes occur and what similarities remain when the square wave is replaced by a rectangular pulse train with the same shape of pulses but a longer repetition period?

5-3   Using the defining integral, compute the Fourier transform of the pulse signal shown and sketch its amplitude spectrum.

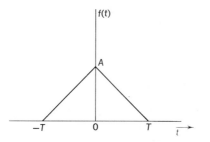

5-4   Show that the duration-bandwidth product of the pulse signal in Problem 5-3 is equal to 2π radian-seconds per second.

5-5   Show that the following relationships represent valid Fourier transformations.

a. $\mathcal{F}[\delta(t - t_0)] = \epsilon^{-j\omega t_0}$

b. $\mathcal{F}\left[\dfrac{d^n}{dt^n}f(t)\right] = (j\omega)^n F(j\omega)$

5-6 By use of the two transforms given in Problem 5-5 it is possible to simplify computation of Fourier transforms of signals that can be represented by piecewise linear approximations. The procedure is to differentiate the piecewise linear approximation a sufficient number of times so that only δ functions remain. The transforms of the δ functions are obtained using (a) in Problem 5-5. The desired transform is then obtained by multiplication of the δ function transforms by the correct negative power of $j\omega$ as indicated in (b) in Problem 5-5. Using this method, find the transforms of the signals shown.

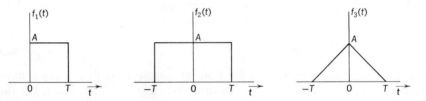

5-7 If $f_c(t)$ is a causal time function, show that the even function $f_2(t)$ $= f_c(t) + f_c(-t)$ has a Fourier transform $F_2(j\omega) = 2 \operatorname{Re}[F_c(j\omega)]$ and similarly show that the odd function $f_3(t) = f_c(t) - f_c(-t)$ has a Fourier transform $F_3(j\omega) = 2j \operatorname{Im}[F_c(j\omega)]$.

5-8 Using the relationships established in Problem 5-7 and the Fourier transforms of the rectangular pulse and one-sided exponential pulse given in the text, determine the Fourier transforms of the signals shown.

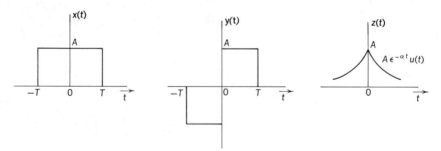

5-9 Find the system function corresponding to each of the following impulse responses:

a. $h(t) = [\epsilon^{-t} - \epsilon^{-3t}]u(t)$

b. $h(t) = \delta(t) - \epsilon^{-2t}u(t)$

c. $h(t) = \epsilon^{-t} \cos t \, u(t)$

5-10 **a.** Find the system function,

$$H(j\omega) = \frac{V_o(j\omega)}{V_i(j\omega)}$$

for the network shown.

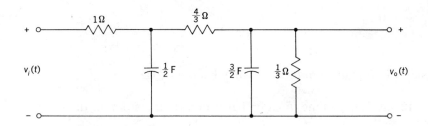

b. Sketch $|H(j\omega)|$ for this network.

5-11 Compare the frequency response of the two systems shown. What

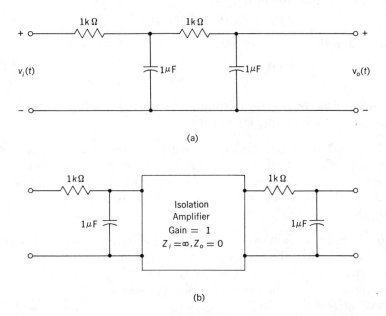

(a)

(b)

accounts for the differences in the two responses? How could you obtain a response closely approximating that of (b), except for an amplitude scale factor, by direct cascading of networks as in (a)? Give an example.

5-12 Using numerical methods, compute and sketch the amplitude spectrum $A(\omega)$ of the function shown. What fraction of the total energy of this

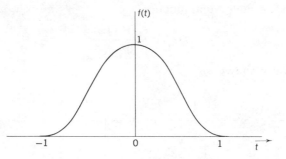

signal is contained in the frequency band 0–1 Hz?

5-13 A voltage time function has a Fourier transform of the form

$$F(j\omega) = \frac{8}{4 + j\omega}$$

What is the energy (on a 1-ohm basis) contained in this voltage waveform?

5-14 A time function of the form

$$v_i(t) = te^{-t} u(t)$$

is applied to the input of an ideal low-pass filter for which

$$H(j) = 1 \qquad -2\pi W \le \omega \le 2\pi W$$
$$= 0 \qquad \text{elsewhere}$$

For what value of W does this filter pass exactly one half of the energy (on a 1-ohm basis) of the input signal?

5-15 What half-power bandwidth must a single stage R-C low-pass filter have in order to transmit 90 percent of the energy in a rectangular pulse? For the same fractional power transmission would the required bandwidth be increased or decreased if the pulse were an isosceles triangle? Why?

5-16 In order for a network to transmit a waveform without distortion it is necessary that the output waveform be identical to the input waveform; that is, $y(t) = x(t - t_0)$, where t_0 is an arbitrary delay factor. What characteristics must the system function possess for distortionless transmission to occur?

5-17 A time function, $f(t)$, has a Fourier transform of

$$F(j\omega) = \frac{1 + j\omega}{8 - \omega^2 + j6\omega}$$

Using the results of Section 5-9, write the Fourier transform for each of the following time functions:

a. $f(3t)$ **c.** $f(3t - 2)$

b. $f(t - 2)$ **d.** $5f(t/2)$

5-18 An ideal delay line is a device for which the output signal has the same size and shape as the input signal, but occurs at a later time. Consider the following system which contains an ideal delay line with a delay of 1 second. Determine the system function, $H(j\omega)$. ($Z_i = \infty$, $Z_o = 0$.)

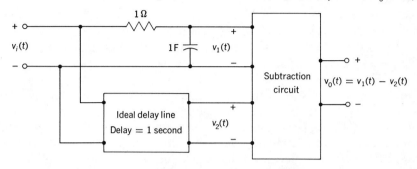

5-19 If $F(j\omega)$ is the Fourier transform of $f(t)u(t)$, what is the Fourier transform of $\epsilon^{-\alpha t}f(t)u(t)$, when α is real and positive?

5-20 For the time function and Fourier transform of Problem 5-17, write the Fourier transform for each of the following time functions.

a. $\epsilon^{j6t}f(t-2)$

b. $6\dfrac{df(t)}{dt}$

c. $f(-2t)$

d. $5tf(3t)$

e. $5f(2-t)$

f. $f(t)\cos t$

5-21 A time function $f_1(t)$ has the form

$$f_1(t) = \epsilon^{-t}u(t)$$

Using the relations in Table 5-1, determine the Fourier transform of each of the time functions shown.

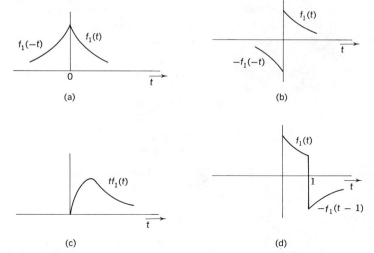

5-22   A network consisting of resistance, inductance, and capacitance has a system function $H(j\omega)$ based on a voltage ratio as shown below. Find the system function that would result in each of the following situations:
a.   Resistance unchanged, inductances increased in value by a factor of 10, and capacitance increased in value by a factor of 10.
b.   Resistances increased in value by a factor of 5, inductances increased in value by a factor of 5, capacitances decreased in value by a factor of 5.

5-23   A good measure of the high-frequency performance of an amplifier is the response of the amplifier to a step input. Two measures of performance that can be obtained from such a test are the rise time and the overshoot. We will define the rise time as the time required for the output to go from 10 to 90 percent of its final value and overshoot as the maximum amount by which the output exceeds its final value. Compute the rise time and overshoot for an ideal low-pass filter having a bandwidth of W hertz. What would be the half-power bandwidth of a single stage low-pass R-C filter having the same rise time as the ideal filter?

5-24   Transmission of a modulated carrier through a bandpass system can often be analyzed very simply in terms of an analogous low-pass system. The procedure is as follows. A time function identical to the envelope of a modulated carrier is applied to the low-pass analog of a bandpass system. The output of the low-pass system is identical to the envelope of the output of the bandpass system. What restrictions on the signal spectrum and system function are required for this procedure to give valid results? How is the low-pass analog related to the bandpass system function?

5-25   As was pointed out in Problem 5-24, it is often possible to compute the response of a bandpass system by analyzing the response of an analogous low-pass system to the envelope of the bandpass excitation. An algorithm for generating a bandpass circuit from a low-pass circuit is as follows:
    1. Leave all resistances unchanged.
    2. Reduce all capacitances by a factor of 2 and place in parallel with each an inductor of the proper value to resonate at the center frequency, ω_0, of the bandpass system.
    3. Reduce all inductances by a factor of 2 and place in series with each a capacitor of the proper value to resonate at ω_0.
The resulting bandpass system will have a response to a modulated carrier whose envelope is approximately the same as the response of the low-pass system to the envelope of the excitation. The approximation is very good for narrow-band systems. There is no formal procedure for

going from a bandpass circuit to an analogous low-pass circuit since such analogs do not always exist. Using the foregoing procedure find the equivalent bandpass filter corresponding to the low-pass filter shown in (a) and (b). Determine and sketch the response of the circuit in (c).

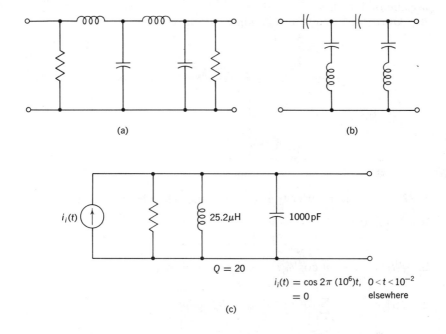

(a)   (b)

$i_i(t)$ $25.2\mu H$ $1000\,pF$

$Q = 20$

$i_i(t) = \cos 2\pi\,(10^6)t, \quad 0 < t < 10^{-2}$
$\qquad = 0 \qquad\qquad\qquad \text{elsewhere}$

(c)

5-26 By proper design a passive network can be made to approximate the behavior of an ideal low-pass filter. One such design is the maximally flat or Butterworth filter, which has a transfer function whose magnitude is

$$|H(j\omega)| = \frac{K}{\left[1 + \left(\dfrac{\omega}{\omega_0}\right)^{2n}\right]^{1/2}}$$

where

$$K = \text{a constant}$$
$$\omega_0 = \text{half-power bandwidth}$$
$$n = \text{order of the filter}$$

a. By expanding $|H(j\omega)|$ in a power series and considering the derivatives of $|H(j\omega)|$ with respect to ω at $\omega = 0$, show why this is called a maximally flat transfer function.

b. Show that the circuit below has a maximally flat transfer function by computing $|H(j\omega)|$. What is the order of the filter?

c. Plot the frequency response of this circuit and compare it with that of a single stage R-C filter having the same half-power bandwidth.

d. By proper scaling of the circuit shown, compute the circuit element values for a Butterworth filter with a half-power bandwidth of 1 kHz and generator internal resistance of 1 kΩ (that is, the resistor will have a value of 1 kΩ).

e. Draw the circuit for a bandpass Butterworth filter.

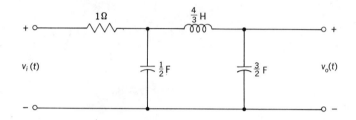

5-27 Find the Fourier transforms of the following time functions

a. $f(t) = 0$ $-\infty < t \le 0$
$ = A \sin \omega_0 t$ $0 \le t < \infty$

b. $f(t) = [1 + m \cos \omega_1 t] \cos \omega_0 t$ $-\infty < t < \infty$

c. $f(t) = \dfrac{a_0}{2} + \displaystyle\sum_{n=1}^{\infty} a_n \cos n\omega_0 t + b_n \cos n\omega_0 t$ $-\infty < t < \infty$

5-28 Find the Fourier transform of the following periodic time function, which is composed of segments of exponentials with time constants of unity.

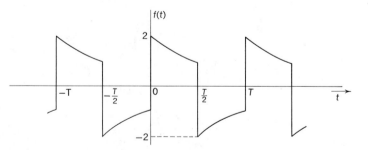

5-29 Find the Fourier transform of $f(t)$ by using the general result for the Fourier transform of a periodic function.

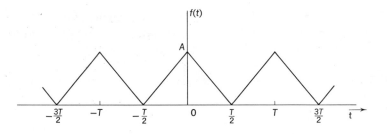

5-30 Find the Fourier transform of the following time functions by using frequency convolution

a. $[1 + m(t)] \cos \omega_0 t \qquad M(j\omega) = \mathscr{F}\{m(t)\}$

b. $f(t) = \left[u\left(t + \dfrac{T}{2}\right) - u\left(t - \dfrac{T}{2}\right) \right] \cdot \displaystyle\sum_{n=-\infty}^{\infty} \delta(t - nt_1) \qquad \dfrac{T}{4} < t_1 < \dfrac{T}{2}$

c. $f(t) = u(t)\, \epsilon^{-at} \cdot \sin \omega_0 t$

5-31 A low-pass waveform $m(t)$ has a maximum frequency content of 10 Hz. After sampling, the signal is to be reconstructed by passing the samples through a single-section $R\text{-}C$ low-pass filter. Specify appropriate sampling rates and filter bandwidth, as well as the relationship of these parameters to the distortion of the recovered signal.

5-32 A bandpass waveform $f(t)$ is to be sampled and then reconstructed by passing the samples through a bandpass filter. If the samples are to be taken every T seconds and the sampling width is Δt, determine the minimum sampling rate if $\mathscr{F}[f(t)] = F(f)$ only exists for $100 \leq f \leq 120$ and $-120 \leq f \leq -100$. Does there exist a maximum sampling rate?

5-33 The time function $f(t) = 5 \cos (2\pi \cdot 500)t \cos^2(2\pi \cdot 1000)t$ is to be sampled 4500 times each second. If reconstruction is to be accomplished by passing the sampled signal through an ideal low-pass filter of bandwidth 2600 Hz, determine the output time function, assuming the filter has zero phase shift and unity gain over its passband. Compute the mean-square error of the output time function. What is the minimum sampling rate that permits the signal to be uniquely reconstructed?

5-34 Determine the minimum sampling rate required and suggest a value for the bandwidth of a low-pass filter to be used to reconstruct the output of a microphone into which a female vocalist is singing a sexy song. Her song could be preserved on a record, tape, etc., or it could be stored as a set of numbers. Approximately how many numbers (samples) would have to be stored in order that her song can be reproduced without distortion for a 3-minute recording? Would the numbers have to be kept in order? What would she sound like if you lost half her numbers?

5-35 The impulse response of a system is as shown. If the input to the

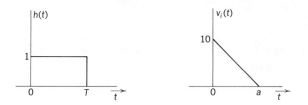

system $v_i(t)$ is a triangular pulse as shown, compute the response for pulse durations of $a = T/10, T, 10T$. Why is a system of this type called a finite time integrator?

5-36 The introduction of feedback in a system can materially alter the system function. For the feedback system shown, compute the system

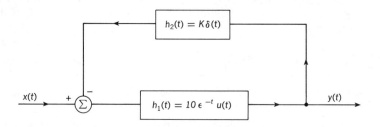

function and sketch the amplitude spectrum for $K = 0, 0.5, 1$. Assume that any loading effects of one circuit on another are negligible.

5-37 In the system shown, the ideal low-pass filter has a system function of

$$H(j\omega) = 1 \qquad -100\pi \leqq \omega \leqq 100\pi$$

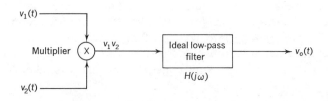

The two input voltages are

$$v_1(t) = u(t) \, \epsilon^{-0.01t} \cos (2\pi \times 10^6 t)$$

and

$$v_2(t) = 10 \cos(2\pi \times 10^6 t) \qquad -\infty < t < \infty$$

a. Find the approximate Fourier transform of the output voltage, $v_o(t)$.
b. What would the approximate Fourier transform of the output voltage be if

$$v_2(t) = 10 \sin (2\pi \times 10^6 t) \qquad -\infty < t < \infty$$

5-38 Let $f(t)$ be a low-pass, band-limited time function whose spectrum is zero outside the range from $-W$ to W hertz. This function is sampled at a rate of $2W$ samples per second and the samples are designated as $f(n/2W)$, where $n = 0, \pm 1, \pm 2$.
a. Prove that

$$\frac{1}{2W} \sum_{n=-\infty}^{\infty} \left[f\left(\frac{n}{2W}\right) \right]^2 = \int_{-\infty}^{\infty} f^2(t) \, dt$$

b. Discuss the significance of this result.

CHAPTER

6

Laplace Transforms

6-1 Introduction

In the previous discussion of the Fourier transform, it was noted that a time function had to be absolutely integrable in order to assure that the transform actually existed. In certain special cases, in which the energy of the time function was concentrated at discrete frequencies, it was possible to circumvent the strict realization of this requirement by utilizing the concept of δ functions in the frequency domain, but this obviously does not include all time functions of practical interest. For example, the random time functions to be considered later *never* have Fourier transforms that exist. In general, the same problem would arise for any nonperiodic signal with nonzero average power.

In view of the convenience and usefulness of frequency-domain representations in the analysis of linear systems, it would seem desirable to have a procedure that would preserve the useful aspects of the Fourier transform but would be applicable to a larger class of time functions. The Laplace transform accomplishes this feat, and provides some additional conveniences as well.

One method of arriving at the Laplace transform is to consider the Fourier transform of the function $\epsilon^{-\sigma t}f(t)$ rather than just $f(t)$. In this case the factor $\epsilon^{-\sigma t}$ is a convergence factor that tends to make $\epsilon^{-\sigma t}f(t)$ absolutely integrable even if $f(t)$ is not. Assuming that this is actually true (this point will be elaborated on later), the Fourier transform is

$$\mathscr{F}\{\epsilon^{-\sigma t}f(t)\} = \int_{-\infty}^{\infty} f(t)\,\epsilon^{-\sigma t}\,\epsilon^{-j\omega t}\,dt$$

$$= \int_{-\infty}^{\infty} f(t)\,\epsilon^{-(\sigma+j\omega)t}\,dt$$

$$= F(\sigma+j\omega)$$

The corresponding inverse transform is

$$f(t)\epsilon^{-\sigma t} = \mathscr{F}^{-1}\{F(\sigma+j\omega)\}$$

$$= \frac{1}{2\pi}\int_{-\infty}^{\infty} F(\sigma+j\omega)\epsilon^{j\omega t}\,d\omega$$

and the convergence factor can be taken to the right side of the equation to give

$$f(t) = \frac{1}{2\pi}\int_{-\infty}^{\infty} F(\sigma+j\omega)\,\epsilon^{(\sigma+j\omega)t}\,d\omega$$

Since σ and $j\omega$ always appear together, it is convenient to define a new variable $s = \sigma + j\omega$ (and $ds = jd\omega$). The inverse and direct transforms now become

$$f(t) = \frac{1}{2\pi j}\int_{\sigma-j\infty}^{\sigma+j\infty} F(s)\epsilon^{st}\,ds \tag{6-1}$$

and

$$F(s) = \int_{-\infty}^{\infty} f(t)\epsilon^{-st}\,dt \tag{6-1a}$$

Equation (6-1a) is an expression for the *two-sided* or *bilateral Laplace transform*, which exists whenever the integral exists.

With the two-sided Laplace transform it is possible to handle functions existing for both positive and negative time. Such functions and their transforms will be considered in more detail later in this chapter. For the present it is convenient to restrict consideration to functions existing only for positive time or to the positive time portion of functions existing in both positive and negative time. The transforms of such functions may be expressed as

$$F(s) = \int_{-\infty}^{\infty} f(t)u(t)\epsilon^{-st}\,dt = \int_{0}^{\infty} f(t)\epsilon^{-st}\,dt \tag{6-2}$$

This is the definition of the *one-sided* or *unilateral Laplace transform.* The corresponding inverse transform is still given by (6-1) and, of course, leads to a function $f(t)u(t)$, which is restricted to positive time.

In (6-2) the lower limit of zero is interpreted to mean 0^-, which implies that any discontinuities and impulses in $f(t)$ at $t = 0$ are included in the integral. The use of this convention simplifies the handling of initial conditions and singularities at the origin and will be discussed in more detail in a later section.

This definition of the Laplace transform is consistent with the classical mathematical definition except for the convention regarding the lower limit. In the classical definition the lower limit is taken as 0^+ and does not include any irregularities occurring at the origin. Whenever the integral

$$\int_{0^-}^{0^+} |f(t)| \ dt = 0$$

for example, when $f(t)$ is continuous or has a finite discontinuity at the origin, the results will be identical for the two definitions and all of the classical results will apply to situations in which the lower limit of 0^- is used. Whenever this integral has a value other than zero, there will be a difference in the resulting transforms.

Unless otherwise stated, all Laplace transforms to be considered in the following sections are assumed to be one-sided as defined by (6-2), and consideration of time functions will be restricted to their positive time portions only. This restriction is not so severe as it might seem, since it permits handling almost all system analysis problems involving nonrandom signals. For example, the impulse response of any physical system satisfies this restriction. Likewise, all practical signals must start at some finite time that can usually be taken to be zero or later.

In using the Laplace transform, it will be found that the integral relationships (6-1) and (6-2) do not actually enter into the calculations very often. They are of great importance in transform theory and can be used to carry out fundamental operations. However, it will be found that much simpler computational methods are available that do not involve direct evaluation of (6-1) and (6-2).

The principal advantages of the Laplace transform over the Fourier transform are: the ease of computing transforms; the simplicity of the transforms themselves; the ease of including initial conditions in the solution of differential equations; the insight into system performance that is possible through use of the complex frequency concept; and the ability to deal with time functions that are not absolutely integrable. After we examine the conditions under which a function may be Laplace-transformed, a number of elementary transforms will be computed and a number of theorems useful in the application of transforms will be developed. Following this, a variety of techniques for finding the time function corresponding to a given transform will be considered.

6-2   Existence of the One-sided Laplace Transform

Requirements on $f(t)$ for the existence of the one-sided Laplace transform $F(s)$ are not at all severe. In order for $F(s)$ to exist it is necessary that the Laplace integral (6-2) converge. The following set of conditions on $f(t)$ is sufficient to assure the convergence of the integral and will cover virtually all waveforms and signals likely to be encountered in the application of Laplace transform theory to physical problems.

Theorem 1.[1]   If $f(t)$ is integrable in every finite interval $a < t < b$ (where $0 \leq a < b < \infty$), and for some value of c the limit

$$\lim_{t \to \infty} \epsilon^{-ct} |f(t)|$$

exists, then the Laplace integral converges absolutely and uniformly for Re $(s) > c$; that is,

$$F(s) = \int_0^\infty f(t)\epsilon^{-st} \, dt < \infty \qquad \text{Re } (s) > c$$

There are two important properties of this theorem that should be noted: the presence of a finite number of infinite discontinuities is permissible so long as they have finite area under them; and because of the uniform convergence, it is permissible to invert the order of integration in multiple integrals without altering the result. Most functions encountered in analysis of engineering problems satisfy the requirements of Theorem 1. Even such functions as ϵ^{100t} or t^n are seen to be sufficiently well behaved to have Laplace transforms. It is possible to specify functions, such as ϵ^{ϵ^t}, that do not have a Laplace transform, but they are of no practical importance in system analysis.

As in the case of Fourier transforms, some shorthand notation is very convenient. To this end the Laplace transform of a function $f(t)$ will be indicated by

$$\mathscr{L}\{f(t)\} = F(s) = \int_0^\infty f(t)\epsilon^{-st} \, dt$$

Similarly, for the inverse transform,[2]

$$\mathscr{L}^{-1}\{F(s)\} = f(t) = \frac{1}{2\pi j} \int_{c-j\infty}^{c+j\infty} F(s)\epsilon^{st} \, ds$$

---

[1] N. M. Nicholson, *Fundamentals and Techniques of Mathematics for Scientists*, John Wiley and Sons, Inc., New York, 1961, p. 330.

W. M. Brown, *Analysis of Linear Time Invariant Systems*, McGraw-Hill Book Co., Inc., New York, 1963, pp. 26–39.

[2] The limits on the integral were changed from $\sigma - j\infty$ and $\sigma + j\infty$ to $c - j\infty$ and $c + j\infty$, where it is assumed that $c > \sigma$. This is a more general formulation in that it allows any path of integration to the right of the line $s = \sigma$ in the complex plane.

Another notation for the transform relation is the following:

$$f(t) \Longleftrightarrow F(s)$$

It is generally assumed that the function $f(t)$ is zero for $t < 0$ unless some indication to the contrary is given. If it is necessary to show this relationship explicitly, then the function can be written $f(t)u(t)$. Some confusion in this regard is possible when the transforms of delayed functions are computed and will be discussed in detail when such transforms are considered.

When a Laplace transform is computed there is a restricton on the value of σ for which the transform is valid. This value of σ determines the region in the complex s plane in which the integral converges. The value of σ is of importance in determining whether or not a Fourier transform exists for the function, and in determining a path of integration that could be used for evaluation of (6-1) by contour integration in the complex plane. However, in most practical calculations, the restrictions on σ are clear and are not tabulated as part of the computation. When the restrictions are pertinent, they must be included. The restrictions on σ will be given in a number of the derivations of the transforms that follow.

6-3 Computation of Some Elementary Transforms

As an example of the computation of the Laplace transform from the defining integral, consider the function $f(t) = \epsilon^{-\alpha t}u(t)$

$$\mathscr{L}\{\epsilon^{-\alpha t}u(t)\} = \int_0^\infty \epsilon^{-\alpha t}\epsilon^{-st}\,dt$$

$$= \frac{\epsilon^{-(\alpha+s)t}}{-(\alpha+s)}\bigg|_0^\infty$$

In order for this integral to converge, it is necessary for Re $(s) = \sigma > -\alpha$, in which case the transform becomes

$$\epsilon^{-\alpha t}u(t) \Longleftrightarrow \frac{1}{s+\alpha} \qquad \sigma > -\alpha \tag{6-3}$$

This transform is valid for complex α, provided $\sigma >$ Re $(-\alpha)$. The Laplace transform of the unit impulse is readily found to be

$$\mathscr{L}\{\delta(t)\} = \int_{0^-}^\infty \delta(t)\epsilon^{-st}\,dt = 1 \qquad \sigma > -\infty$$

The transform of the unit step function can be obtained from (6-3) by allowing $\alpha \to 0$, giving

$$u(t) \Longleftrightarrow \frac{1}{s} \tag{6-4}$$

For the unit ramp function, $f(t) = tu(t)$, the transform is found to be

$$\mathcal{L}\{tu(t)\} = \int_0^\infty te^{-st}\, dt = \frac{\epsilon^{-st}}{s^2}(-st+1)\bigg|_0^\infty \qquad (6\text{-}5)$$

It is seen that this converges for $\sigma > 0$; therefore,

$$tu(t) \Longleftrightarrow \frac{1}{s^2} \qquad \sigma > 0$$

Other transforms could be computed in the same manner, but it is much simpler to build up a table of transforms through application of various operational properties of the transform. In addition, familiarity with these operational properties of the transform greatly aids in understanding and appreciating its applications to practical problems.

6-4 Transform Theorems

The utility of the transform approach to system analysis stems from the fact that when the variables and operations in one domain are transformed to new variables and operations in another domain, simplified relationships among the variables result. In particular, for the Laplace transform it will be found that differential equations in the t domain (time) are transformed into algebraic equations in the s domain (complex frequency), and furthermore it will be found that the initial conditions are automatically included in the solution obtained. In order to establish the relationships between operations in the two domains, a series of theorems relating such operations will be developed and their applications illustrated with suitable examples.

Linearity. If $f_1(t) \Longleftrightarrow F_1(s)$, for $\sigma > \sigma_1$, and $f_2(t) \Longleftrightarrow F_2(s)$, for $\sigma > \sigma_2$, then

$$af_1(t) + bf_2(t) \Longleftrightarrow aF_1(s) + bF_2(s), \qquad \sigma > \sigma_1, \sigma_2 \qquad (6\text{-}6)$$

This relationship follows directly from the definition of the Laplace transform. Its principal use is in allowing the decomposition of time functions and transforms to simplify transformations and inversions. For example, suppose

$$f(t) = \sin \omega_0 t$$

$$\sin \omega_0 t \Longleftrightarrow \mathcal{L}\{\sin \omega_0 t\} = \mathcal{L}\left\{\frac{\epsilon^{j\omega_0 t} - \epsilon^{-j\omega_0 t}}{2j}\right\}$$

From (6-3) we have

$$\sin \omega_0 t \Longleftrightarrow \frac{1}{2j}\left[\frac{1}{s - j\omega_0} - \frac{1}{s + j\omega_0}\right]$$

$$\qquad (6\text{-}7)$$

$$\sin \omega_0 t \Longleftrightarrow \frac{\omega_0}{s^2 + \omega_0^2}$$

Time delay.   If a causal function $f(t)u(t)$ is delayed along the t axis by an amount t_0, its Laplace transform is given by the transform of the undelayed function multiplied by the exponential ϵ^{-st_0}.

$$f(t - t_0)u(t - t_0) \Longleftrightarrow \epsilon^{-st_0} F(s) \qquad t_0 \geq 0 \qquad \text{(6-8)}$$

Thus, delay in the time domain corresponds to multiplication by an exponential in the s domain. This result may be derived as follows:

$$\mathscr{L}\{f(t - t_0)u(t - t_0)\} = \int_0^\infty f(t - t_0)u(t - t_0)\epsilon^{-st}\, dt$$

$$= \int_{t_0}^\infty f(t - t_0)\epsilon^{-st}\, dt$$

Make the change of variable $t - t_0 = \tau$, and obtain

$$\mathscr{L}\{f(t - t_0)u(t - t_0)\} = \int_0^\infty f(\tau)\epsilon^{-s(t_0 + \tau)}\, d\tau$$

$$= \epsilon^{-st_0} \int_0^\infty f(\tau)\epsilon^{-s\tau}\, d\tau$$

$$= \epsilon^{-st_0} F(s)$$

There are many interesting applications of the time delay, or *t-shift theorem* as it is often called. However, there are also some possibilities for confusion. Consider the following formulations involving the basic function $f(t) = t$:

$$f_1(t) = f(t)u(t) = tu(t)$$
$$f_2(t) = f(t - 1)u(t) = (t - 1)u(t)$$
$$f_3(t) = f(t)u(t - 1) = tu(t - 1)$$
$$f_4(t) = f(t - 1)u(t - 1) = (t - 1)u(t - 1)$$

These functions are shown in Fig. 6-1. It is seen that these functions are quite different. We will now compute the Laplace transform of each.

$$F_1(s) = \mathscr{L}\{tu(t)\} = \frac{1}{s^2} \qquad \text{(6-9)}$$

$$F_2(s) = \mathscr{L}\{(t - 1)u(t)\} = \mathscr{L}\{tu(t) - u(t)\} = \frac{1}{s^2} - \frac{1}{s} \qquad \text{(6-10)}$$

$$F_3(s) = \mathscr{L}\{tu(t - 1)\} = \mathscr{L}\{(t - 1)u(t - 1) + u(t - 1)\}$$

$$= \frac{\epsilon^{-s}}{s^2} + \frac{\epsilon^{-s}}{s} \qquad \text{(6-11)}$$

$$F_4(s) = \mathscr{L}\{(t - 1)u(t - 1)\} = \frac{\epsilon^{-s}}{s^2} \qquad \text{(6-12)}$$

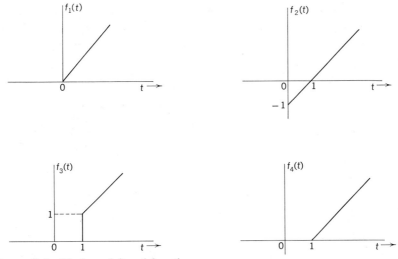

Figure 6-1   Various delayed functions.

It is important to note the manipulations that were made in (6-11) to make the arguments of the time function and the step function the same to simplify the transformation. If this is not done the transformation takes on the following form:

$$\{f(t)u(t-\tau)\} = \int_{\tau}^{\infty} f(t)\epsilon^{-st}\,dt$$

$$= \int_{0}^{\infty} f(t)\epsilon^{-st}\,dt - \int_{0}^{\tau} f(t)\epsilon^{-st}\,dt \qquad (6\text{-}13)$$

$$= F(s) - F_{\tau}(s)$$

where $F_{\tau}(s)$ is the truncated Laplace transform, which must be evaluated for the particular function involved. Tables of such transforms are available, but it is generally easier to compute the transformation directly or to find some other manipulation that will give the desired result than it is to use the truncated transform.

As another example of the use of the t-shift theorem we will determine the Laplace transform of a pulse consisting of a single loop of a sine wave, as shown in Fig. 6-2. This wave can be formed from the summation of a

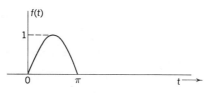

Figure 6-2   Sinusoidal pulse.

sinusoid having period 2π and another sinusoid of the same period which is delayed by a half period. These waveforms are shown in Fig. 6-3. The

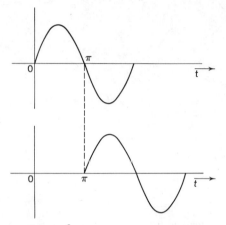

Figure 6-3   Component waveforms.

transform of the resulting pulse is obtained as follows:

$$\mathscr{L}\{f(t)\} = \mathscr{L}\{\sin(t)u(t) + \sin(t - \pi)u(t - \pi)\}$$

$$= \frac{1}{s^2 + 1} + \frac{\epsilon^{-s\pi}}{s^2 + 1} \qquad (6\text{-}14)$$

$$\frac{1}{s^2 + 1}\left[1 + \epsilon^{-s\pi}\right]$$

By use of the t-shift theorem, the transform of the rectangular pulse

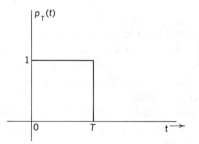

Figure 6-4   The pulse function.

function shown in Fig. 6-4 can be found readily to be

$$\mathscr{L}\{p_T(t)\} = P_T(s) = \mathscr{L}\{u(t) - u(t - T)\}$$

$$= \frac{1}{s} - \frac{\epsilon^{-sT}}{s} \qquad (6\text{-}15)$$

$$= \frac{1}{s}\left[1 - \epsilon^{-sT}\right]$$

The pulse function finds considerable application in formation of pulse-type signals since a valid time function description of any signal extending over the interval t_0 to $t_0 + T$ can be obtained by multiplying the generating signal by $p_T(t - t_0)$. For example, consider the sinusoidal pulse in Fig. 6-2. This pulse is also given by

$$f(t) = p_\pi(t) \sin t \tag{6-16}$$

The transform of (6-16) can be evaluated as follows:

$$\mathscr{L}\{p_\pi(t) \sin t\} = \mathscr{L}\{\sin(t)[u(t) - u(t - \pi)]\}$$
$$= \mathscr{L}\{\sin(t)u(t) - \sin(t)u(t - \pi)\} \tag{6-17}$$

Evaluating the two terms separately we have

$$\mathscr{L}\{\sin t\, u(t)\} = \frac{1}{s^2 + 1}$$

$$\mathscr{L}\{\sin t\, u(t - \pi)\} = \mathscr{L}\{\sin[(t - \pi) + \pi]\, u(t - \pi)\}$$
$$= \mathscr{L}\{\sin(t - \pi)\cos\pi\, u(t - \pi)$$
$$+ \cos(t - \pi)\sin(\pi)\, u(t - \pi)\}$$
$$= \mathscr{L}\{-\sin(t - \pi)u(t - \pi)\}$$
$$= -\frac{\epsilon^{-s\pi}}{s^2 + 1}$$

Therefore,

$$\mathscr{L}\{\sin(t)\, p_\pi(t)\} = \frac{1}{s^2 + 1}[1 + \epsilon^{-s\pi}] \tag{6-18}$$

Scale change. When the independent variable t is multiplied by a positive constant or a variable independent of both t and s, the corresponding transform is given by

$$f(at) \Longleftrightarrow \frac{1}{a} F\left(\frac{s}{a}\right) \qquad a > 0 \tag{6-19}$$

This may be proved by carrying out formally the transformation with a suitable change of variable. As an example of the use of (6-19) consider the transform of a sinusoidal pulse of duration T. Using the expression in (6-18) for the transform of a pulse of duration π we have

$$f_1(t) = \sin t\, p_\pi(t) \Longleftrightarrow \frac{1}{s^2 + 1}[1 + \epsilon^{-s\pi}]$$

$$f_2(t) = f_1\left(\frac{t\pi}{T}\right) \Longleftrightarrow \frac{T}{\pi} \frac{1}{(sT/\pi)^2 + 1}[1 + \epsilon^{-(sT/\pi)\pi}] \tag{6-20}$$

$$f_2(t) \Longleftrightarrow \frac{\pi/T}{s^2 + (\pi/T)^2}[1 + \epsilon^{-sT}]$$

Through the use of this theorem, transforms derived for normalized time functions can be modified to cover a wide range of related functions.

Differentiation.   It is principally as a result of the simple form taken by the Laplace transform of time derivatives that transform methods have found such wide acceptance as a tool for solving differential equations. The expression for the transform of a derivative can be derived from the defining equation for the transform. Let it be assumed that $f(t)$ has a Laplace transform $F(s)$. Then

$$\mathcal{L}\left\{\frac{df}{dt}\right\} = \int_0^\infty \frac{df}{dt}\epsilon^{-st}\, dt$$

Integrating by parts, with $u = \epsilon^{-st}$ and $v = f(t)$,

$$\mathcal{L}\left\{\frac{df}{dt}\right\} = f(t)\,\epsilon^{-st}\,\bigg|_0^\infty + s\int_0^\infty f(t)\epsilon^{-st}\, dt$$

Since $f(t)\epsilon^{-st}$ must be zero for $t \to \infty$ in order for $F(s)$ to exist, it follows that

$$\mathcal{L}\left\{\frac{df}{dt}\right\} = sF(s) - f(0) \tag{6-21}$$

It is thus seen that differentiation in the time domain corresponds to multiplication by s in the s domain with the addition of a constant equal to the value of the time function at $t = 0$. The value of $f(0)$ must be taken in such a way as to be consistent with the definition of the transform and in such a way as to give consistent results with the various functions to which it may be applied. In particular, when there is a discontinuity in $f(t)$ at the origin, there will be a δ function present in the derivative whose strength is equal to the magnitude of the discontinuity. If this δ function is to be included in the Laplace transform, then the value of $f(0)$ must be taken as $f(0^-)$. Similarly, if it is considered that $f(t)$ is an impulse at the origin, the defining integral must have a lower limit of 0^- in order to include this impulse in the integration.

In rigorous mathematical treatments of the Laplace transform, the value $f(0^+)$ is always used to avoid derivatives of discontinuous functions since impulses are not legitimate mathematical functions. However, for practical analysis in which the δ function is used, a much more consistent methodology results by using a lower limit $f(0^-)$. This convention will be followed here. The lower limit will usually be written as 0, but when there is a discontinuity at $t = 0$, it will be understood that what is meant is $t = 0^-$.

As an example of (6-21) consider the function $f(t) = \cos \omega_0 t$. From (6-7) and (6-21), we have:

$$F(s) = \mathcal{L}\{\cos \omega_0 t\} = \mathcal{L}\left\{\frac{1}{\omega_0}\frac{d}{dt}\sin \omega_0 t\right\} = \frac{1}{\omega_0}\left[\frac{s\omega_0}{s^2 + \omega_0^2} - \sin 0\right]$$

$$= \frac{s}{s^2 + \omega_0^2}$$

Now consider the transform of the derivative of the time function $\cos \omega_0 t$.

$$\mathcal{L}\{f'(t)\} = \mathcal{L}\left\{\frac{d}{dt}\cos \omega_0 t\right\} = \mathcal{L}\{-\omega_0 \sin \omega_0 t\}$$

$$= -\frac{\omega_0^2}{s^2 + \omega_0^2}$$

(6-22)

If the time function had been $\cos \omega_0\, tu(t)$ instead of $\cos \omega_0 t$, there would be no difference in the Laplace transform of the time functions. However, the transforms of the derivatives of these two functions will be quite different. The function $\cos (\omega_0 t)\, u(t)$ is shown in Fig. 6-5.

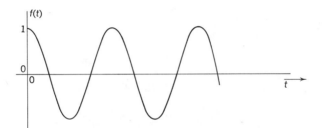

Figure 6-5 The function $\cos \omega_0 t\, u(t)$.

It is seen that in this case $f(t)$ has a jump discontinuity at the origin of unit magnitude. The transform of the derivative of $f(t)$ can be found by the formal application of (6-21):

$$\mathcal{L}\left\{\frac{d}{dt}\cos (\omega_0 t)\, u(t)\right\} = s\left[\frac{s}{s^2 + \omega_0^2}\right] - \cos (0^-)\, u(0^-)$$

(6-23)

$$= \frac{s^2}{s^2 + \omega_0^2}$$

By comparison with (6-22), it is seen that this is quite different from the expression resulting when $f(t)$ is not discontinuous at the origin. The result given in (6-23) can also be obtained by differentiating first and then transforming as follows:

$$\frac{d}{dt}[\cos \omega_0 t\, u(t)] = \frac{d}{dt}[(\cos \omega_0 t)]\, u(t) + \cos \omega_0 t\, \frac{d}{dt}[u(t)]$$

$$= - \omega_0 \sin (\omega_0 t) \, u(t) + \delta(t) \cos \omega_0 t$$

$$= - \omega_0 \sin (\omega_0 t) \, u(t) + \delta(t)$$

$$\mathcal{L}\left\{ \frac{d}{dt} \cos (\omega_0 t) \, u(t) \right\} = \mathcal{L}\{ - \omega_0 \sin (\omega_0 t) \, u(t) + \delta(t) \} \qquad \textbf{(6-24)}$$

$$= - \omega_0 \left(\frac{\omega_0}{s^2 + \omega_0^2} \right) + 1$$

$$= \frac{s^2}{s^2 + \omega_0^2}$$

It is seen that the result obtained by differentiating first is identical to the result obtained by using the expression for the transform of a derivative. Consistent results can be obtained by use of the 0^- limit, provided that care is taken in specifying the signal $f(t)$ at the origin.

The transform of the unit impulse can be found as the transform of the derivative of the unit step function

$$\mathcal{L}\{\delta(t)\} = \mathcal{L}\left\{ \frac{d}{dt} u(t) \right\} = s \left(\frac{1}{s} \right) - u(0^-)$$

$$= 1 \qquad \textbf{(6-25)}$$

Using the same method the transform of the unit doublet is found to be

$$\mathcal{L}\{\delta'(t)\} = s(1) - \delta(0^-)$$

$$= s \qquad \textbf{(6-26)}$$

Many other transforms can be calculated by use of the derivative relationship. However, the principal use of transforms of derivatives is in the transformation of differential equations, which will be discussed in the next chapter.

Integration.   The Laplace transform of a definite integral may be obtained as follows. Let $f(t)$ be a function having the Laplace transform $F(s)$. Then the Laplace transform of

$$\int_0^t f(\lambda) \, d\lambda$$

is found as follows:

$$\mathcal{L}\left\{ \int_0^t f(\lambda) \, d\lambda \right\} = \int_0^\infty \left[\int_0^t f(\lambda) \, d\lambda \right] \epsilon^{-st} \, dt$$

Integrating by parts with

$$u = \int_0^t f(\lambda) \, d\lambda \quad \text{and} \quad dv = \epsilon^{-st} \, dt$$

we obtain

$$\mathscr{L}\left\{\int_0^t f(\lambda)\, d\lambda\right\} = -\frac{1}{s}\,\epsilon^{-st}\int_0^t f(\lambda)\, d\lambda\,\Big|_0^\infty + \frac{1}{s}\int_0^\infty f(t)\epsilon^{-st}\, dt$$

Since

$$\epsilon^{-st} \to 0 \text{ as } t \to \infty \quad \text{and} \quad \int_0^t f(\lambda)\, d\lambda\,\Big|_{t=0} = 0$$

it follows that

$$\mathscr{L}\left\{\int_0^t f(\lambda)\, d\lambda\right\} = \frac{1}{s} F(s) \tag{6-27}$$

The integral theorem is useful in transforming integrodifferential equations and also in developing and interpreting transforms. Thus, whenever we see a transform in which an s can be factored out, we know we can express the inverse transform as the integral of the time function corresponding to the transform with the s removed. Consider, for example, the following transform:

$$F(s) = \frac{1}{s^3} = \frac{1}{s}\left(\frac{1}{s^2}\right)$$

The inverse transform of $1/s^2$ is known from previous work to be $tu(t)$; therefore, the inverse transform of $F(s)$ is given by

$$\mathscr{L}^{-1}\left\{\frac{1}{s^3}\right\} = \int_0^t \lambda\, d\lambda = \frac{t^2}{2} \tag{6-28}$$

This can also be written as

$$t^2 \Longleftrightarrow \frac{2}{s^3} \tag{6-29}$$

The s-shift theorem.   Another theorem frequently of use in determining transforms or in obtaining inverse transforms is the so-called s-shift theorem, which may be stated as follows:

$$\mathscr{L}\{\epsilon^{-\alpha t}f(t)\} = F(s + \alpha) \qquad \alpha > 0 \tag{6-30}$$

In words, this theorem states that shifting $F(s)$ by an amount α in the s domain corresponds to multiplication of the original time function by an exponential $\epsilon^{-\alpha t}$. The derivation of (6-30) follows from direct application of the defining integral.

   Example:
Given

$$\mathscr{L}\{\cos(\omega_0 t)\, u(t)\} = \frac{s}{s^2 + \omega_0^2}$$

It follows from (6-30) that

$$\mathscr{L}\{\epsilon^{-\alpha t} \cos(\omega_0 t)\, u(t)\} = \frac{s + \alpha}{(s + \alpha)^2 + \omega_0^2} \tag{6-31}$$

This theorem (along with all of the others) has many applications in simplifying movement between the t and s domains.

Convolution.   The convolution integral arises in the time-domain determination of the output of a linear system. The Laplace transform of the convolution of two functions is a particularly simple and important relationship in the solution of system problems by transform methods. Let $F_1(s)$ and $F_2(s)$ be the Laplace transforms of two functions $f_1(t)$ and $f_2(t)$. We now propose to find the inverse transform of the product of $F_1(s)$ and $F_2(s)$.

$$F_1(s)\, F_2(s) = F_1(s) \left[\int_0^\infty f_2(t)\epsilon^{-st}\, dt \right] \tag{6-32}$$

Changing the variable of integration and bringing $F_1(s)$ under the integral gives

$$F_1(s) F_2(s) = \int_0^\infty F_1(s) f_2(\lambda)\epsilon^{-s\lambda}\, d\lambda \tag{6-33}$$

Noting that $F_1(s)\epsilon^{-s\lambda}$ is $\mathscr{L}[f_1(t - \lambda)u(t - \lambda)]$ we can write (6-33) as

$$F_1(s)F_2(s) = \int_0^\infty \left[\int_0^\infty f_1(t - \lambda)u(t - \lambda)\epsilon^{-st}\, dt \right] f_2(\lambda)\, d\lambda \tag{6-34}$$

Inverting the order of integration and noting that λ cannot exceed t because of $u(t - \lambda)$ we can write this as

$$F_1(s)F_2(s) = \int_0^\infty \left[\int_0^t f_1(t - \lambda)f_2(\lambda)\, d\lambda \right] \epsilon^{-st}\, dt \tag{6-35}$$

The expression on the right is seen to be the Laplace transform of the convolution of $f_1(t)$ and $f_2(t)$. Accordingly, it can be written as

$$\mathscr{L}\left\{ \int_0^t f_1(\lambda)f_2(t - \lambda)\, d\lambda \right\} = F_1(s) F_2(s) \tag{6-36}$$

or, using the shorthand notation for convolution,

$$\mathscr{L}\{f_1(t) \star f_2(t)\} = F_1(s)F_2(s) \tag{6-37}$$

The theorem as developed above applies to causal time functions and is of frequent use in evaluating transforms, understanding results, and taking inverse transforms. A more general relationship involving infinite limits was given previously for the Fourier transform and a comparable relationship applies to the double-sided Laplace transform. As an example of the application of the convolution theorem, consider the following functions:

$$f_1(t) = \epsilon^{-\alpha t} u(t)$$
$$f_2(t) = u(t)$$

Here $f_1(t)$ might be the impulse response of an *R-C* network and $f_2(t)$ might be a unit step applied to the network input. The output of the network would be given by the convolution $f_1 \star f_2$. The result can be obtained in the frequency domain quite readily as follows:

$$f_3(t) = f_1 \star f_2$$

$$F_3(s) = F_1(s)F_2(s) = \left(\frac{1}{s + \alpha} \right) \left(\frac{1}{s} \right)$$

$$= \frac{1}{\alpha} \left(\frac{1}{s} - \frac{1}{s + \alpha} \right)$$

$$f_3(t) = \mathscr{L}^{-1} \left\{ \frac{1}{\alpha} \left(\frac{1}{s} - \frac{1}{s + \alpha} \right) \right\}$$

$$= \frac{1}{\alpha} \left[u(t) - \epsilon^{-\alpha t} u(t) \right]$$

$$= \frac{1}{\alpha} (1 - \epsilon^{-\alpha t}) u(t)$$

Notice that in determining the inverse transform of $F_3(s)$ it was found convenient to break $F_3(s)$ up into a sum of simpler terms that could be more readily transformed. This partial fraction expansion will be considered in detail in connection with finding inverse transforms.

6-5 Tables of Laplace Transforms

There are many additional theorems which on occasion are useful in manipulating transforms. A number of these are listed in Table 6-1, along with the theorems previously discussed. These theorems may be derived by the same methods as used previously and several of the derivations are included as problems at the end of the chapter. The use of the theorems in Table 6-1 will be illustrated in the various systems analysis problems discussed in the next chapter.

Table 6-1 LAPLACE TRANSFORMS CORRESPONDING
TO MATHEMATICAL OPERATIONS

	TIME DOMAIN	s DOMAIN	
PROPERTY	TIME FUNCTION	LAPLACE TRANSFORM	PROPERTY
Linearity	$a_1 f_1(t) + a_2 f_2(t)$	$a_1 F_1(s) + a_2 F_2(s)$	Linearity
Time differentiation	$f'(t)$	$sF(s) - f(0)$	s multiplication
Time integration	$\int_0^t f(\xi)\,d\xi$	$\dfrac{1}{s} F(s)$	Division by s
t multiplication	$tf(t)$	$-\dfrac{dF(s)}{ds}$	Differentiation
Division by t	$\dfrac{1}{t} f(t)$	$\int_0^\infty F(\xi)\,d\xi$	Integration
Delay (t shift)	$f(t - t_0)\,u(t - t_0)$	$\epsilon^{-st_0} F(s)$	Multiplication by exponential
Multiplication by exponential	$\epsilon^{-\alpha t}f(t)$	$F(s + a)$	s shift
Scale change	$f(at)\ a > 0$	$\dfrac{1}{a} F\left(\dfrac{s}{a}\right)$	Scale change
Time convolution	$f_1 \star f_2 = \int_0^t f_1(\lambda) f_2(t - \lambda)\,d\lambda$	$F_1(s) F_2(s)$	Multiplication of transforms
Initial value	$f(0^+)$	$\lim\limits_{s \to \infty} sF(s)$	Limit as $s \to \infty$
Final value	$f(\infty)$	$\lim\limits_{s \to 0} sF(s)$ $[F(s)$ left half plane poles only$]$	Limit as $s \to 0$
Second derivative	$f''(t)$	$s^2 F(s) - sf(0) - f'(0)$	s multiplication

A collection of the most frequently occurring elementary transforms is provided in Table 6-2. When used in conjunction with the expansion methods to be discussed in the next chapter, these transforms will be found adequate for the solution of a wide range of problems.

Table 6-2 LAPLACE TRANSFORMS OF ELEMENTARY FUNCTIONS

TIME FUNCTION	TRANSFORM
$\delta(t)$	1
$u(t)$	$\dfrac{1}{s}$
$tu(t)$	$\dfrac{1}{s^2}$
$t^n u(t)$	$\dfrac{n!}{s^{n+1}}$
$\epsilon^{-\alpha t} u(t)$	$\dfrac{1}{s+\alpha}$
$t\epsilon^{-\alpha t} u(t)$	$\dfrac{1}{(s+\alpha)^2}$
$\sin(\beta t)\, u(t)$	$\dfrac{\beta}{s^2+\beta^2}$
$\cos(\beta t)\, u(t)$	$\dfrac{s}{s^2+\beta^2}$
$\epsilon^{-\alpha t}\sin(\beta t)\, u(t)$	$\dfrac{\beta}{(s+\alpha)^2+\beta^2}$
$\epsilon^{-\alpha t}\cos(\beta t)\, u(t)$	$\dfrac{s+\alpha}{(s+\alpha)^2+\beta^2}$

6-6 Laplace Transform of a Periodic Function

In many applications it is of interest to determine the response of linear systems to the application of periodic driving functions. When the one-sided Laplace transform is used, it is understood that the functions are only periodic for $t > 0$. A typical function of this form would be $\sin(\omega_0 t) u(t)$. Even though the waveforms are not simple sinusoids, it is still relatively simple to obtain the Laplace transform. Consider a function, $f(t)$, which repeats with period T. We can express the function in the first period as $f_1(t)$, the function in the second period as $f_2(t) = f_1(t - T)$, and so forth. The composite function $f(t)$ is given by the following sum:

$$\begin{aligned}
f(t) &= f_1(t) + f_2(t) + \cdots + f_{k+1}(t) + \cdots \\
&= f_1(t) + f_1(t - T) + \cdots + f_1(t - kT) + \cdots
\end{aligned} \tag{6-38}$$

Taking the Laplace transform of (6-38) gives

$$\begin{aligned}
F(s) &= F_1(s) + F_1(s)\epsilon^{-sT} + \cdots + F_1(s)\,\epsilon^{-ksT} + \cdots \\
&= F_1(t)\left[1 + \epsilon^{-sT} + \cdots + \epsilon^{-ksT} + \cdots\right]
\end{aligned} \tag{6-39}$$

The right-hand factor can be represented as $(1 - \epsilon^{-sT})^{-1}$ as can be shown readily by means of the binomial expansion theorem. Accordingly, (6-39) can be written as

$$F(s) = \frac{F_1(s)}{1 - \epsilon^{-sT}} \tag{6-40}$$

where $f(t)$ is periodic with period T, and $F_1(s)$ is the Laplace transform of the waveform corresponding to the first period.

As an example of the application of (6-40) consider the square wave shown in Fig. 6-6.

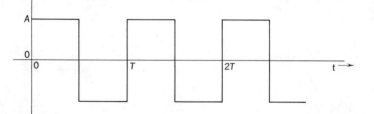

Figure 6-6   Square wave.

$$f_1(t) = A\left[u(t) - 2u\left(t - \frac{T}{2}\right) + u(t - T) \right]$$

$$F_1(s) = \frac{A}{s}(1 - 2\epsilon^{-sT/2} + \epsilon^{-sT})$$

$$= \frac{A}{s}(1 - \epsilon^{-sT/2})^2$$

$$\tag{6-41}$$

$$F(s) = \frac{A}{s}\frac{(1 - \epsilon^{-sT/2})^2}{(1 - \epsilon^{-sT})}$$

$$= \frac{A}{s}\frac{(1 - \epsilon^{-sT/2})}{(1 + \epsilon^{-sT/2})}$$

This result can be extended to cover other waveforms by carrying out operations on $f(t)$ and appropriately modifying the transform. Consider the integral of the square wave as shown in Fig. 6-7(a). This integral can be

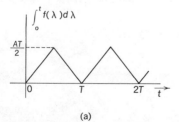

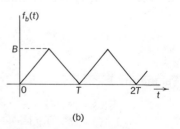

(a)   (b)

Figure 6-7   Triangular wave.

related to the triangular waveform $f_b(t)$ shown in Fig. 6-7(b), and the corresponding transform found using the theorem for the transform of a definite integral.

$$f_b(t) = \frac{2B}{AT} \int_0^t f(\lambda)\, d\lambda$$

$$F_b(s) = \frac{2B}{AT} \left(\frac{1}{s}\right) F(s)$$

$$= \frac{2B}{AT} \left(\frac{1}{s}\right) \frac{A(1 - \epsilon^{-sT/2})}{s(1 + \epsilon^{-sT/2})}$$

$$= \frac{2B}{T} \frac{1 - \epsilon^{-sT/2}}{s^2(1 + \epsilon^{-sT/2})}$$

(6-42)

6-7 The Two-sided Laplace Transform

Now that the one-sided Laplace transform has been considered in some detail, it is desirable to return to the two-sided transform that was originally defined as

$$F_{II}(s) = \int_{-\infty}^{\infty} f(t)\epsilon^{-st}\, dt \tag{6-43}$$

for all values of s for which the integral converges. The subscript II has been introduced in order to distinguish this transform from the one-sided transform.

The values of s for which (6-43) exists can be determined by considering the positive time and negative time portions of $f(t)$ separately. Thus,

$$F_{II}(s) = \int_{-\infty}^{0} f(t)\epsilon^{-st}\, dt + \int_{0}^{\infty} f(t)\,\epsilon^{-st}\, dt \tag{6-44}$$

The first integral will exist for all values of s for which the real part, σ, (Re $s = \sigma$) is *less* than some value β, while the second integral exists for σ *greater* than some value α. These regions are shown in Fig. 6-8 for a case in which

$$\alpha < \sigma < \beta$$

Since the two regions overlap, there is a *strip of convergence* in which $F_{II}(s)$ exists. If, on the other hand, the time function were such that $\beta < \alpha$, there would be no region of overlap and $F_{II}(s)$ would not exist.

The foregoing discussion may be made somewhat clearer by considering some specific cases. In the first case, let

$$f(t) = \epsilon^{at} \qquad a > 0, t < 0$$
$$= \epsilon^{-bt} \qquad b > 0, t \geq 0$$

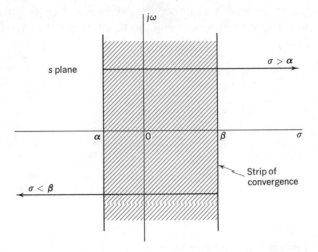

Figure 6-8 Illustrating the strip of convergence for $F_{II}(s)$.

Then,

$$F_{II}(s) = \int_{-\infty}^{0} \epsilon^{at}\epsilon^{-st}\, dt + \int_{0}^{\infty} \epsilon^{-bt}\epsilon^{-st}\, dt$$

$$= \int_{-\infty}^{0} \epsilon^{-(s-a)t}\, dt + \int_{0}^{\infty} \epsilon^{-(s+b)t}\, dt$$

It is clear that the first integral will exist if Re $s = \sigma$ is *less* than a, while the second one exists for Re $s = \sigma$ *greater* than $-b$. Thus, the strip of convergence is defined by

$$-b < \text{Re } s < a$$

and includes the $j\omega$-axis. The corresponding two-sided Laplace transform becomes

$$F_{II}(s) = \frac{-1}{s-a} + \frac{1}{s+b} = \frac{-(a+b)}{(s-a)(s+b)}, \qquad -b < \text{Re } s < a$$

As a second example, let

$$f(t) = 1 \qquad\qquad t < 0$$
$$= \epsilon^{-bt} \qquad\quad b > 0, t \geq 0$$

Then

$$F_{II}(s) = \int_{-\infty}^{0} \epsilon^{-st}\, dt + \int_{0}^{\infty} \epsilon^{-bt}\epsilon^{-st}\, dt$$

$$= \int_{-\infty}^{0} \epsilon^{-st}\, dt + \int_{0}^{\infty} \epsilon^{-(s+b)t}\, dt$$

The first integral converges only when Re $s < 0$, whereas the second one converges for Re $s > -b$. Thus, the strip of convergence is defined by

$$-b < \text{Re } s < 0$$

and does not include the $j\omega$ axis. The resulting two-sided Laplace transform is

$$F_{II}(s) = \frac{-1}{s} + \frac{1}{s+b} = \frac{-b}{s(s+b)} \qquad -b < \text{Re } s < 0$$

As a final example, let

$$f(t) = \epsilon^{-bt} \qquad b > 0, \, -\infty < t < \infty$$

Then,

$$F_{II}(s) = \int_{-\infty}^{0} \epsilon^{-bt} \epsilon^{-st} \, dt + \int_{0}^{\infty} \epsilon^{-bt} \epsilon^{-st} \, dt$$

$$= \int_{-\infty}^{0} \epsilon^{-(s+b)t} \, dt + \int_{0}^{\infty} \epsilon^{-(s+b)t} \, dt$$

The first integral converges only when Re $s < -b$ and the second integral converges only when Re $s > -b$. Thus, the two regions of convergence do not overlap and the two-sided Laplace transform does not exist.

Many of the properties of two-sided Laplace transforms are the same as for one-sided transforms. These are summarized as follows:

Linearity. Equation (6-6) holds for two-sided Laplace transforms provided that the strip of convergence of the sum is taken as the *common* area of the strips of convergence of the individual transforms.

Time translation. Equation (6-8) holds for two-sided Laplace transforms except that the restriction to $t_0 \geq 0$ is no longer necessary.

Scale change. Equation (6-19) for two-sided Laplace transforms can be extended to include negative constants. The relation is

$$\mathscr{L}_{II} \{f(at)\} = \frac{1}{|a|} F_{II}\left(\frac{s}{a}\right)$$

Differentiation. For two-sided Laplace transforms, (6-21) must be modified to read

$$\mathscr{L}_{II}\left\{\frac{df}{dt}\right\} = sF_{II}(s) \qquad \qquad \textbf{(6-45)}$$

Note that there are *no* terms corresponding to the difference between $f(0^-)$ and $f(0^+)$ even though such a discontinuity contributes a δ function to the derivative.

Integration.   In the case of the two-sided Laplace transform the integration of the time function is assumed to start at $-\infty$. Hence, (6-27) is modified to read

$$\mathscr{L}_{II}\left\{\int_{-\infty}^{t} f(\lambda)\ d\lambda\right\} = \frac{1}{s}F_{II}(s) \tag{6-46}$$

The s-shift theorem.   Equation (6-30) holds for the two-sided Laplace transform except that the strip of convergence for $\epsilon^{-\alpha t}f(t)$ is that for $f(t)$, but shifted to the *left* by the amount Re α.

Convolution.   Equation (6-37) holds for two-sided Laplace transforms except that the strip of convergence of the product is the common area of the strips of convergence of the individual transforms.

t Multiplication.   For the two-sided Laplace transform

$$\mathscr{L}_{II}\{tf(t)\} = -\frac{dF_{II}(s)}{ds} \tag{6-47}$$

The strip of convergence for this transform is the same as that for $F_{2}(s)$.

Initial- and final-value theorems.   These theorems (see Problems 6-12 and 6-13) do not hold for the two-sided Laplace transform in general. It is possible to apply these theorems individually to the two parts of $F_{II}(s)$ which come from the negative-time portion and the positive-time portion of $f(t)$.

■ REFERENCES

See references for Chapter 7.

■ PROBLEMS

6-1   Use the defining integral to find the Laplace transform of each of the following time functions:

a.	$u(t - t_0)$	**e.**	t^n
b.	$(t - t_0)u(t - t_0)$	**f.**	$t^{1/2}$
c.	$3t^2u(t - 5)$	**g.**	$t^{-1/2}$
d.	$5u(t)u(3 - t)$	**h.**	$\epsilon^{-\alpha t^2}$

6-2   Find the Laplace transform of each of the following time functions:
a. $10u(t) - 10u(t - 2)$
b. $t\epsilon^{-\alpha t}$

c. $\cosh(\beta t)$

d. $\epsilon^{-\alpha t} \cosh(\beta t)$

6-3 Find $F_2(s)$ from $F_1(s)$, using the scaling and t-shift theorems.

$f_1(t)$	$F_1(s)$	$f_2(t)$
$\sinh(t)$	$\dfrac{1}{s^2 - 1}$	$\sinh(\beta t)$
$\sin(t)$	$\dfrac{1}{s^2 + 1}$	$\sin(\beta t)$
$t\epsilon^{-t}u(t)$	$\dfrac{1}{(s+1)^2}$	$(t-1)\epsilon^{-t}u(t-1)$

6-4 Find the Laplace transforms of the following time functions using the t-shift theorem.

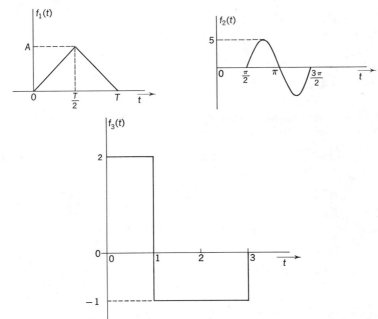

6-5 Using two methods, find the Laplace transform of

$$f(t) = \frac{d}{dt}\left[\epsilon^{-\alpha t}u(t)\right]$$

6-6 Consider a time function of the form

$$f(t) = t\epsilon^{-t}\,u(t)$$

a.   Find the Laplace transform of the derivative of $f(t)$.
b.   Find the Laplace transform of the second derivative of $f(t)$.
c.   Find the Laplace transform of the integral of $f(t)$.

6-7   Derive the following Laplace transform relationship. (Note: $t \geq 0$.)

$$\mathcal{L}\left\{\int_{-\infty}^{t} f(\lambda)\, d\lambda\right\} = \frac{1}{s} F(s) + \frac{1}{s} \int_{-\infty}^{0^-} f(t)\, dt$$

6-8   Find the Laplace transforms of the nth derivatives of the functions $f(t)$ and $f(t)u(t)$.

6-9   A set of functions that is orthonormal on the interval $0 < t < \infty$ can be used as basis functions for the orthogonal expansion of Laplace transformable signals. Such a set is the following

$$\phi_n(t) = \frac{\epsilon^{-t/2}}{n!} L_n(t)$$

where $L_n(t)$ is the nth-order Laguerre polynomial, defined by

$$L_n(t) = \epsilon^t \frac{d^n}{dt^n}(t^n \epsilon^{-t})$$

Find the Laplace transform of $\phi_n(t)$.

6-10   Find the Laplace transforms of the following functions.
a. $f(t) = \epsilon^{-\alpha(t-t_0)} \sin(\omega_0 t + \phi_0) u(t)$
b. $f(t) = t\epsilon^{-\alpha t} \cos \omega_0 t\, u(t)$
c. $f(t) = \displaystyle\int_0^t \epsilon^{-\alpha(t-\lambda)} \sin \omega_0 \lambda\, u(t - \lambda)\, d\lambda$

6-11   Find the Laplace transforms of the signals shown and compare them with the corresponding Fourier transforms.

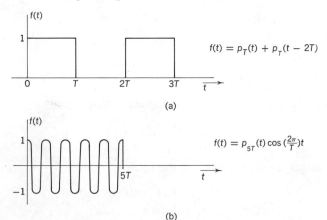

$$f(t) = p_T(t) + p_T(t - 2T)$$

(a)

$$f(t) = p_{5T}(t) \cos \left(\tfrac{2\pi}{T}\right)t$$

(b)

6-12 Prove the initial-value theorem, which states that

$$\lim_{t \to 0^+} f(t) = \lim_{s \to \infty} sF(s)$$

6-13 Prove the final-value theorem, which states that

$$\lim_{t \to \infty} f(t) = \lim_{s \to 0} sF(s)$$

6-14 Find the Laplace transforms of the following functions by use of the convolution theorem.

a. $f_2(t) = \int_0^t f_1(\lambda)d\lambda$

b. $f_2(t) = \int_t^{t+a} f_1(\lambda)d\lambda$

c.

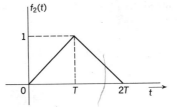

6-15 Find the Laplace transforms of the periodic waveforms shown.

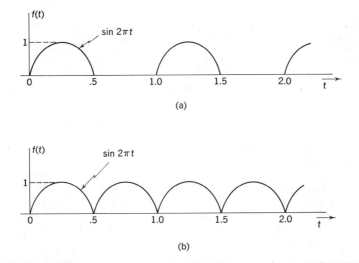

(a)

(b)

6-16 Find the two-sided Laplace transform of the following functions and indicate the strip of convergence in each instance.

a. $p_T\left(t + \dfrac{T}{2}\right)$ **c.** $\epsilon^{-\alpha|t|} \cos \omega_0 t$

b. $(t - a)u(-t)$ **d.** $\epsilon^{-\alpha t^2}$

6-17   A time function is defined as follows:

$$f(t) = te^{-\alpha|t|} \qquad -\infty < t < \infty$$

a.   Find the two-sided Laplace transform of $f(t)$.
b.   Specify the strip of convergence for $F_{II}(s)$.
c.   Repeat parts (a) and (b) for the function

$$\epsilon^{\beta t} f(t) \qquad \beta < \alpha$$

6-18   Find the two-sided Laplace transform for the following functions. (Hint: Use the same procedure as for Fourier transforms in which the functions are considered as limiting forms of functions having known transforms.)
a. $f(t) = K \qquad -\infty < t < \infty$
b. $f(t) = \cos \omega_0 t \qquad -\infty < t < \infty$

7

Inverse Laplace Transforms and Applications to System Analysis

7-1 Introduction

Application of the Laplace transform to the solution of differential equations requires that the transformation from the s domain to the t domain be accomplished readily. This "inverse transformation" can be carried out by a variety of methods, and it is our purpose to consider the most useful of these methods. The most obvious method is to carry out the formal inversion given by (6-1) which is

$$f(t) = \mathscr{L}^{-1}\{F(s)\} = \frac{1}{j2\pi} \int_{c-j\infty}^{c+j\infty} F(s)\epsilon^{st}\,ds \qquad \text{(7-1)}$$

repeated here as (7-1). In actuality, the effective use of this expression requires an understanding of the theory of complex variables, and the integration is normally carried out as a contour integral. It will not be necessary for us to resort to use of (7-1), however, since all of the transforms required for our purposes can be obtained by other methods. The Laplace transform has a very important property that greatly simplifies the problem of obtaining transforms and inverse transforms. This property is the unique relationship that exists between a function and its Laplace transform. For any function there is only one Laplace transform corresponding to that function. In the case of the inverse transform, it is found that for a given $F(s)$ there can be more than one $f(t)$ corresponding to this $F(s)$. These different functions can differ from each other only by a so-called "null function" $n(t)$, which has the property

$$\int_0^t n(t)\, dt = 0 \qquad \text{for all } t > 0$$

An example of two functions differing by a null function would be functions with discontinuities which are defined to have different finite values at the discontinuity but are the same elsewhere. When we consider all time functions that differ only by null functions to be the same, as is usual in mathematical analysis, the inversion of the Laplace transform is unique. This uniqueness of $\mathscr{L}$ and $\mathscr{L}^{-1}$ means that any valid means of obtaining the transform or inverse transform will provide the correct relationship. The most generally useful method of obtaining inverse transforms will be to modify, expand, or otherwise alter the transform so as to put it into a form that can be inverted by inspection. The chief tools for carrying out this process will be the partial fraction expansion and judicious use of the theorems concerning the Laplace transforms of operations.

Once the techniques for returning from the complex frequency domain to the time domain have been presented, application of the transform technique to a variety of problems will be considered. The Laplace transform is particularly useful in analyzing the transient behavior of systems, and often much insight into system behavior can be obtained from study of the s-plane properties of the system response function. Network synthesis problems are also carried out quite frequently in the s plane but will not be considered here.

7-2 Partial Fraction Expansion

The transform analysis of linear time-invariant systems with lumped parameters generally leads to transforms that are rational functions of s — that is, transforms that are ratios of polynomials in s. For example, the transfer function relating the current in the nth mesh of an electric circuit to a voltage source in the circuit is the ratio of two determinants, each of which is a polynomial in s. Rational functions of this form can be expressed as the sum of simple fractions whose denominators are the factors of the denominator of the original function. There will be one term in the expansion for each first-order pole in the original function. As an example, consider the following rational function:

$$F(s) = \frac{5s + 12}{s^2 + 5s + 6} = \frac{2}{s + 2} + \frac{3}{s + 3}$$

The inverse transform is easily obtained from the expanded form as $(2\epsilon^{-2t} + 3\epsilon^{-3t})u(t)$.

In order to expand a rational function in partial fractions it is necessary that the numerator be of lower degree than the denominator. If this requirement is not satisfied by the given function, it can always be met by dividing the denominator into the numerator until the remainder is of lower degree than the divisor. The function can then be expressed as the sum of the quotient terms and the remainder terms, divided by the original denominator. This procedure for reducing the degree of the numerator is illustrated by the following example:

$$F(s) = \frac{s^4 + 8s^3 + 23s^2 + 34s + 19}{s^3 + 7s^2 + 15s + 9}$$

$$
\begin{array}{r}
s + 1 \\
s^3 + 7s^2 + 15s + 9 \overline{\smash{\big)}\ s^4 + 8s^3 + 23s^2 + 34s + 19} \\
\underline{s^4 + 7s^3 + 15s^2 + \ \ 9s} \\
s^3 + \ \ 8s^2 + 25s + 19 \\
\underline{s^3 + \ \ 7s^2 + 15s + \ \ 9} \\
s^2 + 10s + 10
\end{array}
$$

Therefore,

$$F(s) = s + 1 + \frac{s^2 + 10s + 10}{s^3 + 7s^2 + 15s + 9}$$

The inverse transforms of the first two terms are obtained readily, and the primary job is to obtain the inverse transform of the remaining term, which is now a proper rational function. In future discussions of partial fraction expansions it will be assumed that the function has first been reduced to a proper rational function.

Let the rational function to be expanded be of the form

$$F(s) = \frac{P(s)}{Q(s)}$$

where the denominator polynomial $Q(s)$ is now assumed to be of higher degree than the numerator polynomial $P(s)$. According to a fundamental theorem of algebra, if $Q(s)$ is an nth-degree polynomial it will have n roots, not all of which need be different, and it can be factored into n factors, using these roots as follows:

$$
\begin{aligned}
Q(s) &= s^n + a_{n-1}s^{n-1} + \cdots + a_1 s + a_0 \\
&= (s - \alpha_1)(s - \alpha_2) \cdots (s - \alpha_{n-1})(s - \alpha_n)
\end{aligned}
$$

where $\alpha_1, \alpha_2 \cdots \alpha_n$ are the roots of $Q(s)$ and are solutions to the equation $Q(s) = 0$. Some of the α_k's may not be distinct, and some may be imaginary or complex. The variable s is the complex frequency, and the values of the complex frequency corresponding to the zeros of $Q(s)$ are called the *poles* of the function $F(s)$. Similarly, the complex frequencies corresponding to the roots of the numerator $P(s)$ are called the *zeros* of $F(s)$. The terminology is quite descriptive of the behavior of $P(s)$ at these critical frequencies, since, when the denominator approaches zero the function increases without limit (a pole) and when the numerator approaches zero the function also approaches zero (a zero). In taking the inverse transform of a rational function it is found that the locations of the poles in the complex s plane completely determine the form of the solution, and the locations of the zeros affect only the amplitudes of the various components present in the solution. This will be readily apparent when the partial fraction expansion is considered in detail.

If it is desired to exclude imaginary and complex roots from the factorization of $Q(s)$, then the factored form can be expressed as the product of linear and quadratic factors, some of which may be repeated. The partial fraction expansion will then be given as a sum of simple fractions having these factors as denominators and each having a numerator of lower degree than its denominator. The most frequently occurring cases are as follows.

Nonrepeated linear factors.   Assume that the denominator polynomial contains a nonrepeated linear factor $(s - \alpha_1)$. It is then possible to write the denominator as $Q(s) = (s - \alpha_1)Q_1(s)$, where $Q_1(s)$ is the remainder after $(s - \alpha_1)$ has been factored out of $Q(s)$. The rational function then becomes

$$F(s) = \frac{P(s)}{Q(s)} = \frac{P(s)}{(s - \alpha_1)Q_1(s)} = \frac{A}{s - \alpha_1} + \frac{P_1(s)}{Q_1(s)} \tag{7-2}$$

In (7-2) A is a constant (since this is the only polynomial of lower degree than $(s - \alpha_1)$) to be determined, and $P_1(s)$ is a polynomial of lower degree than $Q_1(s)$. The polynomial $P_1(s)$ will be ignored for the moment since we are presently concerned only with the first term. Multiplying both sides of (7-2) by $(s - \alpha_1)$ gives

$$(s - \alpha_1)F(s) = \frac{P(s)}{Q_1(s)} = A + (s - \alpha_1)\frac{P_1(s)}{Q_1(s)}$$

If this equation is now evaluated at $s = \alpha_1$, the second term on the right-hand side goes to zero, and A is found to be

$$A = \frac{(s - \alpha_1)P(s)}{Q(s)}\bigg|_{s=\alpha_1} = \frac{P(\alpha_1)}{Q_1(\alpha_1)} \tag{7-3}$$

In words, (7-3) may be stated as follows: the constant A in (7-2) can be found by deleting the factor $(s - \alpha_1)$ on the left-hand side and then putting $s = \alpha_1$ in the remaining fraction. As an example, consider the following rational function:

$$F(s) = \frac{3s^2 + 2s + 1}{(s + 1)(s^2 + 12s + 36)} = \frac{A}{s + 1} + \text{other terms}$$

$$A = \frac{3s^2 + 2s + 1}{s^2 + 12s + 36}\bigg|_{s = -1} = \frac{2}{25}$$

Exactly the same procedure is used to evaluate the numerators of the partial fractions corresponding to other linear factors in the same expression. Consider the following example:

$$F(s) = \frac{s^2 + 1}{(s + 1)(s + 3)(s + 4)} = \frac{A}{s + 1} + \frac{B}{s + 3} + \frac{C}{s + 4}$$

$$A = \frac{s^2 + 1}{(s + 3)(s + 4)}\bigg|_{s = -1} = \frac{1}{3}$$

$$B = \frac{s^2 + 1}{(s + 1)(s + 4)}\bigg|_{s = -3} = -5$$

$$C = \frac{s^2 + 1}{(s + 1)(s + 3)}\bigg|_{s = -4} = \frac{17}{3}$$

$$F(s) = \frac{1/3}{s + 1} - \frac{5}{s + 3} + \frac{17/3}{s + 4}$$

The expansion can always be checked by recombining the terms on the right. The foregoing expansion is valid for complex roots also, but this case will be discussed in connection with quadratic factors, since complex roots always occur as complex conjugate pairs and can be expressed as a single quadratic factor with real coefficients.

Repeated linear factors. If $(s - \alpha_1)^k$, with $k \geq 2$, is a factor of $Q(s)$, then the foregoing method is not sufficient, for there must be k terms in the partial fraction expansion corresponding to this repeated factor. These terms can be expressed in either of the following equivalent forms:

$$\frac{A_1}{(s - \alpha_1)^k} + \frac{A_2}{(s - \alpha_1)^{k-1}} + \cdots + \frac{A_k}{(s - \alpha_1)} \qquad \text{(7-4)}$$

or

$$\frac{B_0 + B_1 s + B_2 s^2 + \cdots + B_{k-1} s^{k-1}}{(s - \alpha_1)^k} \qquad \text{(7-5)}$$

where the A's or B's must be determined. Generally it will be found that the form given in (7-4) leads to more convenient terms for actually carrying out the inverse transformation. There are several methods available for determining the A's or B's. Consider the following example.

$$\frac{s^2}{(s + 1)^2(s + 2)} = \frac{A_1}{(s + 1)^2} + \frac{A_2}{s + 1} + \frac{A_3}{s + 2}$$

A_3 is determined as before and found to be $A_3 = 4$. The constant A_1 can be found in a similar manner—that is, by multiplying both sides by $(s + 1)^2$ and then setting $s = -1$. This leads to a value for A_1 of 1. Unfortunately the same procedure will not yield the value of A_2, since multiplication by $(s + 1)$ will not remove this factor from the denominator of the first term; so if s were set equal to -1, the expression would go to infinity. This problem can be handled directly by clearing fractions and then equating coefficients of like powers of s or by substituting convenient values of s into the expression to give numerical equations. In the present case this latter procedure leads to the following result:

$$\frac{s^2}{(s + 1)^2(s + 2)} = \frac{1}{(s + 1)^2} + \frac{A_2}{s + 1} + \frac{4}{s + 2}$$

Setting $s = 0$ and solving the resulting equation for A_2 leads to the value $A_2 = -3$. Exactly the same result could be obtained by equating the coefficients of s^2, etc. The final expansion is, therefore,

$$\frac{s^2}{(s + 1)^2(s + 2)} = \frac{1}{(s + 1)^2} - \frac{3}{s + 1} + \frac{4}{s + 2}$$

Another method that is very effective for the case of repeated roots involves differentiation. Assume that we have a rational function involving a linear factor in the denominator that is repeated k times; that is,

$$F(s) = \frac{P(s)}{Q(s)} = \frac{P(s)}{(s - \alpha)^k Q_1(s)}$$

$$= \frac{A_1}{s - \alpha} + \frac{A_2}{(s - \alpha)^2} + \cdots + \frac{A_k}{(s - \alpha)^k} + \frac{P_1(s)}{Q_1(s)} \qquad (7\text{-}6)$$

If now we multiply both sides of (7-6) by the repeated factor $(s - \alpha)^k$, we obtain

$$(s - \alpha)^k \, F(s) = A_1(s - \alpha)^{k-1} + A_2(s - \alpha)^{k-2} + \cdots + A_k + \frac{P_1(s)(s - \alpha)^k}{Q_1(s)}$$

$$(7\text{-}7)$$

Setting $s = \alpha$ gives the value of A_k as

$$A_k = (s - \alpha)^k F(s)\big|_{s = \alpha} \qquad (7\text{-}8)$$

To simplify the notation, let $(s - \alpha)^k F(s) = F_1(s)$. We then have

$$A_k = F_1(s)\big|_{s = \alpha} \qquad (7\text{-}9)$$

Differentiating (7-7) with respect to s and setting $s = \alpha$ gives

$$A_{k-1} = \frac{d}{ds} F_1(s) \Big|_{s=\alpha} \tag{7-10}$$

Repeating once more, we obtain

$$A_{k-2} = \frac{1}{2} \frac{d^2}{ds^2} F_1(s) \Big|_{s=\alpha} \tag{7-11}$$

The nth term becomes

$$A_{k-n} = \frac{1}{n!} \frac{d^n}{ds^n} F_1(s) \Big|_{s=\alpha} \tag{7-12}$$

Applying this procedure to the previous problem, we have

$$F(s) = \frac{s^2}{(s+1)^2(s+2)} = \frac{A_1}{(s+1)} + \frac{A_2}{(s+1)^2} + \frac{A_3}{s+2}$$

As before, A_3 is found to be $A_3 = 4$. The function $F_1(s)$ is now formed and A_1 and A_2 are evaluated.

$$F_1(s) = \frac{s^2}{s+2}$$

$$A_2 = F_1(s) \Big|_{s=-1} = \frac{s^2}{s+2} \Big|_{s=-1} = 1$$

$$A_1 = \frac{d}{ds} \left(\frac{s^2}{s+2} \right) \Big|_{s=-1} = \frac{s^2 + 4s}{(s+2)^2} \Big|_{s=-1} = -3$$

In the case of repeated roots it is always possible to evaluate directly the constant in the numerator of the partial fraction corresponding to the highest power of the factor. This evaluation is made by multiplying through by the factor raised to the highest power and evaluating the resulting expression with s set equal to the root corresponding to this factor. The resulting numerator terms will have to be evaluated by clearing fractions and equating powers of s, by choosing values of s to give simple equations in the unknowns, or by using the differentiation technique of (7-12).

Complex roots and quadratic factors. Some of the roots of the denominator polynomial may be complex. Such roots of polynomials with real coefficients always occur in complex conjugate pairs; that is, for each root $a_1 = -\alpha - j\omega_0$ there is another root $a_2 = a_1^* = -\alpha + j\omega_0$. These factors can be multiplied together to give a quadratic factor having real coefficients.

$$(s + \alpha + j\omega_0)(s + \alpha - j\omega_0) = (s + \alpha)^2 + \omega_0^2 \tag{7-13}$$

Alternatively, this factor can be expressed as the quadratic factor

$$(s + \alpha)^2 + \omega_0^2 = s^2 + 2\alpha s + \omega_0^2 + \alpha^2 = s^2 + as + b \tag{7-14}$$

The corresponding partial fraction expansion can then take any of the following forms:

$$\frac{P(s)}{Q(s)} = \frac{P(s)}{Q_1(s)\,(s^2 + as + b)} \tag{7-15}$$

$$= \frac{A_1 s + A_2}{s^2 + as + b} + \frac{P_1(s)}{Q_1(s)} \tag{7-16}$$

$$= \frac{B_1 + jB_2}{s + (\alpha + j\omega_0)} + \frac{B_1 - jB_2}{s + (\alpha - j\omega_0)} + \frac{P_1(s)}{Q_1(s)} \tag{7-17}$$

$$= \frac{C_1 s + C_2}{(s + \alpha)^2 + \omega_n^2} + \frac{P_1(s)}{Q_1(s)} \tag{7-18)^1}$$

In all cases the constants A, B, and C are real numbers. The last two forms are generally most convenient to use and are obtained from the first by factoring or completing the square. It should be noted that in (7-17) the numerators are complex conjugates of each other; thus, if one numerator is found the other can be written down immediately. Also, the constants A_1 and A_2 are equal to C_1 and C_2, respectively, since (7-16) and (7-18) are identical expressions. The constants are determined by clearing fractions and equating powers of s or, in the case of (7-17), by multiplying them by one of the factors and then evaluating at the value of s corresponding to that factor. The following examples illustrate expansion of functions containing quadratic factors.

$$F(s) = \frac{2s^2 + 6s + 6}{(s + 2)(s^2 + 2s + 2)} = \frac{A}{s + 2} + \frac{Bs + C}{s^2 + 2s + 2} \tag{7-19}$$

The constant A is found by the usual method to be $A = 1$. The values of B and C are found by clearing fractions and equating the coefficients of powers of s.

$$2s^2 + 6s + 6 = s^2 + 2s + 2 + Bs^2 + 2Bs + Cs + 2C$$
$$B = 2 - 1 = 1$$
$$C = \frac{1}{2}(6 - 2) = 2 \tag{7-20}$$
$$F(s) = \frac{1}{s + 2} + \frac{s + 2}{s^2 + 2s + 2}$$

---

[1] This expansion could also be written as

$$\frac{D_1(s + \alpha)}{(s + \alpha)^2 + \omega_0^2} + \frac{D_2}{(s + \alpha)^2 + \omega_0^2} + \frac{P_1(s)}{Q_1(s)}$$

which leads more directly to the transform in many cases. However, (7-18) is more consistent with previous procedures and easier to remember. Furthermore, it can be connected to this form by inspection.

Another, and frequently more simple, method of determining the constants B and C in (7-19) is to set $s = 0$, obtaining $6/4 = 1/2 + C/2$ which readily gives $C = 2$. The value for B can be obtained by multiplying (7-19) by s and letting $s \to \infty$. This leads to the equation $2 = 1 + B$, or $B = 1$. The inverse transform is found readily by completing the square in the denominator of the quadratic term and then adjusting the numerator by adding and subtracting quantities to make it complementary to the denominator.

$$F(s) = \frac{1}{s+2} + \frac{s+2}{(s+1)^2+1} = \frac{1}{s+2} + \frac{s+1}{(s+1)^2+1} + \frac{1}{(s+1)^2+1}$$

$$\tag{7-21}$$

$$f(t) = [\epsilon^{-2t} + \epsilon^{-t}\cos t + \epsilon^{-t}\sin t]u(t)$$

In obtaining the final form, use was made of inverse transforms for exponentials and sinusoids, and of the s-shift theorem.

This example can also be worked by using the linear factors, as follows:

$$F(s) = \frac{2s^2 + 6s + 6}{(s+2)(s^2+2s+2)} = \frac{2s^2 + 6s + 6}{(s+2)[s+(1+j1)][s+(1-j1)]}$$

$$= \frac{K_1}{s+2} + \frac{K_2}{s+1+j1} + \frac{K_3}{s+1-j1}$$

$$\tag{7-22}$$

$K_1 = 1$, as before.[2]

---

[2] The evaluation of complicated expansions, such as the following one for K_2, can often be more simply accomplished by use of the so-called remainder theorem, which may be stated as follows: If $D(s)$ is the quotient polynomial and R_0 is the remainder on division of $F(s)$ by $(s-a)$, then the following relation

$$F(s) = (s-a)D(s) + R_0$$

is an identity. If s is set equal to a then it follows that

$$R_0 = F(a)$$

Therefore, a polynomial can be evaluated at a given value, a, by determining the remainder when the polynomial is divided by $(s-a)$. In the above example the numerator can be evaluated at $s = -1 - j$ as follows:

$$
\begin{array}{r}
2s + (4-2j) \\
s+1+j\,\overline{\smash{\big)}\,2s^2 + 6s + 6} \\
\underline{2s^2 + (2+2j)s} \\
(4-2j)s + 6 \\
\underline{(4-2j)s + 6 - 2j} \\
2j
\end{array}
$$

Therefore, $R = 2j =$ value of numerator at $s = -1 - j$.

Although not so convenient in this instance, the remainder theorem is of great use in evaluating higher-order polynomials.

$$K_2 = \frac{2s^2 + 6s + 6}{(s + 2)[s + 1 - j1]}\bigg|_{s = -1 - j} = \frac{2(1 + j2 - 1) - 6 - j6 + 6}{(-1 - j + 2)(-1 - j + 1 - j)}$$

$$= \frac{1}{1 - j} = \frac{1}{2} + j\frac{1}{2}$$

$$K_3 = K_2{}^* = \frac{1}{2} - j\frac{1}{2}$$

Therefore,

$$F(s) = \frac{1}{s + 2} + \frac{\frac{1}{2} + j\frac{1}{2}}{s + 1 + j} + \frac{\frac{1}{2} - j\frac{1}{2}}{s + 1 - j}$$

This expression could be inverted as it stands and would lead to complex exponentials, which could be converted to sinusoids. However, it is generally more convenient to combine the complex roots giving a term of the following form:

$$\frac{K}{s + (\alpha + j\omega_0)} + \frac{K^*}{s + (\alpha - j\omega_0)}$$

$$= \frac{Ks + K\alpha - jK\omega_0 + K^*s + K^*\alpha + jK^*\omega_0}{(s + \alpha)^2 + \omega_0{}^2}$$

$$= \frac{2 \text{ Re } (K)(s + \alpha)}{(s + \alpha)^2 + \omega_0{}^2} + \frac{2 \text{ Im } (K)\omega_0}{(s + \alpha)^2 + \omega_0}$$

The inverse transform of these terms is

$$[2 \text{ Re } (K)\epsilon^{-\alpha t} \cos \omega_0 t + 2 \text{ Im } (K)\epsilon^{-\alpha t} \sin \omega_0 t] u(t)$$

Using this relationship, the inverse transform in the example is thus found to be

$$f(t) = [\epsilon^{-2t} + \epsilon^{-t} \cos \omega_0 t + \epsilon^{-t} \sin \omega_0 t] u(t)$$

Repeated quadratic factors.   When a quadratic factor is repeated it is necessary to use the same approach as for repeated linear factors. An example will illustrate the expansion in the case of a double quadratic factor.

$$F(s) = \frac{4s^2}{(s^2 + 1)^2(s + 1)}$$

(7-23)

$$= \frac{A}{s + 1} + \frac{Bs + C}{(s^2 + 1)^2} + \frac{Ds + E}{s^2 + 1}$$

A can be found using the normal procedure of multiplying through by $s + 1$ and setting $s = -1$. This gives $A = 1$. The remaining constants can be evaluated by clearing fractions and equating powers of s, as follows:

$$4s^2 = (s^2 + 1)^2 + (Bs + C)(s + 1) + (Ds + E)(s^2 + 1)(s + 1)$$

Equating powers of s gives the following equations.

$$
\begin{array}{llll}
D + 1 = 0 & \text{therefore} & D = -1 \\
D + E = 0 & \text{therefore} & E = -D = 1 \\
-2B + D + E = 0 & \text{therefore} & B = 2 \\
C + B + D + E = 0 & \text{therefore} & C = -B = -2 \\
1 + C + E = 0 & \text{therefore} & -1 - 2 + 1 = 0 \text{ (check)}
\end{array}
$$

$$F(s) = \frac{1}{s + 1} + \frac{2s - 2}{(s^2 + 1)^2} - \frac{s - 1}{s^2 + 1} \qquad \textbf{(7-24)}$$

This expression can be inverted easily by use of a table.

7-3 Solution of Differential Equations

A very straightforward application of Laplace transform theory is the solution of linear differential equations with specified initial conditions. As an example, consider the electric circuit shown in Fig. 7-1. Suppose

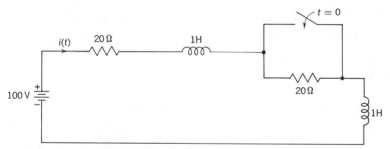

Figure 7-1 Switched R-L circuit.

that it is required to find the current in the circuit after the switch is closed. The differential equation for this circuit can be written by using Kirchhoff's voltage law and summing voltages around the loop.

$$20i + 2\frac{di}{dt} = 100$$

$$i(0^-) = 2.5 \text{ amperes} \qquad \textbf{(7-25)}$$

Taking the Laplace transform of (7-25) gives

$$20I(s) + 2[sI(s) - i(0^-)] = \frac{100}{s}$$

Substituting for $i(0^-)$ from (7-25) and solving for $I(s)$ gives

$$I(s) = \frac{2.5s + 50}{s(s + 10)} = \frac{5}{s} - \frac{2.5}{s + 10} \tag{7-26}$$

The current in the time domain is then found by taking the inverse transform of (7-26).

$$i(t) = \mathscr{L}^{-1}\left\{ \frac{5}{s} - \frac{2.5}{s + 10} \right\} \tag{7-27}$$

$$= [5 - 2.5\,\epsilon^{-10t}]\,u(t)$$

It is clear from this example that the solution of the differential equation has been reduced to the problem of making the transformation to the s domain, carrying out some algebraic manipulation, and then obtaining the inverse transform. This same procedure can be applied to much more complicated differential equations.

As an example of a somewhat more complicated system consider the artificial delay line shown schematically in Fig. 7-2. This type of circuit

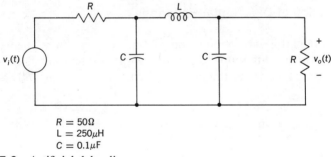

$$R = 50\Omega$$
$$L = 250\mu H$$
$$C = 0.1\mu F$$

Figure 7-2   Artificial delay line.

is used to cause a signal to be delayed by a specified time interval. By cascading a number of the π networks formed by the L's and C's in Fig. 7-2, it is possible to obtain a delay proportional to the number of sections cascaded. Let it be assumed that a signal $v_i(t)$ is applied to the network and that it is required to determine the output $v_o(t)$. The circuit equations will be obtained by converting the input to a current source as shown in Fig. 7-3 and writing nodal equations.

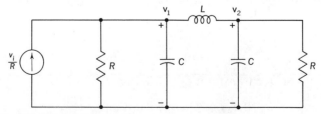

Figure 7-3   Modified delay circuit.

The node voltages will be designated $v_1 = v_1(t)$ and $v_2 = v_2(t)$, and it will be assumed that there is no initial energy stored in the network. The circuit equations are obtained from Kirchhoff's current law as follows:

$$\frac{v_1}{R} + C\frac{dv_1}{dt} + \frac{1}{L}\int_0^t v_1\,d\lambda - \frac{1}{L}\int_0^t v_2\,d\lambda = \frac{v_i}{R} \tag{7-28}$$

$$-\frac{1}{L}\int_0^t v_1\,d\lambda + \frac{1}{L}\int_0^t v_2\,d\lambda + C\frac{dv_2}{dt} + \frac{v_2}{R} = 0 \tag{7-29}$$

Taking the Laplace transform of (7-28) and (7-29) gives

$$V_1(s)\left[\frac{1}{Ls} + \frac{1}{R} + Cs\right] + V_2(s)\left[-\frac{1}{sL}\right] = \frac{V_i(s)}{R} \tag{7-30}$$

$$V_1(s)\left[-\frac{1}{Ls}\right] + V_2(s)\left[\frac{1}{Ls} + \frac{1}{R} + Cs\right] = 0 \tag{7-31}$$

These equations can now be solved as a set of simultaneous algebraic equations in the variables $V_1(s)$ and $V_2(s)$. From (7-31) we obtain

$$V_1(s) = Ls\left[\frac{1}{Ls} + \frac{1}{R} + Cs\right]V_2(s) \tag{7-32}$$

Substituting (7-32) into (7-30) gives

$$V_2(s)Ls\left[\frac{1}{Ls} + \frac{1}{R} + Cs\right]^2 - V_2(s)\left[\frac{1}{Ls}\right] = \frac{V_i(s)}{R} \tag{7-33}$$

Multiplying out the factors, combining terms and solving for $V_2(s)$ gives

$$V_2(s) = \frac{V_i(s)}{RLC^2\left\{s^3 + \frac{2}{RC}s^2 + \left[\frac{2}{LC} + \left(\frac{1}{RC}\right)^2\right]s + \frac{2}{RLC^2}\right\}} \tag{7-34}$$

This expression can be written as

$$V_2(s) = V_i(s)H(s) \tag{7-35}$$

where $H(s)$ is given by

$$H(s) = \frac{1/RLC^2}{s^3 + \frac{2}{RC}s^2 + \left[\frac{2}{LC} + \left(\frac{1}{RC}\right)^2\right]s + \frac{2}{RLC^2}} \tag{7-36}$$

In order to proceed further, it is necessary to expand $V_2(s)$ in partial fractions. To obtain a complete expression for $V_2(s)$ it would be necessary to put in the correct expression for $V_i(s)$. However, this will be deferred until later at the possible risk of requiring an additional partial fraction expansion when the substitution for $V_i(s)$ is made. In the present instance the denominator of $H(s)$ can be factored by inspection to give

$$H(s) = \frac{1/RLC^2}{\left(s + \dfrac{1}{RC}\right)\left(s^2 + \dfrac{1}{RC}s + \dfrac{2}{LC}\right)} \tag{7-37}$$

When factoring by inspection is not possible, as is almost always the case for high-order polynomials, it is necessary to resort to numerical methods to obtain answers. The partial fraction expansion of $H(s)$ can be seen from (7-37) to be of the following form:

$$H(s) = \frac{A}{s + \dfrac{1}{RC}} + \frac{Bs + C}{s^2 + \dfrac{1}{RC}s + \dfrac{2}{LC}} \tag{7-38}$$

The numerator of the first term is found to be

$$A = \frac{1}{2RC} \tag{7-39}$$

The second term will be found by subtracting the first term from $H(s)$, thus from (7-38) and (7-39)

$$\frac{Bs + C}{s^2 + \dfrac{1}{RC}s + \dfrac{2}{LC}} = H(s) - \frac{A}{s + \dfrac{1}{RC}}$$

$$= \frac{\dfrac{1}{RLC^2} - \dfrac{1}{2RC}s^2 - \dfrac{1}{2R^2C^2}s - \dfrac{1}{RLC^2}}{\left(s + \dfrac{1}{RC}\right)\left(s^2 + \dfrac{1}{RC}s + \dfrac{2}{LC}\right)} \tag{7-40}$$

$$= \frac{-\dfrac{1}{2RC}s}{s^2 + \dfrac{1}{RC}s + \dfrac{2}{LC}}$$

The output voltage can therefore be written as

$$V_2(s) = \frac{V_i(s)}{2RC}\left[\frac{1}{s + \dfrac{1}{RC}} - \frac{s}{s^2 + \dfrac{1}{RC}s + \dfrac{2}{RC}}\right]$$

$$\tag{7-41}$$

$$= \frac{V_i(s)}{2RC}\left[\frac{1}{s + \dfrac{1}{RC}} - \frac{\left(s + \dfrac{1}{2RC}\right) - \dfrac{1}{2RC}}{\left(s + \dfrac{1}{2RC}\right)^2 + \dfrac{2}{LC} - \left(\dfrac{1}{2RC}\right)^2}\right]$$

An idea of the behavior of the delay network can be obtained by considering its response to a very short pulse. To simplify the computations let the input signal be a unit impulse; that is, $v_i(t) = \delta(t)$. In this case, $V_i(s) = 1$ and, if the delay unit were ideal, we would expect that the output $v_2(t)$ would be an impulse delayed by some specified amount. The solution for $v_2(t)$ is obtained as follows:

$$v_2(t) = \mathcal{L}^{-1}\left\{\frac{1}{2RC}\left[\frac{1}{s + \dfrac{1}{RC}} - \frac{\left(s + \dfrac{1}{2RC}\right) - \dfrac{1}{2RC}}{\left(s + \dfrac{1}{2RC}\right)^2 + \dfrac{2}{LC} - \left(\dfrac{1}{2RC}\right)^2}\right]\right\}$$

(7-42)

This could be carried out in general form very readily, but since we are not interested in a detailed study of the effect of various parameters on the performance we will convert to numerical values before proceeding. From the values for R, L, and C given in Fig. 7-2 the various constants in (7-42) can be evaluated and the resulting expression is

$$v_2(t) = \mathcal{L}^{-1}\left\{10^5\left[\frac{1}{s + 2 \times 10^5} - \frac{(s + 10^5) - 10^5}{(s + 10^5) + (7 \times 10^{10})}\right]\right\}$$

$$= 10^5\left[\epsilon^{-2 \times 10^5 t} - \epsilon^{-10^5 t}\cos(\sqrt{7} \times 10^5 t)\right.$$

(7-43)

$$\left. + \frac{1}{\sqrt{7}}\epsilon^{-10^5 t}\sin(\sqrt{7} \times 10^5 t)\right]u(t)$$

It is evident from (7-43) that $v_2(0) = 0$ and that $v_2(\infty) = 0$. The actual shape is shown in Fig. 7-4. It is seen that a delay does indeed occur,

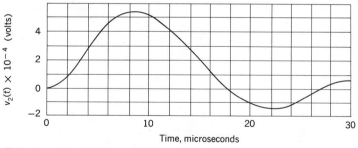

Figure 7-4 Impulse response of delay network.

which in this case might be considered to be of the order of 6 to 8 microseconds. The primary defect of the network is the distortion of the pulse shape. This particular delay network is actually designed as a low-pass network and would be quite effective for longer pulses. Its behavior for a step function can be obtained by re-solving (7-41), using as an input

$V_1(s) = \mathscr{L}[u(t)] = 1/s$. However, the same result can be more easily obtained by using the relation

$$\mathscr{L}^{-1}\left\{\frac{1}{s} F(s)\right\} = \int_0^t f(\lambda)\, d\lambda \tag{7-44}$$

From this it follows that the response to a step function is just the integral of the impulse response and this can be obtained by direct integration of (7-43). For our purposes it is sufficient to carry out a numerical integration of the curve of Fig. 7-4. The result, as seen in Fig. 7-5, shows that the delay network does approximate the desired response.

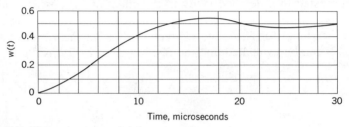

Figure 7-5   Step response of delay network.

7-4   The Transform Network

When electrical networks are specified in the time domain, the element values correspond to the constants in the equations characterizing the behavior of the various elements. For example, in the case of an inductance the relationship between the voltage and current is

$$v(t) = L\frac{di}{dt} \tag{7-45}$$

In this equation, L is the constant of proportionality between the voltage and the rate of change of current. The Laplace transform of (7-45) gives

$$V(s) = sLI(s) - Li(0) \tag{7-46}$$

The transformed equation contains an additional term resulting from the presence of an initial current in the inductor. In (7-46) this additional term adds directly to the transform of the voltage $V(s)$ and, therefore, can be represented as an ideal voltage generator having a transform of $-Li(0)$. The s-domain equivalent circuit of an inductance can therefore be thought of as an impedance sL in series with an ideal voltage source. Such an equivalent circuit is shown in Fig. 7-6.

(a)   (b)

Figure 7-6 The s-domain equivalent of an inductance. **(a)** Time domain. **(b)** s domain.

Using Norton's theorem, the s-domain equivalent circuit of Fig. 7-6 can be converted to another form as shown in Fig. 7-7. This second relation

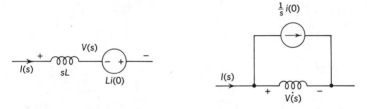

Figure 7-7 Two s-domain equivalent circuits of an inductance.

can also be derived from the expression for the current through an inductance in terms of the voltage. Thus

$$i(t) = \frac{1}{L} \int_0^t v(\lambda) \, d\lambda + i(0)$$

$$I(s) = \frac{1}{Ls} V(s) + \frac{1}{s} i(0)$$

The second equation corresponds to the circuit on the right in Fig. 7-7. Similar s-domain circuits are readily found for resistances and capacitances and are tabulated in Table 7-1. By use of the equivalents of Table 7-1, it is very simple to sketch the s-domain or transform network from which the circuit operations can be immediately written down including all initial conditions. This method is particularly useful in the solution of transient problems. When the initial conditions are zero, the concept of the transfer function becomes very useful and usually leads to further simplifications in the solution of network response problems.

Table 7-1   S-DOMAIN EQUIVALENTS FOR ELECTRIC
CIRCUIT ELEMENTS. (ALL ELEMENTS ARE
REPRESENTED IN TERMS OF THEIR IMPEDANCE.)

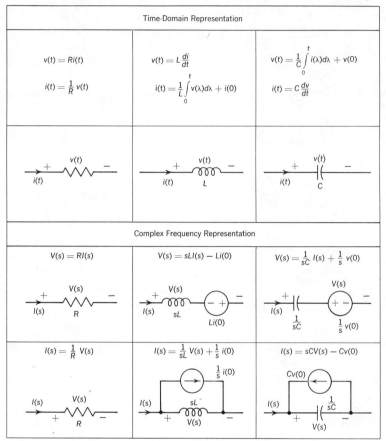

7-5   Transients Involving Initial Conditions

Solution of transient problems involving initial conditions can be illustrated best by considering some specific examples. In Fig. 7-8 is shown a network that is assumed to have reached an equilibrium state prior to the time $t = 0$ when the switch is opened. It is required to find the current $i_1(t)$ for $t > 0$. The transform network is most easily obtained by replacing the coupled circuit by an equivalent T network, as shown in Fig. 7-9. The transform network is then as shown in Fig. 7-10.

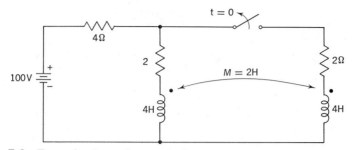

Figure 7-8 Example of transient analysis.

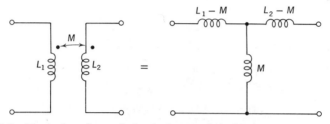

Figure 7-9 Equivalent for an inductively coupled circuit.

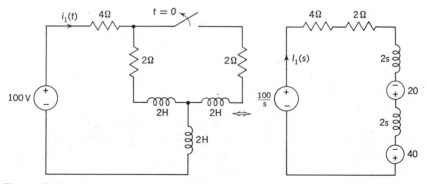

Figure 7-10 Transform network of Fig. 7-9.

From Fig. 7-10 the expression for $I_1(s)$ is found to be

$$I(s) = \frac{100/s + 20 + 40}{4 + 2 + 2s + 2s}$$

$$= \frac{15s + 25}{s(s + 3/2)} = \frac{50/3}{s} - \frac{5/3}{s + 3/2}$$

$$i(t) = \left[\frac{50}{3} - \frac{5}{3}\epsilon^{-3t/2} \right] u(t)$$

Suppose it is desired to find the voltage across the secondary inductance.

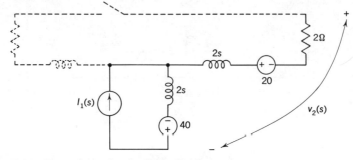

Figure 7-11   Secondary circuit of Fig. 7-10.

The equivalent transform circuit is shown in Fig. 7-11. Using the value for $I_1(s)$ found above, the transform of $V_2(s)$ is

$$V_2(s) = -20 - 40 + 2sI_1(s)$$

$$= -60 + \frac{30s + 50}{s + 3/2} = -30 + \frac{5}{s + 3/2}$$

Therefore,

$$v_2(t) = -30\delta(t) + 5\epsilon^{-3/2t}u(t)$$

7-6   The Transfer Function

The transfer function $H(s)$ of a network is defined as the ratio of the transforms of the output and input signals when the initial conditions are zero. If the excitation or input signal is $v_i(t)$ and the response or output signal is $v_o(t)$, then the transfer function $H(s)$ is given by

$$H(s) = \frac{\mathscr{L}\{v_o(t)\}}{\mathscr{L}\{v_i(t)\}} = \frac{V_o(s)}{V_i(s)} \tag{7-47}$$

This function will be independent of $V_i(s)$ since in a linear system the output is porportional to $V_i(s)$, and therefore $V_i(s)$ will cancel out in the ratio given in (7-47). The transfer function is a fundamental characteristic of a system and finds use in studies of system response, system stability, and system synthesis. For example, if one knows the desired output for a particular input signal, then it is possible to determine the transfer function of the system which will produce that output-input relationship by taking the ratio of the transforms of the signals. As an example of the computation of a transfer function, consider the network shown in Fig. 7-12, along with the corresponding transform network. For purposes of

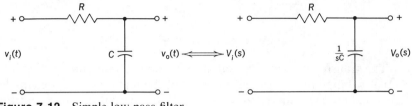

Figure 7-12   Simple low-pass filter.

computing the transfer function it is not necessary to know the nature of $V_i(s)$. The input can be left arbitrary and the output computed in terms of this arbitrary input. Dividing this output by $V_i(s)$ then gives $H(s)$. The analysis proceeds essentially the same way as for steady-state ac analysis. In the present example the output can be found using the voltage division between the impedances R and $1/sC$ or by determining the current and multiplying by the impedance $1/sC$. In either case we find

$$V_o(s) = \frac{1/sC}{R + 1/sC}\, V_i(s) = \frac{1/RC}{s + 1/RC}\, V_i(s)$$

Therefore, the transfer function is

$$H(s) = \frac{V_o(s)}{V_i(s)} = \frac{1/RC}{s + 1/RC} \qquad \text{(7-48)}$$

Once the transfer function has been determined, the output for any input can be found as the inverse transform of the product of the transfer function and the transform of the input signal. Thus,

$$V_o(s) = H(s)\, V_i(s) \qquad \text{(7-49)}$$

$$v_o(t) = \mathscr{L}^{-1}\{V_o(s)\} = \mathscr{L}^{-1}\{H(s)V_i(s)\} \qquad \text{(7-50)}$$

As an example of this use of the transfer function we will determine the output of the R-C circuit of Fig. 7-12 for an input of $u(t)\cos(100t)$ and a time constant $RC = 0.01$. Using the transfer function from (7-48), we have

$$V_o(s) = H(s)\, V_i(s) = \left[\frac{100}{s + 100}\right]\left[\frac{s}{s^2 + (100)^2}\right]$$

$$\qquad \text{(7-51)}$$

$$= \frac{A}{s + 100} + \frac{Bs + C}{s^2 + (100)^2}$$

$$A = \frac{100\,(-100)}{(100)^2 + (100)^2} = -\frac{1}{2} \qquad \text{(7-52)}$$

Setting $s = 0$ in (7-52) gives $C = 50$, and multiplying through by s and letting $s \to \infty$ gives $B = 1/2$. Therefore,

$$V_o(s) = \frac{1}{2}\left[\frac{-1}{s + 100} + \frac{s + 100}{s^2 + 10^4}\right] \tag{7-53}$$

$$v_o(t) = \frac{1}{2}\left[-\epsilon^{-100t} + \cos(100t) + \sin(100t)\right]u(t) \tag{7-54}$$

The transfer function can often be computed without carrying out a formal solution for the output in terms of the input. One of the simplest and quickest methods is to assume that the output is unity, and then compute what input must have been present to produce this output. The reciprocal of this input is the required transfer function. This method is especially useful for ladder networks because the computations are almost trivial. An example will clarify the method. In carrying out the actual computations of the input, the simplest procedure is to label the voltages and currents on the transform network. Figure 7-13(a) shows

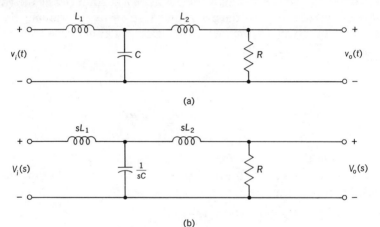

(a)

(b)

(c)

Figure 7-13   Computation of $H(s)$.

an R-L-C circuit for which the voltage transfer function is required. The transform circuit is shown in Fig. 7-13(b) with an assumed output of $V_o(s) = 1$. The currents and voltages in the rest of the network are computed as shown in Fig. 7-13(c). Starting at the right-hand terminals it is assumed that the voltage is one volt. Accordingly, the current in the resistance across the output terminals must be $1/R$ and this is also the current flowing through the inductance L_2. The voltage across L_2 is the product of the current $1/R$ and the impedance sL_2, or sL_2/R. The voltage across the capacitor is obtained as the sum of the voltage across the inductance and the output voltage, and is $1 + sL_2/R$. This computation process is continued until the input voltage is found to be

$$V_i(s) = 1 + \frac{sL_2}{R} + \frac{sL_1}{R} + s^2 L_1 C + \frac{s^3 L_1 L_2 C}{R} \tag{7-55}$$

Since the transfer function is $V_o(s)/V_i(s)$ and $V_o(s)$ is unity, it follows that $H(s)$ is the reciprocal of (7-55), or

$$H(s) = \frac{V_o(s)}{V_i(s)} = \frac{1}{1 + \dfrac{sL_2}{R} + \dfrac{sL_1}{R} + s^2 L_1 C + \dfrac{s^3 L_1 L_2 C}{R}} \tag{7-56}$$

$$= \frac{R/L_1 L_2 C}{s^3 + \dfrac{R}{L_2} s^2 + \left(\dfrac{1}{L_1 C} + \dfrac{1}{L_2 C}\right) s + \dfrac{R}{L_1 L_2 C}} \tag{7-57}$$

This method of computing transfer functions is also valid for ratios of currents or mixed variables, such as the ratio of the output voltage to input current. The method of computation is identical.

7-7 Physical Realizability and Stability in the s Domain

Since the transfer function of a system, $H(s)$, is the Laplace transform of the impulse response, $h(t)$, it follows that whatever constraints exist on $h(t)$ in the time domain will lead to corresponding constraints on $H(s)$ in the complex frequency domain. The constraints on $h(t)$ of primary interest relate to physical realizability (causality) and stability.

The requirement for physical realizability in the time domain is that $h(t)$ be zero for negative time; that is, the system must be nonanticipatory. The corresponding relationship in the frequency domain when the system function is expressed in terms of ω, was discussed in Section 5-5. When the system function can be taken as a one-sided Laplace transform, physical realizability is automatically implied.

Before we state the requirements on $H(s)$ that assure stability of the system, it is instructive to examine the effects of the various factors that can occur in a transfer function. Consideration will be restricted to lumped-parameter, linear systems so that the transfer function will be a rational function and, therefore, can be expanded into partial fractions. Each term in the partial fraction expansion will represent a separate contribution to the impulse response of the system when the inverse transform is taken. Consider first a term of the form $k_a/(s + a)$, which corresponds to a pole at $s = -a$, as shown in Fig. 7-14. The inverse

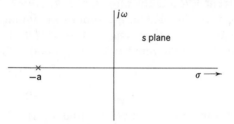

Figure 7-14   Simple pole for a first-order system.

transform of this term is a decaying exponential $k_a \epsilon^{-at} u(t)$. If a were a negative number the exponential would be increasing instead of decreasing. It is evident from this that for a system to be stable in the sense that a bounded input gives a bounded output (BIBO stability) there can be no simple poles in the right half of the s plane. The magnitude of the response corresponding to a simple pole is proportional to the residue, k_a, at the pole and the exponent of the damping factor is the distance of the poles from the origin along the $j\omega$ axis. Repeated simple poles also lead to exponentially damped terms as long as the poles are in the left half of the s plane.

Another typical term occurring in transform functions is of the form

$$\frac{k}{s^2 + \omega_0^2} = \frac{jk_1}{s - j\omega_0} - \frac{jk_1}{s + j\omega_0}$$

Terms of this form represent conjugate imaginary poles on the $j\omega$ axis as shown in Fig. 7-15. In this case the response $h(t)$ is an undamped

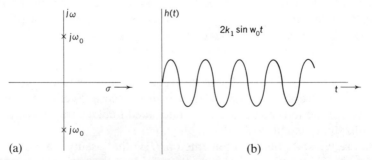

(a)   (b)

Figure 7-15   (a) Conjugate imaginary poles for a second-order system. (b) Impulse response of a system, having the poles shown in (a).

sinusoid. The amplitude is again proportional to the residue k_1, and the frequency is proportional to the distance of the poles from the origin along the $j\omega$ axis. Also the exponential damping is proportional to the σ coordinate of the pole—in this case, zero. Terms of this type do not correspond to stable systems in the BIBO sense, since an input at the resonant frequency would result in an infinite response. This is further borne out by the fact that the area under the absolute value of the impulse response (a sinusoid) is not finite. Only a singular signal (that is, a signal at a single specific frequency) leads to an unbounded output for a bounded input. A transfer function containing terms of this type is often called *marginally stable*. A similar situation occurs when the pole is at the origin. The impulse response in this latter case is a step function and the system would correspond to an ideal integrator. Such a system would also be considered marginally stable. When repeated poles are present on the $j\omega$ axis the corresponding time function has an amplitude that increases with time. For example, a term of the form

$$\frac{1}{(s^2 + \omega_0{}^2)^2}$$

leads to a time response of the form

$$\frac{1}{2\omega_0{}^3} (\sin \omega_0 t - \omega_0 t \cos \omega_0 t)u(t)$$

which is seen to increase without bound. In view of this, multiple poles on the $j\omega$ axis are not permissible in the transfer function of a stable system. A third type of term encountered in rational transfer functions involves complex roots and is of the form

$$\frac{k}{(s + \alpha)^2 + \beta^2} = \frac{k_1}{s + \alpha + j\beta} + \frac{k_1{}^*}{s + \alpha - j\beta}$$

A term of this type is shown plotted in Fig. 7-16 along with the corresponding time-domain response. As before, the damping factor is determined by the σ coordinate of the pole, the oscillation frequency by the $j\omega$

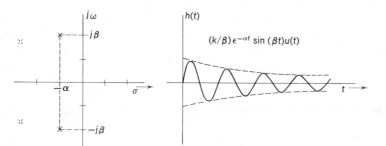

Figure 7-16   Transfer function with complex roots.

coordinate of the pole, and the amplitude by the residue at the pole. If we were to alter the transfer function, so that the poles moved to a new position as shown by the dotted X's in Fig. 7-16, we could immediately conclude that the corresponding time function would have a lower frequency and a higher damping factor. More information would be required to determine the amplitude. If, on the other hand, the poles were shifted to the right half plane it would be found that the exponent in the damping factor became positive and the result would be of growing sinusoid instead of a decaying sinusoid. Accordingly, for BIBO stability it is necessary that complex poles lie in the left half plane.

In summary, the requirements for (marginal) stability in terms of the poles of the transfer function of a time invariant lumped parameter system are:

1. No poles in the right half of the s plane.
2. No (repeated) poles on the $j\omega$ axis.

In formulating these criteria, we have implicitly assumed that the system function was a proper rational function. A general rational system function can always be expressed as the sum of a polynomial in s plus a proper rational function, as discussed in Section 7-2. If this polynomial has a term in s^k, where $k > 0$, with a nonzero coefficient, then a portion of the system is acting as a kth-order differentiator. Hence the response to the bounded input, $\sin \omega t$, will include a term having amplitude proportional to ω^k, and therefore it can be made arbitrarily large by increasing the frequency of the unit-amplitude sinusoid. Thus, we have a third requirement for stability:

3. The degree of the numerator of $H(s)$ cannot exceed that of the denominator.

Taken together, conditions 1, 2, and 3 are both necessary and sufficient for determining whether a rational system function corresponds to a stable system.

7-8 Frequency Response from Pole-Zero Plots

The transfer function $H(s)$ evaluated along the $j\omega$ axis is the frequency response of the system. Certain general characteristics of the frequency response and an alternate method of evaluating the transfer function at a specific frequency can be obtained directly from a pole-zero plot of $H(s)$ in the s plane. In order to estimate $H(s)$ along the $j\omega$ axis it is helpful to visualize $|H(s)|$ as a surface lying above the s plane. The height of the surface above this plane at any point is proportional to the magnitude of $H(s)$ at that point. As an example consider the function

$$H_1(s) = \frac{1}{s^2 + 4s + 13}$$

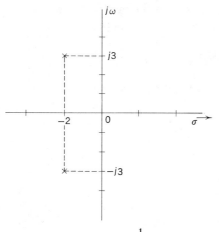

Figure 7-17   Poles for plot of $H_1(s) = \dfrac{1}{(s + 2)^2 + 9}$.

The pole zero plot of $H_1(s)$ is shown in Fig. 7-17, and consists of complex conjugate poles at $s = -2 \pm j3$. At each pole the magnitude of $H(s)$ becomes infinite. If we now visualize $|H(s)|$ as a surface above the s plane we obtain the surface shown in Fig. 7-18. In this figure only the position to the left of the $j\omega$ axis is shown. The height along the $j\omega$ axis is the desired response. The surface in Fig. 7-18 can be thought of as an originally flat rubber sheet that has been stretched, as shown, by the poles pushing up at the critical frequencies. When there are zeros present the

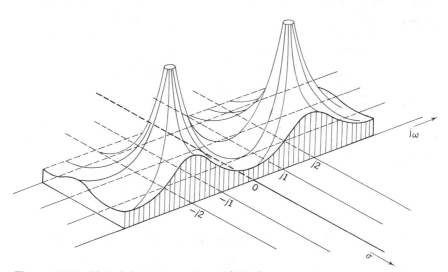

Figure 7-18   Pictorial representation of $|H(s)|$.

rubber sheet is considered to be fastened down at each zero. As a further example, consider the transfer function

$$H_2(s) = \frac{s^2 + 2s + 2}{s^2 + 4s + 13} = \frac{(s + 1)^2 + 1}{(s + 2)^2 + 9}$$

The pole-zero plot of this transfer function is shown in Fig. 7-19. It is

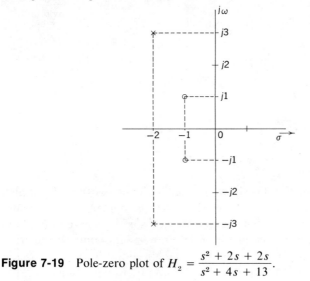

Figure 7-19   Pole-zero plot of $H_2 = \dfrac{s^2 + 2s + 2s}{s^2 + 4s + 13}$.

seen that this plot is very similar to the previous case considered except that now there are two zeros between the poles and the origin. Using the rubber-sheet analogy, it would be expected that since the zeros tack the sheet down at $s = 1 \pm j1$, the height along the $j\omega$ axis from the origin on out for some distance would be reduced from what it is without the zeros. If the zeros were moved to the other side of the poles, as in Fig. 7-20,

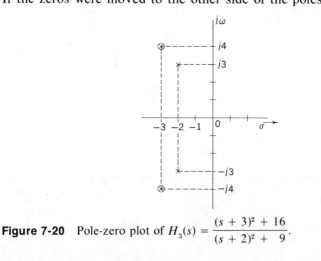

Figure 7-20   Pole-zero plot of $H_3(s) = \dfrac{(s + 3)^2 + 16}{(s + 2)^2 + 9}$.

it is clear that these zeros would have little effect on the amplitude at the origin because of the "shielding" effect of the poles that lie between the zeros and the origin. The effect of the zeros would be more pronounced at frequencies slightly greater than $\omega = 3$. The magnitudes of the frequency responses for these cases are shown in Fig. 7-21 and clearly

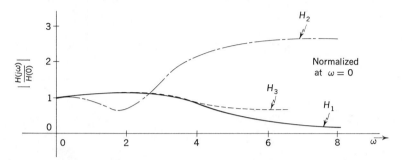

Figure 7-21   Amplitude spectra of $H_1(j\omega)$, $H_2(j\omega)$, and $H_3(j\omega)$.

indicate the effects that have been discussed. Much additional insight into system behavior can be obtained from pole-zero plots and they are widely used in system analysis and design. Further discussion of this method is contained in the references at the end of the chapter.

Before leaving the subject of pole-zero plots there is one additional use of this representation that should be discussed. Consider a general transfer function of the form

$$H(s) = k_0 \frac{(s - \gamma_0)(s - \gamma_2) \cdots (s - \gamma_m)}{(s - \Gamma_1)(s - \gamma_3) \cdots (s - \gamma_n)} \tag{7-58}$$

where γ_k are the complex roots of the numerator and denominator polynomials and K_0 is a real constant. Suppose now that it is required to evaluate $H(s)$ at some complex frequency $s = s_0 = \sigma_0 + j\omega_0$. This may be done algebraically by substituting $(\sigma_0 + j\omega_0)$ for s in (7-58) and evaluating the resulting expression. If this procedure is carried out, each factor in the numerator and denominator will be a complex number and can be expressed as a magnitude $M_k = |s_0 - \gamma_0|$ and an angle

$$\psi_a = \tan^{-1}\left[\frac{\text{Im}(s_0 - \gamma_k)}{\text{Re}(s_0 - \gamma_k)}\right]$$

The complete expression for $H(s_0)$ can then be written as

$$H(s_0) = k_0 \frac{M_0 \cdot M_2 \cdots M_m}{M_1 \cdot M_3 \cdots M_n} \frac{\underline{/\psi_0 + \psi_2 + \cdots + \psi_m}}{\underline{/\psi_1 + \psi_3 + \cdots + \psi_n}} \tag{7-59}$$

The magnitude and phase angles in (7-59) can be obtained from the pole-zero diagram of $H(s)$ in a very simple manner. Consider a typical pole-

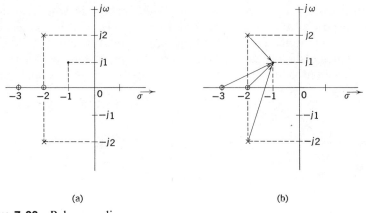

(a)   (b)

Figure 7-22   Pole-zero diagram.

zero plot as shown in Fig. 7-22 and suppose it is desired to evaluate $H(s)$ at $s = -1 + j1$. By drawing directed line segments from each critical frequency to the point $s_0 = -1 + j1$ we will obtain a set of vectors which represent the factors in (7-59). The magnitudes are equal to the lengths of the lines and the phase angles are the angles the vectors make with the positive σ axis. For rapid computation the lengths and angles can be measured directly from an accurate plot or if desired the plot can be used to clarify the geometric and trigonometric relations necessary to allow analytical computations. For the example shown it is easily seen that the magnitude is given by

$$|H(-1 + j1)| = k_0 \frac{\sqrt{2^2 + 1^2 + 1^2 + 1^2}}{\sqrt{1^2 + 1^2 + 1^2 + 3^2}} = k_0 \sqrt{\frac{7}{12}}$$

and the phase angle by

$$\underline{/H(-1 + j1)} = \tan^{-1}\left(\frac{1}{1}\right) + \tan\left(\frac{1}{2}\right) - \tan^{-1}\left(\frac{-1}{1}\right) - \tan^{-1}\left(\frac{3}{1}\right)$$

$$= 45° + 26.6° + 45° - 71.6° = 45°$$

Rapid estimates of the magnitude of the frequency response can be made by moving the point of evaluation along the $j\omega$ axis. Another place where this method is particularly useful is in evaluating the residue at a pole in the partial fraction expansion of a rational function of s. As an example of this application consider a transfer function of the form

$$H(s) = \frac{2s(s + 2)}{(s + 3)(s^2 + 2s + 5)}$$

The pole-zero plot of $H(s)$ is shown in Fig. 7-23(a). In order to find the residue at a pole, the procedure is to multiply the gain constant (in this

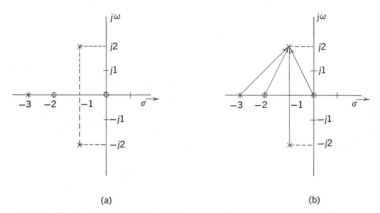

(a)   (b)

Figure 7-23   Evaluation of the residue at a pole.

case, 2) by the vectors from each zero to the pole in question and to divide by the vectors from each pole to the pole in question. Using this procedure the residue at the pole located at $-1 + j2$ is found from Fig. 7-23(b) to be

$$k_{-1+j2} = \frac{2(2.23\angle 63.4°)(2.23\angle 116.6°)}{(3.60\angle 33.6°)(4.00\angle 90°)}$$

$$= 0.347\angle 56.4°$$

The residue at $s = -1 - j2$ is found as the complex conjugate of this quantity; that is, $k_{-1-j2} = 0.347 \angle -56.4°$.

7-9   Relationship between Laplace and Fourier Transforms

The Laplace transform and the Fourier transform are very closely related, as is evident from the derivation of the Laplace transform from the Fourier transform given at the beginning of Chapter 6. The one-sided or unilateral Laplace transform, which has been considered so far, is concerned only with the behavior of time functions for $t > 0$. The Fourier transform, on the other hand, includes both positive and negative time but cannot handle functions having finite average power without using special limiting operations which are accounted for by means of δ functions. In carrying out computation, it is generally more convenient to use the variable s rather than the variable $j\omega$ since the algebra is much simpler. However, whenever it is required to consider frequency spectra, it is necessary to return to the variable $j\omega$. It is, therefore, useful to be able to move easily between the variables s and $j\omega$ in working with transforms. For certain classes of functions, the change from $\mathcal{L}[f(t)]$ to $\mathcal{F}[f(t)]$ is quite simple; for others, it is more involved. The important situations are given in the discussion that follows. In all cases it is assumed that $F(s)$ is a legitimate unilateral Laplace transform.

F(s) with poles in the left half plane only.   When $F(s)$ has poles only in the left half of the s plane (not including the $j\omega$ axis), the transformation between $F(s)$ and $F(j\omega)$ is accomplished simply by making the substitution $s = j\omega$. These transforms include all finite energy signals defined for positive time only. As an example consider the following Laplace transform.

$$\mathcal{L}\{\epsilon^{-\alpha t}u(t)\} = \frac{1}{s + \alpha} \qquad \mathrm{Re}\,(s) > -\alpha$$

If α is a positive constant, the only pole in $F(s)$ is in the left half plane (LHP) at $s = -\alpha$, and it follows that

$$\mathcal{L}\{\epsilon^{-\alpha t}u(t)\} = F(s)\big|_{s=j\omega} = \frac{1}{s + \alpha}\bigg|_{s=j\omega} = \frac{1}{j\omega + \alpha}$$

The same simple relationship holds for all other transforms meeting the conditions stated above.

F(s) with poles in the left half plane and on the $j\omega$ axis.   By partial fraction expansion, transforms of this class can be separated into terms having poles in the LHP and terms having poles on the $j\omega$ axis. The terms with LHP poles can be handled in the same manner described in the preceding paragraph. The terms containing poles on the $j\omega$ axis require modified handling and, in general, lead to Fourier transforms containing δ functions. For example, if

$$F(s) = \frac{\omega_0}{s^2 + \omega_0{}^2}$$

we immediately recognize this as the transform of $\sin \omega_0 t\, u(t)$. By the methods discussed in Chapter 5, it is readily shown that

$$\mathcal{F}[\sin \omega_0 t\, u(t)] = \frac{\omega_0}{\omega_0{}^2 - \omega^2} + j\frac{\pi}{2}[\delta(\omega + \omega_0) - \delta(\omega - \omega_0)]$$

To obtain this result directly from $F(s)$ we must recognize that *each simple pole* on the $j\omega$ axis leads to two terms in the Fourier representation: one is obtained by the substitution $s = j\omega$; the other is a δ function having a strength of π times the residue at the pole. This can be written in equation form as:

$$F(s) = \sum_n \frac{k_n}{s - j\omega_n} \quad \text{poles at } s = j\omega_n \tag{7-60}$$

$$F(j\omega) = F(s)|_{s = j\omega} + \pi \sum_n k_n \delta(\omega - \omega_n) \tag{7-61}$$

The residue at a simple pole is just the numerator of the term in the partial fraction expansion containing the pole. Consider the Laplace transform given above:

$$F(s) = \frac{\omega_0}{s^2 + \omega_0^2} = \frac{j/2}{s + j\omega_0} - \frac{j/2}{s - j\omega_0}$$

Using (7-61), the Fourier transform is found to be

$$F(j\omega) = \frac{\omega_0}{(j\omega)^2 + \omega_0^2} + j\frac{\pi}{2}[\delta(\omega + \omega_0) - \delta(\omega - \omega_0)]$$

as previously noted. As a further example, consider the following transform:

$$F(s) = \frac{2s^2 + \omega_0^2}{s(s^2 + \omega_0^2)}$$

Expanding in partial fractions gives

$$F(s) = \frac{1}{s} + \frac{1/2}{s + j\omega_0} + \frac{1/2}{s - j\omega_0}$$

The corresponding Fourier transform is

$$F(j\omega) = \frac{-2\omega + \omega_0^2}{j\omega(-\omega^2 + \omega_0^2)} + \pi[\delta(\omega) + \frac{1}{2}\delta(\omega + \omega_0) + \frac{1}{2}\delta(\omega - \omega_0)]$$

$$= j\frac{\omega_0^2 - 2\omega^2}{\omega(\omega^2 - \omega_0^2)} + \pi\delta(\omega) + \frac{\pi}{2}[\delta(\omega - \omega_0) + \delta(\omega - \omega_0)]$$

When $F(s)$ contains higher-order poles, the relationship becomes somewhat more complicated and leads to higher-order singularity functions. Such cases can always be handled by converting from $F(s)$ back to the time domain and then taking the Fourier transform.

F(s) with poles in the right half plane.   When $F(s)$ has poles in the right half plane (RHP) and is a legitimate unilateral Laplace transform, it means that the convergence region Re $s = \sigma > 0$. Therefore, the integral does not converge on the $j\omega$ axis and no corresponding Fourier transform exists. An example of such a function is

$$F(s) = \frac{1}{s-1} \qquad \sigma > 1$$

This is the Laplace transform of the function $\epsilon^t u(t)$, and we have not defined a Fourier transform for such a function.

There are legitimate Laplace transforms, having poles in the right half of the s plane, that are defined so that their strip of convergence includes the $j\omega$ axis. Such transforms correspond to noncausal time functions and are based on the bilateral or two-sided Laplace transform. These transforms are closely related to the Fourier transform, but details of the relationship must be deferred until the two-sided Laplace transform has been discussed.

7-10   Inverse Two-sided Laplace Transforms

Although the inversion integral for two-sided Laplace transforms is identical to that for the unilateral transform, the methods for carrying out the inversion are somewhat more involved — partly because the positive time and negative time portions must be handled separately and partly because of a fundamental ambiguity that exists in the interpretation of a two-sided Laplace transform.

In order to examine this ambiguity in more detail, consider the two time functions defined by

$$f_a(t) = \epsilon^{-\alpha t} \qquad t > 0$$
$$\quad\;\;\, = 0 \qquad\;\; t < 0$$

and

$$f_b(t) = -\epsilon^{-\alpha t} \qquad t < 0$$
$$\quad\;\;\, = 0 \qquad\quad\;\; t > 0$$

and sketched in Fig. 7-24. The Laplace transforms of these two time

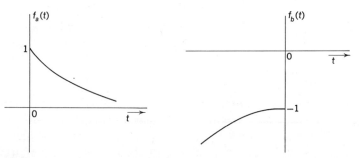

Figure 7-24   Two time functions having the same Laplace transform.

functions are

$$F_a(s) = \int_0^\infty \epsilon^{-\alpha t} \epsilon^{-st} \, dt = \frac{1}{s + \alpha} \qquad \text{Re } (s) > -\alpha$$

and

$$F_b(s) = \int_{-\infty}^0 -\epsilon^{-\alpha t}\epsilon^{-st} \, dt = \frac{1}{s + \alpha} \qquad \text{Re } (s) < -\alpha$$

and these are seen to be identical, except for the regions of convergence. Thus, the unique relationship that existed between a function and its Laplace transform in the one-sided case does *not* exist for the two-sided transform. Hence, if one is given a two-sided Laplace transform, *with no indication of the region of convergence,* it is impossible to determine the corresponding time function uniquely.

Fortunately, in the practical use of the two-sided Laplace transform the ambiguity problem can be resolved on the basis of physical consideration, since time functions that increase without limit as t approaches either $+\infty$ or $-\infty$ do not exist in reality. Thus, it is usually a simple matter to select the one practical time function even though others may be mathematically possible.

In the analysis of linear, time-invariant systems, the two-sided Laplace transforms that arise are almost always rational functions of s, just as in the one-sided case. These can be expanded into partial fractions in exactly the same way as has been discussed in the earlier part of this chapter. Each term in the partial fraction expansion will correspond to a pole of the transform and some of these will be in the left half of the s plane while others will be in the right half. Furthermore, it has been shown that LHP poles correspond to decaying exponentials in positive time, whereas RHP poles yield exponentials that vanish at $-\infty$. Thus, it is possible to select realistic time functions for the inverse transform if one accepts the following convention.

1. All terms in the partial fraction expansion that come from LHP poles will be assumed to yield time functions that exist only for $t \geq 0$.

2. All terms in the partial fraction expansion that come from RHP poles will be assumed to yield time functions that exist only for $t \leq 0$.

This procedure can be illustrated by means of the following example. Let the two-sided transform be

$$F_{II}(s) = \frac{2s - 5}{(s - 1)(s + 2)} = \frac{-1}{s - 1} + \frac{3}{s + 2}$$

in which the partial fraction expansion has been obtained using the procedure discussed in Section 7-2. By analogy to the foregoing example, and employing the stated convention, we find that

$$f(t) = \epsilon^t \qquad t < 0$$
$$= 3\epsilon^{-2t} \qquad t > 0$$

and this function is sketched in Fig. 7-25. Note that this convention leads

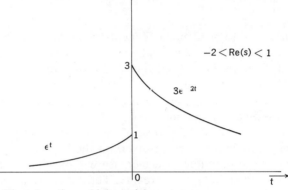

Figure 7-25   Time function which vanishes at $\pm \infty$.

to only one of *four* apparently possible time functions. The other three, sketched in Fig. 7-26 are all unbounded. The regions of convergence are also indicated for each sketch and it is seen that there is *no* region of convergence for Fig. 7-26(b). Hence this is not really a possible inverse transform. The other two sketches in Fig. 7-26 do have regions of convergence and are therefore mathematically acceptable inverse transforms even if they are not physically acceptable.

A useful trick that can be applied to RHP terms automatically en-

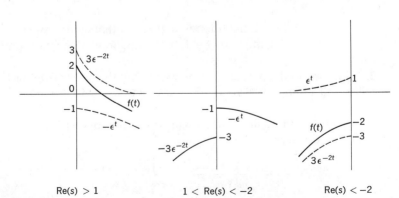

Figure 7-26   Three other time functions from the same transform.

forces the convention stated above. It utilizes the techniques and tabulated transform pairs for the one-sided transform. This can be illustrated
by writing the transform for a function that exists in negative time and
then making a change in variable. Thus,

$$F(s) = \int_{-\infty}^{0} f(t)\epsilon^{-st}\,dt = \int_{\infty}^{0} f(-\lambda)\epsilon^{-(-s)\lambda}\,(-d\lambda)$$

in which $\lambda = -t$. Using the minus sign to interchange the limits gives

$$F(s) = \int_{0}^{\infty} f(-\lambda)\epsilon^{-(-s)\lambda}\,d\lambda \qquad (7\text{-}62)$$

Equation (7-62) may be interpreted as meaning that the Laplace transform of a function existing only in negative time can be obtained by
(1) reflecting the negative-time function into positive time, (2) taking the
ordinary one-sided Laplace transform for this positive-time function,
and (3) replacing s by $-s$.
This procedure may be illustrated by considering the function

$$f(t) = \epsilon^{\alpha t} \qquad\qquad t < 0$$
$$= 0 \qquad\qquad t > 0$$

Its reflection $f_{+}(t)$ is

$$f_{+}(t) = f(-t) = \epsilon^{-\alpha t} \qquad t > 0$$
$$= 0 \qquad\qquad t < 0$$

and this function has a one-sided transform of

$$F_{+}(s) = \frac{1}{s + \alpha}$$

Thus, the transform of $f(t)$, for $t < 0$, is

$$F(s) = F_{+}(-s) = \frac{1}{-s + \alpha} = \frac{-1}{s - \alpha}$$

In taking inverse transforms, the procedure is just reversed. Thus
for an RHP term, (1) replace s by $-s$, (2) take a normal one-sided inverse Laplace transform, and (3) reflect the resulting positive-time
function into negative time by replacing t with $-t$.
The example discussed earlier may be used to illustrate this procedure.

$$F_{II}(s) = \frac{2s - 5}{(s - 1)(s + 2)} = \frac{-1}{s - 1} + \frac{s}{s + 2}$$

The RHP term is

$$F(s) = \frac{-1}{s - 1}$$

from which

$$F(-s) = F_+(s) = \frac{-1}{-s - 1} = \frac{1}{s + 1}$$

and
$$f_+(t) = \epsilon^{-t} \qquad\qquad t > 0$$

The resulting negative-time function is

$$f_-(t) = f_+(-t) = \epsilon^t \qquad t < 0$$

The LHP term is handled in the usual manner, so the total time function becomes

$$\begin{aligned} f(t) &= \epsilon^t & t < 0 \\ &= 3\epsilon^{-t} & t > 0 \end{aligned}$$

which agrees with the preceding result.

So far, the discussion of the inverse transform has carefully avoided any mention of poles *on* the $j\omega$ axis. In this case, practical consideration of accepting only bounded functions give no clue as to how to proceed. For example, if

$$F(s) = \frac{1}{s}$$

the inverse transform may be taken either as

$$f(t) = -u(-t)$$

or as
$$f(t) = u(t)$$

and these are both bounded. Likewise, a pair of conjugate imaginary poles on the $j\omega$ axis would lead to constant-amplitude sinusoids in either positive time or negative time. Thus, it might appear that there is no way of resolving the ambiguity that arises from $j\omega$ axis poles. This, in fact, would be the case if one were presented with a transform with no inkling as to how it arose. In practical system analysis problems, however, one starts with time functions and derives the transforms. Hence, with a little care in notation, one can keep track of how a particular $j\omega$ axis pole was created and how it must be interpreted in the final result.

As a very simple illustration of this, consider the *R-C* circuit and input waveform shown in Fig. 7-27. Although there are some very simple ways of handling this problem without using the two-sided Laplace transform, it is instructive to do so. The input signal is

$$v_i(t) = Au(-t)$$

and its transform is

$$V_i(s) = \frac{-A}{s_-} \qquad \text{Re } (s) < 0$$

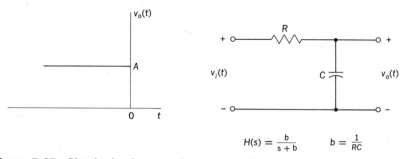

$$H(s) = \frac{b}{s+b} \qquad b = \frac{1}{RC}$$

Figure 7-27   Simple circuit responding to a negative-time input.

Note the minus subscript on the s to indicate that this arose from a negative-time function. The transform of the input signal is

$$V_o(s) = V_i(s)\, H(s) = \frac{-Ab}{(s+b)s_-} \qquad -b < \text{Re } (s) < 0$$

and the partial fraction expansion of this is

$$V_o(s) = \frac{-A}{s_-} + \frac{A}{s+b}$$

Note that this is a valid transform because there is a strip of convergence with nonzero width.

In obtaining the inverse transform of $V_o(s)$, the minus subscript on s_- makes it clear that this is to be interpreted as a negative-time function. Hence, the resulting time function is

$$v_o(t) = Au(-t) + A\epsilon^{-bt}u(t)$$

which is sketched in Fig. 7-28(a). Without this indication, one might be

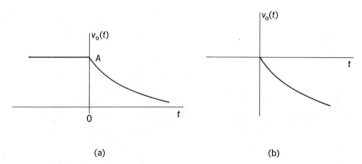

(a)   (b)

Figure 7-28   Response of circuit in Fig. 7-27 for two different interpretations. **(a)** Correct response. **(b)** Incorrect response.

tempted to interpret this term as a positive-time function and this would lead to

$$v_o(t) = -Au(t) + A\epsilon^{-bt}u(t)$$

which is shown in Fig. 7-28(b). Since both responses are bounded, the only way one would have of knowing which is correct is to utilize one's knowledge of how the pole at the origin arose.

One way of easily keeping track of $j\omega$ axis poles is to use the notation s_+ when they arise from positive-time functions and s_- when they arise from a negative-time function. In this way the proper inverse transform can be obtained in even very complicated cases. It should be emphasized, however, that this mechanical procedure does not accomplish anything that could not be done by keeping track of the regions of convergence. Its usefulness lies solely in the fact that it requires less effort than the more fundamental procedure.

■ REFERENCES

There are many references covering the material discussed in Chapter 7. The following are representative of those available and contain most of the information required for engineering applications of the Laplace transform. It should be noted that in all cases except the book by Kuo, the defining integral uses a lower limit of 0^+ rather than 0^-.

1. Cheng, D. K., *Analysis of Linear Systems*. Reading, Mass.: Addison-Wesley Publishing Company, 1959.

   Written as a junior-level text, this book presents a good discussion of system analysis methods using transform techniques. Of particular interest is Chapter 4, which discusses the use of mechanical-electrical analogies for the analysis of mechanical systems.

2. Churchill, R. W., *Operational Mathematics,* 2d ed. New York: McGraw-Hill Book Company, Inc., 1958.

   This book presents the mathematical theory of the Laplace transform at the senior or graduate level. The applications discussed are from the general field of physical science and only few relate directly to electrical engineering. An extensive table of transforms is included.

3. Doetsch, G., *Guide to the Applications of Laplace Transforms*. Princeton, N. J.: D. Van Nostrand Company, Inc. 1961.

   Written by a leading authority on the Laplace transformation, this book contains in summary fashion most of the results of classical Laplace transform theory required in the study of engineering problems. A very wide range of topics is covered and an extensive table of transforms is appended to the text.

4. Kuo, F. F., *Network Analysis and Synthesis*, 2d ed. New York: John Wiley & Sons, Inc., 1966.

   This book is written as a junior- or senior-level text. The Laplace transform is considered in some detail, along with a variety of other methods useful in network analysis. Many applications of the Laplace transform to circuit analysis problems are considered. The last third of the book provides an excellent introduction of synthesis procedures carried out completely in the complex frequency domain (s plane).

5. McCollum, P. A., and B. F. Brown, *Laplace Transform Tables and Theorems*. New York: Holt, Rinehart and Winston, Inc., 1965.

   This book contains conveniently arranged tables of Laplace transform pairs, along with the most important theorems relating to the Laplace transform.

6. Truxal, J., *Control System Synthesis*. New York: McGraw-Hill Book Company, Inc., 1955.

   This classic in the field of automatic control contains an excellent discussion of the Laplace transform and includes many examples of the use of transform methods in system design. In addition to treatment of a wide range of topics relating to automatic control, there is much information lucidly presented on networks and network synthesis.

7. Van Der Pol, B., and H. Bremmer, *Operational Calculus Based on the Two-sided Laplace Integral*, 2d ed. New York: Cambridge University Press, 1955.

   This book is highly recommended to anyone wishing to pursue study of applications of the Laplace transform to a wider range of problems. Although written carefully from a mathematical point of view, the book contains a vast amount of material that is of vital concern to engineers. It contains (for the average engineer) the most readable discussions of advanced topics in Laplace transform theory that are available today. Much of the material in the book relates to the one-sided Laplace transform, which is considered to be a special case of the two-sided transform. One word of caution is in order in that all transforms are multiplied by an extra p (that is, s in our notation). This was done to make the transform pairs identical with the older Heaviside operational calculus transform pairs, and causes little confusion.

■ PROBLEMS

7-1 Find the inverse Laplace transform of each of the following functions:

a. $F(s) = \dfrac{s}{(s + 1)(s + 4)}$

d. $F(s) = \dfrac{\epsilon^{-2s}}{(s + 1)(s + 2)^2}$

b. $F(s) = \dfrac{s^3 + 6s^2 + 6s}{s^2 + 6s + 8}$

e. $F(s) = \dfrac{5s - 12}{s^2 + 4s + 13}$

c. $F(s) = \dfrac{s + 1}{s^2 + 2s}$

f. $F(s) = \dfrac{1 - \epsilon^{-4s}}{3s^3 + 2s^2}$

7-2 Find the inverse transforms of the following functions:

a. $F(s) = \dfrac{s^2 + 3s + 5}{s^2 + 3s + 2}$

c. $F(s) = \dfrac{se^{-s} + 2s^2 + 9}{s(s^2 + 9)}$

b. $F(s) = \dfrac{s^2 + s + 1}{s^2 + 1}\, \epsilon^{-sT}$

d. $F(s) = \dfrac{s}{(s + 1)(s^2 + 1)}$

e. $F(s) = \dfrac{s^5 + 2s^3 + s^2 + s + 4}{(s^2 + 4)(s^2 + 1)^2}$

f. $F(s) = \dfrac{s^3 + 4s^2 + 6s - 6}{(s^2 + 2s + 10)(s^2 + 4s + 4)}$

7-3 When $F(s)$ is the ratio of two polynomials, the residues at simple poles can be evaluated by the following expression

$$k_n = \left. \frac{P(s)}{Q'(s)} \right|_{s = \alpha_n}$$

where α_n is the root of $Q(s)$ at $s = \alpha_n$, and $Q'(s)$ is the derivative of $Q(s)$.
a. Use this expression to find the inverse transform of the functions of Problems 7-1(a) and 7-1(b).
b. How is this formula related to the procedure of multiplying through by a factor and then evaluating the resulting expression at the root of the factor as discussed in the text?
c. Write a general expression for the inverse transform of a rational function of s having only first-order poles in the LHP. The resulting expression is known as Heaviside's expansion theorem.

7-4 Solve the following differential equations using Laplace transform methods:

a. $\dfrac{d^2x(t)}{dt^2} + 4x(t) = 0$

where $x(0) = 1 \quad x'(0) = 0$
b. Find the value of $y(0)$ and $y'(0)$ for the system described by the following differential equation.

$$y''(t) + 2y'(t) + y(t) = 2u(t)$$
$$y(1) = \epsilon^{-1} \qquad y'(1) = 0$$

7-5 Solve the following differential equations using Laplace transform methods:

a. $x''(t) + x'(t) = t^2 + 2t$
where $x(0) = 4 \quad x'(0) = -2$
b. $2x'(t) + 4x(t) + y'(t) - y(t) = 0$
$\quad\quad x'(t) + 2x(t) + y'(t) + y(t) = 0$
where $x(0) = 0 \quad x'(0) = 2$
$\quad\quad y(0) = 1 \quad y'(0) = -3$

7-6 Solve the following integrodifferential equation:

$$\frac{dx}{dt} + 3x(t) + 2 \int_0^t x(\lambda) \, d\lambda = 2u(t)$$

where $x(0^-) = 1$ $x'(0) = 1$

7-7 Solve the following second-order difference equation using Laplace transform methods and sketch for $0 \leq t < 5$. [Hint: Expand $X(s)$ in a series and invert term by term.]

$$x(t) + x(t-1) = tu(t)$$

7-8 Solve the following integral equation for $x(t)$ using Laplace transform methods:

$$(2 - 2 \, \epsilon^{-t})u(t) = x(t) + \int_0^t \epsilon^{-\lambda} x(t-\lambda) \, d\lambda$$

7-9 **a.** Sketch and label the transform network for the circuit shown, in which the switch is closed at $t = 0$.

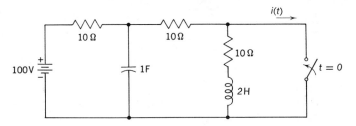

b. Write the Laplace transform for the current in the switch, $i(t)$.
c. Find the current in the switch as a function of time.

7-10 The switch in the circuit shown is moved from position 1 to position 2 at $t = 0$. The capacitor C_2 is initially uncharged.

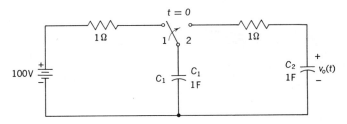

a. Find the voltage $v_o(t)$ that appears across capacitor C_2.
b. At $t = 100$, the switch is returned to position 1, and at $t = 200$ it is moved again to position 2. Write an approximate expression for the voltage $v_o(t)$ for $t \leq 200$.

7-11 Determine the current $i_1(t)$ in the circuit shown when the input is a unit voltage pulse. Assume an ideal transformer.

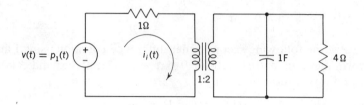

7-12 Compute the voltage $v_2(t)$ in the circuit shown. Assume that the switch has been closed a long time prior to $t = 0$ and that after $t = 0$ it remains open.

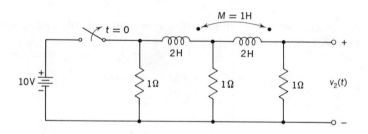

7-13 For the circuit shown, find each of the transfer functions defined as follows:

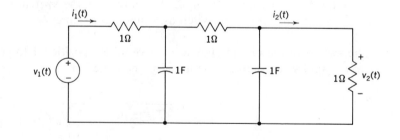

a. $H_a(s) = \dfrac{V_2(s)}{V_1(s)}$

c. $H_c(s) = \dfrac{I_2(s)}{V_1(s)}$

b. $H_b(s) = \dfrac{I_2(s)}{I_1(s)}$

d. $H_d(s) = \dfrac{V_2(s)}{I_1(s)}$

7-14 a. Determine the transfer function of the system shown.

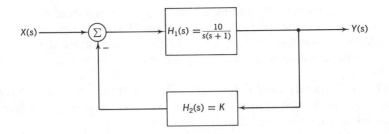

b. Find the response of this system to a unit step and a unit ramp for $K = 0$ and $K = 1/8$. [Note: $H_2(s) = K$.]

7-15 Consider an n-stage R-C-coupled amplifier with identical time constants in each stage.
a. Compute the step response of such an amplifier neglecting all frequency-dependent quantities except the coupling circuits.
b. Sketch the response for one- and two-stage amplifiers assuming a unity gain and unity time constant for each stage.
c. How is the initial slope of step response of an n-stage amplifier related to the initial slope of a single stage?
d. Is there any relationship between the low-frequency half-power bandwidth and the initial slope of the step response?

7-16 When pulse signals are passed through a resistive attenuator as shown in (a), a loss in rise time results because of stray capacitance

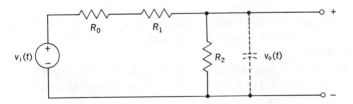

(a)

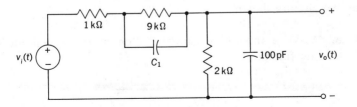

(b)

across R_2 to ground. By adding a small capacitor shunting R_1, the circuit response can be speeded up. Investigate this effect and determine a suitable value for the shunting capacitor C_1, for the circuit shown in (b). Assume the input to be a unit step to simplify calculations.

7-17   A frequently used definition of the "rise time" of a system is the time required for the system response to go from 10 to 90 percent of its final value when the excitation is a unit step.

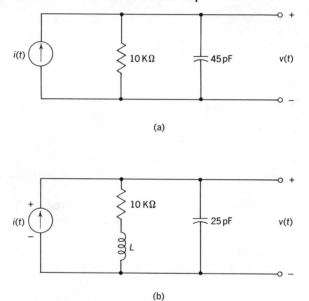

(a)

(b)

a.   For the circuit shown in (a), calculate the rise time and determine the general relationship between the rise time and half-power bandwidth for circuits of this type.

b.   Find the rise time for the "shunt peaked" circuit shown in (b) for values of $L = 0.5$ mH and $L = 2$ mH. What limits the amount of peaking that can be employed?

c.   A general rule for the relationship between rise time T_r (seconds) and half-power bandwidth, B (hertz), of systems without excessive overshoot is $T_r B = 0.35$ to 0.45. Using this relationship compute the bandwidths of the two circuits shown.

7-18   a.   Make a three-dimensional sketch of the magnitude of the transfer function

$$H(s) = \frac{(s + 1)}{s^2 + 2s + 2}$$

b.   Sketch the frequency response, $|H(j\omega)|$, working directly from the pole-zero plot.

7-19 It is occasionally necessary to compute the waveform correspond-ing to the steady-state response of a system excited by a periodic signal. One procedure for such a computation is as follows:
a. Compute the transform of the total response in terms of the trans-form of the input and transfer function.
b. From the partial fraction expansion of the total response select the terms corresponding to the transient response (that is, terms with poles in LHP).
c. Subtract, in the time domain, the transient response during the first period from the total response during the first period, leaving the periodic component that is the steady-state response.

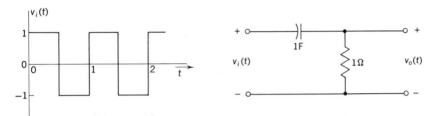

As an example of this procedure, determine and sketch the steady-state response of the circuit shown to a unit-amplitude square-wave in-put having a period of 1 second applied at $t = 0$. In addition, find the total response during the third period of the square wave.

7-20 Computation of the response of a bandpass system to a suddenly applied modulated carrier is generally very tedious. Oftentimes such systems can be analyzed in terms of an equivalent low-pass system. The response of the low-pass system to the envelope of the carrier applied to the bandpass system is determined. This response is then taken as the envelope of the bandpass system response. The exact conditions under which this procedure can be used were considered in Problem 5-24. The method is applicable to bandpass systems that have a frequency response that can be considered as the translation of a low-pass system response and that have a small fractional bandwidth; for example, most tuned RF amplifiers meet these requirements.
a. Using this procedure, compute the step response of a single tuned resonant circuit tuned to a frequency of 1 MHz and having a Q of 100.
b. Compare the calculation in part a with the complete analysis.

7-21 Bandpass filters can be generated from low-pass prototypes by the following procedure:
  1. Leave all resistances unaltered.
  2. Replace each capacitor C_k by a new capacitor of value $\frac{1}{2}C_k$ and put in parallel with the new capacitor an inductance resonating at the center frequency of the passband.

3. Replace each inductor L_k by a new inductor of value $\frac{1}{2}L_k$ and put in series with the new inductor a capacitor resonating at the center frequency of the passband.

Using this procedure find the bandpass equivalent (having a 30 MHz center frequency) of the filter shown and determine the response of the bandpass filter to a 1-μs pulse at the carrier frequency (see Problem 7-20).

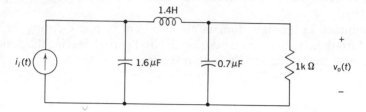

7-22 Write the Fourier transforms for the time functions having the following one-sided Laplace transforms.

a. $F(s) = \dfrac{s}{(s + 8)^2}$

c. $F(s) = \dfrac{s + 3}{(s^2 + 9)(s + 4)}$

b. $F(s) = \dfrac{s^2 + 9}{s(s^2 + 4s + 3)}$

d. $F(s) = \dfrac{1}{s(s^2 + 9)}$

7-23 Find the bounded time functions corresponding to the following two-sided Laplace transforms:

a. $F_2(s) = \dfrac{-10}{s^2 - 4}$

b. $F_2(s) = \dfrac{s - 2}{(s - 2)^2 + 9}$

c. $F_2(s) = \dfrac{-16s}{(s^2 - 16)^2}$

7-24 Find $v_o(t)$ at the output of the circuit shown when the input is $v_i(t)$. Use the two-sided Laplace transform.

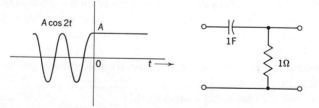

7-25 A given system has a transfer function of

$$H(s) = \frac{V_o(s)}{V_i(s)} = \frac{10s(s + 2)}{s^3 + 8s^2 + 19s + 12}$$

and the input voltage has the form

$$v_i(t) = 5\epsilon^{-2|t|} \qquad -\infty < t < \infty$$

Find the output voltage $v_o(t)$.

7-26 Sound radiated from the back of a loudspeaker is 180° out of phase with that radiated from the front. At low frequencies the wavelengths of sound waves are quite long (135 inches at 100 Hz) and so any leakage of the rearward radiated signal around to the front causes destructive interference in the radiated signal. By placing the speaker in a wall of very large dimensions (called an infinite baffle) this problem is avoided. Another method of combating this problem is to completely enclose the back of the speaker in a box. The acoustical behavior of these systems can be analyzed by means of electrical circuits analogous to the mechanical and acoustical circuits in the system. A simplified equivalent circuit of a completely enclosed system is shown below. In this diagram C_s, L_s, and R_s are the mass, compliance, and mechanical conductance of the diaphragm and its suspension. C_a is the acoustical mass of the diaphragm due to air loading, L_a is the acoustical compliance of the enclosure, and R_a is the acoustical radiation conductance. In this analogy, the radiated signal is proportional to the current in the equivalent resistance R_a. For purposes of analysis assume the values of the components shown below and assume that the speaker has a mechanical resonance of the suspension at 60 Hz.

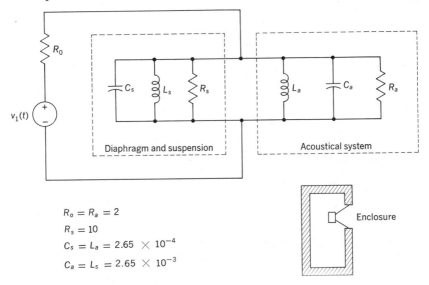

$$R_o = R_a = 2$$
$$R_s = 10$$
$$C_s = L_a = 2.65 \times 10^{-4}$$
$$C_a = L_s = 2.65 \times 10^{-3}$$

a. Determine the step response of the system (that is, determine the voltage across R_a for a step input at v_i).

b. The equivalent circuit can be changed to that of an infinite baffle by letting $L_a \to \infty$, since the air has no compliance when the enclosure is removed. Compare the step response of the infinite baffle with that of the completely enclosed speaker.

c. Investigate the effect of increasing and decreasing the source impedance. How would you select an optimum value?

d. In an actual system the resistance R_a decreases with frequency. Qualitatively, what effect would this have on the step response?

8

State-Space Methods in System Analysis

8-1 Introduction

One of the most striking aspects of current work in engineering systems is the trend toward greater complexity. This increased complexity stems from the need for systems that can perform more tasks, in less time, and with greater accuracy. Such a complex system may have many input signals and many output signals, and these may be interrelated in a complicated fashion. The number of components in such a system may be huge, and the cost astronomical.

As a consequence of this increase in system complexity and cost, the need for system analysis becomes even more acute. It is not feasible, either from a technical or a financial standpoint, to determine system response by experimental methods and to adjust system parameters by trial and error. Unfortunately, the task of system analysis also becomes more complex and time-consuming in such a situation. It becomes essential, therefore, to seek analytical techniques that can cope with the increased complexity and reduce the labor of system analysis to manageable proportions. The *state-space approach* to system analysis is one such technique.

There appear to be three essential steps in the development of an analysis technique that can survive the onslaught of an overwhelming increase in the number of system variables. The first step is to have the freedom to select variables in a manner that is not dictated by the particular configuration of voltages and currents but, if the need arises, to use variables that have no physical counterpoint in the actual system. The second step is to have a method of manipulating many equations that does not become more notationally cumbersome as the number of equations increases. The use of matrix representation of systems of equations accomplishes this feat. The final step is to be able to carry out the actual mechanics of solving for the system response by means of a computer, since it is only by such means that the engineer can be sufficiently freed from the burden of routine computation to make it feasible to consider the analysis of large-scale systems. The purpose of this chapter is to outline some of the fundamentals of the first two steps. Although the third step may well be the most critical one, it represents too large a subject to be included in an elementary discussion.

Before proceeding with the state-space approach to linear systems, it is desirable to review very briefly the methods of system representation that have already been discussed. These include:

1. The use of a *single differential equation* that relates the system output to the system input.

2. The *normal form of the system equations,* which include other system variables in addition to the input and output.

3. The *system impulse response,* which provides an integral relationship between the input and output by means of convolution.

4. The *system function,* which is the Fourier transform of the impulse response and which replaces convolution by multiplication.

5. The *transfer function,* which is the Laplace transform of the impulse response and which also replaces convolution by multiplication.

The impulse response, system function, and transfer function are primarily extensions of the single-differential-equation method of system representation. As such, they deal mostly with the input and output of the system. The state-space methods to be discussed, however, are primarily extensions of the normal equation method of system representation and, hence, can consider quantities *within* the system as well as the input and output. However, these methods also draw upon the concepts of impulse response and transfer functions, so that in this sense they represent a generalization of all that has been discussed previously.

8-2 Block Diagram Representations of Systems

The concept of representing a system by means of a single block with input and output arrows, as shown in Fig. 8-1, was introduced in Chapter

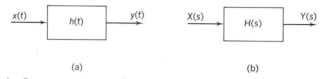

(a)   (b)

Figure 8-1 System representation by a single block. (a) Time-domain representation. (b) Frequency-domain representation.

2 and has been employed numerous times since. It is now appropriate to extend this concept to the representation of complex systems by means of several blocks with suitable interconnections. Although such an extension is not an essential part of the state-space approach, it does provide a convenient means for lending some physical reality to the assignment of state variables.

Figure 8-1 indicates that the block diagram may be used for either a time-domain representation or a frequency-domain representation. In the time-domain case, the block is designated by the impulse response and the input and output are designated as time functions. The relationship between input and output is given by the convolution of the impulse response and the input signal. Thus,

$$y(t) = h(t) \star x(t) \tag{8-1}$$

where, as before, the symbol $\star$ implies convolution. In the frequency-domain case, the block is designated by the transfer function and the input and output are designated by their Laplace transforms. In this case, the input and output are related by

$$Y(s) = H(s)X(s) \tag{8-2}$$

The next step in increasing system complexity is to connect two blocks in cascade as shown in Fig. 8-2. In making such a connection it is assumed that the presence of the second block does not alter the signal appearing at the output of the first block. In an actual system, particularly an electrical network, this may not be true and care must be taken not to employ this concept in situations where the input impedance of the second block is a significant load on the first block.

The single-block system that is equivalent to the two cascaded blocks will have an impulse response $h(t)$ that is the *convolution* of the individual impulse responses, and a transfer function that is the *product* of the individual transfer functions. Because of the greater ease in combining

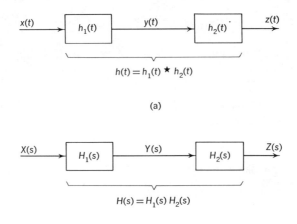

$$h(t) = h_1(t) \ast h_2(t)$$

(a)

$$H(s) = H_1(s) H_2(s)$$

(b)

Figure 8-2 System connected in cascade. **(a)** Time-domain representation. **(b)** Frequency-domain representation.

blocks when the transfer function is used rather than the impulse response, almost all manipulations of block diagrams are done with a frequency-domain representation. The basic concept of finding a single impulse response or transfer function that represents a complete system composed of several parts is an important one in system analysis. One of the advantages of the block diagram representation is that this combining operation can often be accomplished by manipulation of the blocks according to a set of formal rules, thus avoiding a great deal of algebraic manipulation.

Although there are many different rules that can be formulated, those illustrated in Fig. 8-3 are adequate for most manipulations. For convenience, both the time-domain and frequency-domain notations have been employed on each block. The impulse response and transfer function of the equivalent system are stated below each block diagram. The verifications of these equivalences are left as exercises for the student.

The concept of the *inverse system* is introduced in Fig. 8-3(c). Note that a system cascaded with its inverse is equivalent to a straight-through connection, and has a constant transfer function. An important point to remember in connection with inverse systems is that the inverse of a causal system is *not necessarily* causal, although in some cases it is. It should also be noted that the symbol for the inverse of an impulse response, $h^{-1}(t)$, does *not* mean the reciprocal of $h(t)$. However, because of the multiplicative nature of a cascaded transfer function, the inverse of $H(s)$ *is* just the reciprocal.

The concept of a feedback system is shown in Fig. 8-3(d). This situation clearly indicates the greater convenience of the frequency-domain representation. The use of feedback introduces a problem of stability

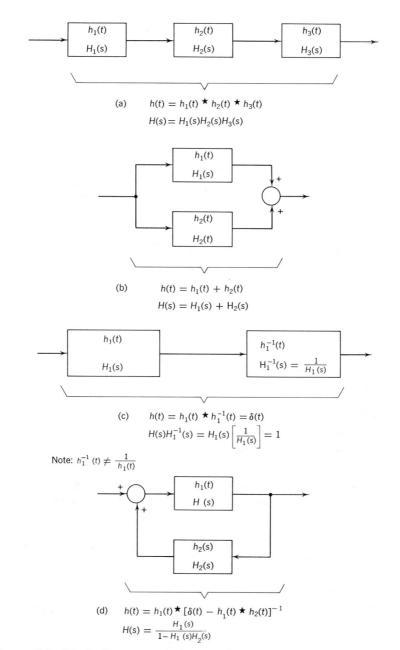

(a) $h(t) = h_1(t) \star h_2(t) \star h_3(t)$

$H(s) = H_1(s)H_2(s)H_3(s)$

(b) $h(t) = h_1(t) + h_2(t)$

$H(s) = H_1(s) + H_2(s)$

(c) $h(t) = h_1(t) \star h_1^{-1}(t) = \delta(t)$

$H(s)H_1^{-1}(s) = H_1(s)\left[\dfrac{1}{H_1(s)}\right] = 1$

Note: $h_1^{-1}(t) \neq \dfrac{1}{h_1(t)}$

(d) $h(t) = h_1(t) \star [\delta(t) - h_1(t) \star h_2(t)]^{-1}$

$H(s) = \dfrac{H_1(s)}{1 - H_1(s)H_2(s)}$

Figure 8-3   Block diagram equivalent (a) Cascade connection. (b) Parallel connection. (c) Inverse system. (d) Feedback system.

even when $H_1(s)$ and $H_2(s)$ both represent stable, causal systems. It was pointed out in Section 7-7 that the transfer function of a stable system must have no poles in the right half of the s plane. In the case of a feedback system, however, the poles of the equivalent transfer function $H(s)$ include the zeros of $1 - H_1(s)H_2(s)$, and there are many circumstances under which these zeros can be in the right half plane. The stability analysis of linear feedback systems is an important aspect of the study of automatic control systems, and the literature contains many excellent discussions of the subject. However, since it represents a digression from the objective of the present chapter, it will not be pursued further here.

A particular form of feedback system that will be useful in drawing block diagrams that can be represented by differential equations in the normal form is shown in Fig. 8-4. In this case, $H_1(s)$ becomes an ideal

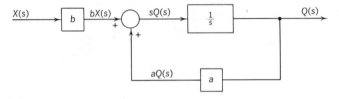

Figure 8-4   A first-order feedback system.

integrator and $H_2(s)$ is simply a constant gain a. In addition, there is another constant gain of b at the input to the system. From the equivalent transfer function given in Fig. 8-3(c), the transfer function of this system can be written as

$$H(s) = \frac{Q(s)}{X(s)} = \frac{b(1/s)}{1 - (1/s)\,a} = \frac{b}{s - a} \qquad (8\text{-}3)$$

It is clear from this result that the feedback system is first order. It is also clear that this system is stable if and only if $a < 0$, so that the pole of $H(s)$ is in the left half plane.

In order to relate the block diagram of Fig. 8-4 to the differential equation representation of the system, it is convenient to consider the time-domain version as shown in Fig. 8-5. It is very easy to write the

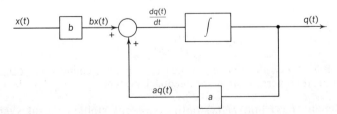

Figure 8-5   First-order system in the time domain.

differential equation for the system by noting that the input to the integrator (which is the derivative of the output) is simply the sum of two components. Thus,

$$\frac{dq(t)}{dt} = aq(t) + bx(t) \tag{8-4}$$

Note that this is a normal-form equation for a first-order system. This feature will be enlarged upon in the next section.

8-3   Block Diagrams for the Normal Equations

It was pointed out in Section 2-6 that an nth-order linear system could be represented by a set of n simultaneous first-order equations. The unknown time functions in these equations were denoted by $q_1(t)$, $q_2(t)$, $\cdots$, $q_n(t)$ and were called *state* variables. The resulting set of differential equations was written as

$$\frac{dq_1(t)}{dt} = a_{11}(t)q_1(t) + a_{12}(t)q_2(t) + \cdots + a_{1n}(t)q_n(t) + b_1(t)x(t)$$

$$\frac{dq_2(t)}{dt} = a_{21}(t)q_1(t) + a_{22}(t)q_2(t) + \cdots + a_{2n}(t)q_n(t) + b_2(t)x(t) \tag{8-5}$$

$$\vdots$$

$$\frac{dq_n(t)}{dt} = a_{n1}(t)q_1(t) + a_{n2}(t)q_2(t) + \cdots + a_{nn}(t)q_n(t) + b_n(t)x(t)$$

and were associated with an output equation of the form

$$y(t) = c_1(t)q_1(t) + c_2(t)q_2(t) + \cdots + c_n(t)q_n(t) + d(t)x(t) \tag{8-6}$$

We have slightly generalized the discussion of Section 2-6 by allowing $x(t)$ to appear explicitly in (8-6). Note that these equations represent a time-varying system, since the coefficients have been designated as functions of time. In the case of a time-invariant system, all of the coefficients are constants.

It was emphasized in the discussion of Section 2-6 that the state variables need not represent physically observable quantities within the system. Nevertheless, it is convenient from a conceptual standpoint to be able to sketch a block diagram in which the state variables appear explicitly, even if the resulting blocks have no physical counterparts. The first-order feedback system of Fig. 8-5 makes it possible to do this.

Consider a very simple system in which there are only two state variables and for which the normal equations are:

$$\frac{dq_1(t)}{dt} = -10q_1(t) + 5q_2(t) + 3x(t)$$

$$\frac{dq_2(t)}{dt} = 7q_1(t) - q_2(t) - 4x(t)$$

(8-7)

and the output equation is

$$y(t) = \tfrac{1}{2} q_1(t) + 2q_2(t)$$

(8-8)

The block diagram that corresponds to these equations is shown in Fig. 8-6. Although this diagram appears to be fairly complicated, it is relatively easy to compare the block diagram with the equation and verify the equivalence.

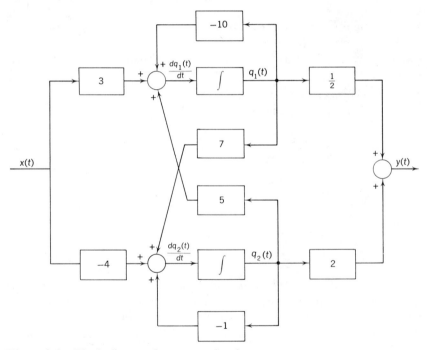

Figure 8-6 Block diagram for a second-order system.

It is certainly possible, in principle, to draw a similar block diagram for systems of any order. However, such a diagram is likely to be so cluttered up with detail that it no longer serves a useful purpose in providing a simple, overall characterization of the system. It is desirable, therefore, to provide some method of simplifying the presentation of both the normal equations and the corresponding block diagram. This is accomplished by the use of matrix notation as will be described in the next section. Before we proceed with this discussion, however, it is desirable to consider a more concrete example of system representation, and, at the same time, introduce the concept of multiple-input, multiple-output systems.

All of the discussion of systems so far has assumed that there was only one input signal and one output signal. Actually, however, there are many systems that have several inputs or several outputs, or both. It is still possible to represent such systems by a set of normal equations by adding to each equation the appropriate contribution from each input. Likewise, the output is expressed in terms of the state variables by a set of equations instead of a single equation. Obviously the complete block diagram for this situation will be even more complicated than in the single input cases already discussed.

As a simple example, consider the two-input, two-output network shown in Fig. 8-7. The two inputs, $x_1(t)$ and $x_2(t)$ are assumed to be

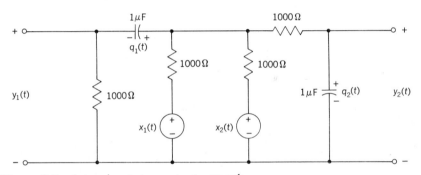

Figure 8-7   A two-input, two-output network.

voltage sources here. The two outputs, $y_1(t)$ and $y_2(t)$, are the open-circuit voltages appearing at the outputs of a high-pass R-C filter and a low-pass R-C filter respectively. This circuit might be used to separate the low-frequency and high-frequency components of the input signals into separate outputs regardless of which input contained which component. The resistance and capacitance values are such as to make the cutoff frequency of these two filters about 100 Hz. Thus, a 10-Hz component in either $x_1(t)$ or $x_2(t)$, for example, would appear predominantly in $y_2(t)$, whereas a 1000-Hz component in either input would appear predominantly in $y_1(t)$.

For reasons that will become clearer later on, the state variables, $q_1(t)$ and $q_2(t)$ have been chosen to be the voltages across the two capacitors. By writing the usual equilibrium equations and converting to normal form, it is easy to obtain the normal system equations as

$$\frac{dq_1(t)}{dt} = -750q_1(t) + 250q_2(t) + 250x_1(t) + 250x_2(t)$$

$$\frac{dq_2(t)}{dt} = 250q_1(t) - 750q_2(t) + 250x_1(t) + 250x_2(t)$$

(8-9)

Note that both input signals appear in each equation.

Since there are two output signals, there will be two output equations. These are

$$y_1(t) = -0.75q_1(t) + 0.25q_2(t) + 0.25x_1(t) + 0.25x_2(t)$$
$$y_2(t) = q_2(t)$$

(8-10)

Note that in this case $y_1(t)$ cannot be expressed solely in terms of the state variable, but must also include contributions from the input signals.

Equations (8-9) and (8-10) can now be used to sketch a block diagram for the system of Fig. 8-7 by using first-order feedback systems to create the state variables. The resulting block diagram is shown in Fig. 8-8. The complexity of the diagram for even a simple case like this clearly

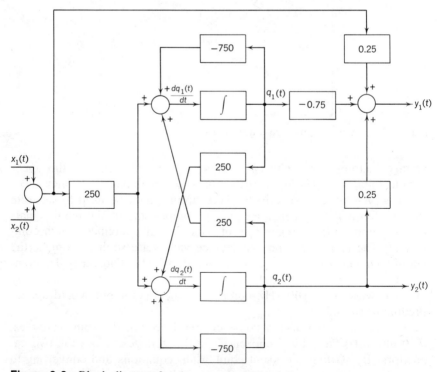

Figure 8-8 Block diagram for the system of Fig. 8-7.

indicates the need for a more compact notation when there are many inputs, outputs, and state variables.

8-4 Matrix Representations of the Normal Equations

The discussion in this section, and throughout the rest of this chapter, assumes that the reader is familiar with concepts of vectors, matrices, and elementary matrix manipulations. A brief summary of the necessary matrix manipulations is given in Appendix B.

The first step is to define an appropriate set of vectors and matrices. If there are n state variables, these can be combined in a column vector, or an $(n \times 1)$ matrix, and designated as $\mathbf{q}(t)$.[1] Thus,

$$\mathbf{q}(t) = \begin{bmatrix} q_1(t) \\ q_2(t) \\ \vdots \\ q_n(t) \end{bmatrix} \qquad (n \times 1)$$

is known as the *state vector*. If there are m input signals, the *input vector* will be designated as

$$\mathbf{x}(t) = \begin{bmatrix} x_1(t) \\ x_2(t) \\ \vdots \\ x_m(t) \end{bmatrix} \qquad (m \times 1)$$

Likewise, if there are p output signals, the *output vector* is

$$\mathbf{y}(t) = \begin{bmatrix} y_1(t) \\ y_2(t) \\ \vdots \\ y_p(t) \end{bmatrix} \qquad (p \times 1)$$

The coefficients of the state variables, as shown in (8-5) can be represented by an $(n \times n)$ matrix. Thus, for a general time-varying system, let

$$\mathbf{A}(t) = \begin{bmatrix} a_{11}(t) & a_{12}(t) \cdots a_{1n}(t) \\ a_{21}(t) & a_{22}(t) \cdots a_{2n}(t) \\ \vdots & \\ a_{n1}(t) & \cdots\cdots\cdots a_{nn}(t) \end{bmatrix} \qquad (n \times n)$$

---

[1] Vectors will be designated by boldface, lower-case letters, such as **a** or **x**. Matrices will be designated by boldface, upper-case letters, such as **A** or **X**.

for a time-invariant system, all of these coefficients are constants and the matrix will be designated simply as $\mathbf{A}$.

The coefficients of the input signal were designated in (8-8) by $b_1(t)$, $\cdots$, $b_n(t)$ since there was only one input. If there are m inputs, then there will be m such coefficients in each of the n equations. Thus, these coefficients may be represented by an $(n \times m)$ matrix as

$$\mathbf{B}(t) = \begin{bmatrix} b_{11}(t) & b_{12}(t) \cdots b_{1m}(t) \\ b_{21}(t) & b_{22}(t) \cdots b_{2m}(t) \\ \vdots & \\ b_{n1}(t) & b_{n2}(t) \cdots b_{nm}(t) \end{bmatrix} \qquad (n \times m)$$

Again, in the time-invariant case these will all be constants and the matrix becomes just $\mathbf{B}$.

If there are p output signals there will be p output equations, each requiring n coefficients as in (8-8). Thus, define a $(p \times n)$ matrix as

$$\mathbf{C}(t) = \begin{bmatrix} c_{11}(t) & c_{12}(t) \cdots c_{1n}(t) \\ c_{21}(t) & c_{22}(t) \cdots c_{2n}(t) \\ \vdots & \\ c_{p1}(t) & c_{p2}(t) \cdots c_{pn}(t) \end{bmatrix} \qquad (p \times n)$$

Likewise, each output equation may contain terms from each of the m input signals. Thus, let

$$\mathbf{D}(t) = \begin{bmatrix} d_{11}(t) & d_{12}(t) \cdots d_{1m}(t) \\ d_{21}(t) & d_{22}(t) \cdots d_{2m}(t) \\ \vdots & \\ d_{p1}(t) & d_{p2}(t) \cdots d_{pm}(t) \end{bmatrix} \qquad (p \times m)$$

Both of these matrices will have constant elements in the time-invariant case and will be designated as $\mathbf{C}$ and $\mathbf{D}$.

Having defined these vectors and matrices, it is now possible to write the complete set of normal equations as

$$\frac{d\mathbf{q}(t)}{dt} = \mathbf{A}(t)\mathbf{q}(t) + \mathbf{B}(t)\mathbf{x}(t) \qquad \text{(8-11)}$$

These equations are frequently referred to as the *state equations*.

Similarly, the set of output equations becomes

$$\mathbf{y}(t) = \mathbf{C}(t)\mathbf{q}(t) + \mathbf{D}(t)\mathbf{x}(t) \qquad \text{(8-12)}$$

The correctness of these equations can be verified easily by carrying out the indicated multiplications and writing an equation relating corresponding elements of the resulting vectors. This will be illustrated by a specific example.

Consider again the circuit shown in Fig. 8-7 and the corresponding equations (8-9) and (8-10). In this case $n = m = p = 2$ and the system is time-invariant. From the equations it is clear that

$$\mathbf{A} = \begin{bmatrix} -750 & 250 \\ 250 & -750 \end{bmatrix} \quad \mathbf{B} = \begin{bmatrix} 250 & 250 \\ 250 & 250 \end{bmatrix}$$

$$\mathbf{C} = \begin{bmatrix} -0.75 & 0.25 \\ 0 & 1 \end{bmatrix} \quad \mathbf{D} = \begin{bmatrix} 0.25 & 0.25 \\ 0 & 0 \end{bmatrix}$$

Thus, (8-11) can be written as

$$\begin{bmatrix} \dfrac{dq_1(t)}{dt} \\[2mm] \dfrac{dq_2(t)}{dt} \end{bmatrix} = \begin{bmatrix} -750 & 250 \\ 250 & -750 \end{bmatrix} \begin{bmatrix} q_1(t) \\ q_2(t) \end{bmatrix} + \begin{bmatrix} 250 & 250 \\ 250 & 250 \end{bmatrix} \begin{bmatrix} x_1(t) \\ x_2(t) \end{bmatrix} \tag{8-13}$$

Carrying out the multiplication yields

$$\begin{bmatrix} \dfrac{dq_1(t)}{dt} \\[2mm] \dfrac{dq_2(t)}{dt} \end{bmatrix} = \begin{bmatrix} -750q_1(t) + 250q_2(t) \\[2mm] 250q_1(t) - 750q_2(t) \end{bmatrix} + \begin{bmatrix} 250x_1(t) + 250x_2(t) \\[2mm] 250x_1(t) + 250x_2(t) \end{bmatrix} \tag{8-14}$$

Since matrices are equal only when corresponding elements are equal, it follows that

$$\frac{dq_1(t)}{dt} = -750q_1(t) + 250q_2(t) + 250x_1(t) + 250x_2(t)$$

results from equating the upper element in each vector. This is exactly the upper equation in (8-9). Equating the lower elements will lead to the lower equation of (8-9).

In a similar way, (8-12) can be written as

$$\begin{bmatrix} y_1(t) \\ y_2(t) \end{bmatrix} = \begin{bmatrix} -0.75 & 0.25 \\ 0 & 1 \end{bmatrix} \begin{bmatrix} q_1(t) \\ q_2(t) \end{bmatrix} + \begin{bmatrix} 25 & 25 \\ 0 & 0 \end{bmatrix} \begin{bmatrix} x_1(t) \\ x_2(t) \end{bmatrix} \tag{8-15}$$

The reader may verify that carrying out the multiplication and equating similar elements will lead to Equation (8-10).

It should be clear from the foregoing discussion that a considerable notational convenience can be achieved by using matrix notation. Furthermore, increasing the order of the system, the number of inputs, or the number of outputs does not make the state equations more cumbersome. In a later section, it will be shown that the matrix form of the normal equation can be solved explicitly to obtain a solution in matrix form. Thus, a great deal of the analysis of complicated systems can be carried out by procedures that are only slightly more involved than those for first-order systems.

It is also possible to draw a simple block diagram for the state equations. In order to distinguish such a block diagram from the type already discussed, we will use double arrows to represent vector quantities and blocks with thicker edges to represent matrices. Thus, (8-11) and (8-12) could be represented by the *matrix block diagram* of Fig. 8-9.

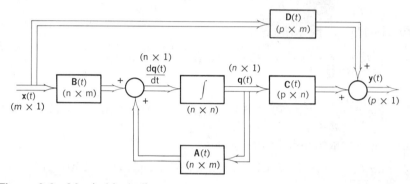

Figure 8-9   Matrix block diagram.

8-5   Elementary State-Space Concepts

Now that the notational preliminaries are out of the way, it is time to discuss some of the basic concepts associated with the state-space approach in a little more detail. The most fundamental concept, of course, is just what is meant by the *state* of a system. For our purposes, it is sufficient to consider the state of a system at any time to be all of the necessary information about the past history of the system needed to determine the future response of the system. This definition glosses over many subtle points that need to be considered in order for us to have a full understanding of the concept of state, but attempting to explain these here would only add confusion.

The mathematical representation of the state of a system at any time is the state vector, $q(t)$. This is not a unique representation since there are many different collections of state variables which would convey the same information about the system. However, if it contains all of the essential information, then it does lead to a unique determination of system response to any excitation $x(t)$. In most cases, it is convenient to pick some time t_0 and assume that all inputs of interest occur for $t \geqq t_0$. If this is done, then $q(t_0)$ is the initial state of the system and contains all of the necessary information about the history of the system prior to the time t_0.

For values of time greater than t_0 the response of the system depends upon both the initial state and the input excitation. For purposes of analysis, it is convenient to separate the total response into the parts dependent upon each. One part, called the *zero-input response,* is the response that would evolve from the initial state if the input excitation were zero. The other part, called the *zero-state response,* is the response that would evolve from the input excitation if the initial state were zero. Each of these concepts requires further clarification.

The input is a vector, $\mathbf{x}(t)$, and in order for it to be zero it is necessary that all of its components be zero. Thus, zero input is designated as $\mathbf{x}(t) = \mathbf{0}$ and implies that $x_1(t) = 0$, $x_2(t) = 0$, $\cdots$, $x_m(t) = 0$ for all $t \geq t_0$. The concept of zero state is a little more involved, since it does *not* necessarily imply that $\mathbf{q}(t_0) = \mathbf{0}$. Instead it implies that the system output $\mathbf{y}(t)$ will be zero when the input is zero. That is, a state $\mathbf{q}_0(t_0)$ is called a *zero state* if, for every t_0, $\mathbf{y}(t) = \mathbf{0}$ when $\mathbf{x}(t) = \mathbf{0}$ for all $t \geq t_0$.

The concept of zero state can be illustrated more concretely by considering two examples. For the first example, refer back to the network shown in Fig. 8-7. A brief examination of this network reveals that $y_1(t)$ and $y_2(t)$ will be zero, when $x_1(t)$ and $x_2(t)$ are zero, if and only if both $q_1(t)$ and $q_2(t)$ are zero. Thus, in this case, the zero state does in fact occur when $\mathbf{q}_0(t_0) = \mathbf{0}$ for any t_0. The second example will illustrate that this is not always so, although it is true most of the time. The situation shown in Fig. 8-10 is somewhat contrived, but it is not too dissimilar from many situations that arise in connection with active networks.

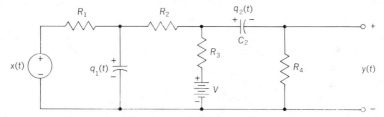

Figure 8-10   Network with an internal voltage source.

The state variables in the network of Fig. 8-10 are again chosen to be the capacitor voltages. It is clear that $y(t)$ will be zero when $x(t)$ is zero only if

$$q_1(t) = \frac{R_1}{R_1 + R_2 + R_3}V \quad \text{and} \quad q_2(t) = \frac{R_1 + R_2}{R_1 + R_2 + R_3}V$$

Thus, the zero state for this system is

$$\mathbf{q}_0(t_0) = \begin{bmatrix} \dfrac{R_1}{R_1 + R_2 + R_3}V \\[2mm] \dfrac{R_1 + R_2}{R_1 + R_2 + R_3}V \end{bmatrix} \tag{8-16}$$

for any t_0.

It was stated earlier that it would be desirable to express the total response of a system as the sum of the zero-input response and the zero-state response. This will be possible only if the system is linear. The concept of linearity was introduced in Chapter 2 for single-input, single-output systems and with no consideration of initial conditions. (Although it was not so stated, the definition of linearity employed there is only applicable if the initial state of the system is a zero state.) It is appropriate at this time to extend the concept of linearity in the light of state-space methods.

Suppose the initial state of a system is a zero-state $\mathbf{q}_0(t_0)$, the zero-state response to input $\mathbf{x}_1(t)$ is $\mathbf{y}_1(t)$, and the zero-state response to $\mathbf{x}_2(t)$ is $\mathbf{y}_2(t)$. Then the system is *zero-state linear* if and only if $[a\mathbf{y}_1(t) + b\mathbf{y}_2(t)]$ is the zero-state response to input $[a\mathbf{x}_1(t) + b\mathbf{x}_2(t)]$ for all a, b, and $t \geq t_0$.

Next, suppose the zero-input response is $\mathbf{y}_{01}(t)$ when the initial state is $\mathbf{q}_1(t_0)$ and the zero-input response is $\mathbf{y}_{02}(t)$ when the initial state is $\mathbf{q}_2(t_0)$. Then the system is *zero-input linear* if and only if $[a\mathbf{y}_{01}(t) + b\mathbf{y}_{02}(t)]$ is the zero-input response when the initial state is $[a\mathbf{q}_1(t_0) + b\mathbf{q}_2(t_0)]$ for all a, b, and $t \geq t_0$.

In the third place, a system is said to be *decomposable* if and only if the response to every input $\mathbf{x}(t)$ for every initial state $\mathbf{q}(t_0)$ can be represented as the sum of the zero-state response for that input and the zero-input response for that initial state.

On the basis of these three concepts, we can now make a more general definition of linearity. A system is *fully linear* if and only if it is *decomposable, zero-state linear,* and *zero-input linear.* It should be noted that this definition is valid for either time-varying or time-invariant systems.

It is of interest to check on the linearity of the networks shown in Figs. 8-7 and 8-10. It is not difficult to show that the network of Fig. 8-7 satisfies all three criteria and, hence, is fully linear. In the case of Fig. 8-10, however, the system is zero-state linear but is *not* zero-input linear. This is easily verified by noting that the zero-input response to an initial state that is a constant times the zero-state, $\mathbf{q}_0(t_0)$, is not zero.

8-6 Time-Domain Solutions of the State Equations — Invariant Systems

The state equations for a linear time-varying system were given in Section 8-5 as Equations (8-11) and (8-12). If the system is time-invariant, these may be written as

$$\frac{d\mathbf{q}(t)}{dt} = \mathbf{A}\mathbf{q}(t) + \mathbf{B}\mathbf{x}(t) \tag{8-17}$$

and
$$y(t) = \mathbf{C}\mathbf{q}(t) + \mathbf{D}\mathbf{x}(t) \tag{8-18}$$

where $\mathbf{A}$, $\mathbf{B}$, $\mathbf{C}$, and $\mathbf{D}$ are constant matrices that characterize the system. For the purpose of the following discussion the system will be assumed to be fully linear as defined in the previous section.

The general problem in system analysis is to find the output $\mathbf{y}(t)$ when the input $\mathbf{x}(t)$ is specified for $t \geq t_0$, and some initial state $\mathbf{q}(t_0)$ is given or can be determined. In order to do this, it is necessary to solve the matrix differential equation (8-17) for the state vector $\mathbf{q}(t)$. Once this has been determined, the evaluation of the output from (8-18) is straightforward.

Since the system is fully linear, it is decomposable, and the total solution can be written as the sum of the zero-input response and zero-state response. This is also true for the state vector as well as the output vector. Thus, the zero-input response for the state vector can be obtained from (8-17) by letting $\mathbf{x}(t) = \mathbf{0}$. The resulting homogeneous equation is

$$\frac{d\mathbf{q}(t)}{dt} = \mathbf{A}\mathbf{q}(t) \tag{8-19}$$

By analogy to the corresponding first-order scalar equation it might be suspected that the solution of this equation would have the form

$$\mathbf{q}_s(t) = \epsilon^{\mathbf{A}(t-t_0)}\mathbf{q}(t_0) \tag{8-20}$$

where the subscript implies that this response is due to the initial state only. It will be shown that this is true by substitution into (8-19). Since $\mathbf{A}$ is a constant matrix, the derivative of (8-20) is[2]

$$\frac{d\mathbf{q}_s(t)}{dt} = \mathbf{A}\left[\epsilon^{\mathbf{A}(t-t_0)}\mathbf{q}(t_0)\right] \tag{8-21}$$

Substitution of (8-20) and (8-21) into (8-19) obviously yields an equality.

The quantity $\epsilon^{\mathbf{A}t}$ is an $(n \times n)$ matrix, which can be defined by the series for an exponential. Thus,

$$\epsilon^{\mathbf{A}t} = \mathbf{I} + \mathbf{A}t + \mathbf{A}^2\frac{t^2}{2!} + \mathbf{A}^3\frac{t^3}{3!} + \cdots \quad (n \times n) \tag{8-22}$$

where $\mathbf{I}$ is the identity matrix. The matrix $\epsilon^{\mathbf{A}t}$ arises so often in the solution of linear equations that it is given a special symbol, $\phi(t)$, and is often called the *fundamental matrix* for the system. Its evaluation and properties are so important to system analysis that the following section will be devoted exclusively to discussing them. For the moment we simply will note that $\phi(t)$ is a solution to the homogeneous equation and that the zero-input response for the state vector may also be written as

$$\mathbf{q}_s(t) = \phi(t - t_0)\mathbf{q}(t_0) \tag{8-23}$$

---

[2] The basic rules of matrix calculus are summarized in Appendix B.

The matrix $\phi(t - t_0)$ is frequently referred to as the *state-transition matrix*, since it specifies the transition from the state at time t_0 to that at some other time $t \geq t_0$.

The zero-state response for the state vector will be determined by the method of variation of parameters. In order to do this, assume that this solution has the form

$$\mathbf{q}_i(t) = \epsilon^{A(t-t_0)} \mathbf{g}(t) \qquad t \geq t_0 \tag{8-24}$$

where the subscript i implies that this is the response due to the input only and where $\mathbf{g}(t)$ is an $(n \times 1)$ vector that is to be determined. The derivative of (8-24) is

$$\frac{d\mathbf{q}_i(t)}{dt} = \mathbf{A}\epsilon^{A(t-t_0)} \mathbf{g}(t) + \epsilon^{A(t-t_0)} \frac{d\mathbf{g}(t)}{dt}$$

and this may be substituted into (8-17) to give, after simplifying,

$$\epsilon^{A(t-t_0)} \frac{d\mathbf{g}(t)}{dt} = \mathbf{B}\mathbf{x}(t)$$

Premultiplying by $\epsilon^{-A(t-t_0)}$ yields[3]

$$\frac{d\mathbf{g}(t)}{dt} = \epsilon^{-A(t-t_0)}\mathbf{B}\mathbf{x}(t) \qquad t \geq t_0$$

which may be integrated to give

$$\mathbf{g}(t) = \int_{t_0}^{t} \epsilon^{-A(\lambda-t_0)} \mathbf{B}\mathbf{x}(\lambda) \, d\lambda \tag{8-25}$$

Substituting (8-25) into (8-24) gives the zero-state response for the state vector as

$$\mathbf{q}_i(t) = \int_{t_0}^{t} \epsilon^{A(t-\lambda)} \mathbf{B}\mathbf{x}(\lambda) \, d\lambda$$

or, using the definition of the state-transition matrix,

$$\mathbf{q}_i(t) = \int_{t_0}^{t} \phi(t - \lambda) \mathbf{B}\mathbf{x}(\lambda) \, d\lambda \tag{8-26}$$

It is now possible to write the total state vector as the sum of the zero-input response, given by (8-23), and the zero-state response, given by (8-26). That is

$$\mathbf{q}(t) = \mathbf{q}_s(t) + \mathbf{q}_i(t)$$

$$= \phi(t - t_0) \mathbf{q}(t_0) + \int_{t_0}^{t} \phi(t - \lambda)\mathbf{B}\mathbf{x}(\lambda) \, d\lambda \tag{8-27}$$

---

[3]This operation is equivalent to premultiplying by the inverse of the matrix $\epsilon^{A(t-t_0)}$, and assumes that the inverse exists.

This result clearly indicates the important role played by the state-transition matrix. It is necessary, therefore, to examine the properties of this matrix and consider ways of evaluating it before we go to a specific example.

8-7 The State-Transition Matrix

The state-transition matrix for time-invariant linear systems was defined to be

$$\phi(t - t_0) = \epsilon^{A(t - t_0)} \tag{8-28}$$

The most basic method for evaluating the elements of this matrix is by using the series expansion for the exponential. Thus,

$$\phi(t - t_0) = I + A(t - t_0) + A^2 \frac{(t - t_0)^2}{2!} + A^3 \frac{(t - t_0)^3}{3!} + \cdots \tag{8-29}$$

This method is tedious to carry out by hand calculation, but can be adapted to computer calculations quite readily. An example that can be carried out easily by hand will be shown in the next section.

A second method of evaluating this matrix in the time domain is based on the *Cayley-Hamilton theorem,* which states that a square matrix A satisfies its own characteristic equation.[4] This makes it possible to express *all* powers of A in terms of a polynomial in A of degree no higher than $n - 1$. Thus, the entire series of (8-29) can be written as

$$\phi(t - t_0) = \alpha_0(t - t_0) I + \alpha_1(t - t_0) A + \cdots \alpha_{n-1}(t - t_0) A^{n-1} \tag{8-30}$$

in which the coefficients $\alpha_i(t - t_0)$ are to be determined by substituting the eigenvalues of A into the scalar equivalent of (8-30) and obtaining a set of n simultaneous equations. An example will illustrate this procedure.

Suppose that A is (2×2) and has the form

$$A = \begin{bmatrix} -3 & 1 \\ 2 & -2 \end{bmatrix}$$

Since the characteristic equation comes from the determinant equation

$$|A - \lambda I| = 0$$

it follows that

$$\begin{vmatrix} -3 - \lambda & 1 \\ 2 & -2 - \lambda \end{vmatrix} = 0$$

and, hence,

$$\lambda^2 + 5\lambda + 4 = 0$$

---

[4] See Appendix B for a summary of characteristic equation concepts.

from which the two eigenvalues of $\mathbf{A}$ are $\lambda_1 = -1$ and $\lambda_2 = -4$. The state-transition matrix can then be expressed as

$$\boldsymbol{\phi}(t - t_0) = \alpha_0(t - t_0)\mathbf{I} + \alpha_1(t - t_0)\mathbf{A} = \epsilon^{\mathbf{A}(t - t_0)} \tag{8-31}$$

and the scalar form of this is simply

$$\alpha_0(t - t_0) + \alpha_1(t - t_0)\lambda = \epsilon^{\lambda(t - t_0)}$$

Substituting in $\lambda = \lambda_1 = -1$ gives

$$\alpha_0(t - t_0) - \alpha_1(t - t_0) = \epsilon^{-(t - t_0)}$$

while $\lambda = \lambda_2 = -4$ yields

$$\alpha_0(t - t_0) - 4\alpha_1(t - t_0) = \epsilon^{-4(t - t_0)}$$

from which

$$\alpha_0(t - t_0) = \frac{4}{3}\epsilon^{-(t - t_0)} - \frac{1}{3}\epsilon^{-4(t - t_0)}$$

$$\alpha_1(t - t_0) = \frac{1}{3}\epsilon^{-(t - t_0)} - \frac{1}{3}\epsilon^{-4(t - t_0)}$$

Inserting these values into (8-31) yields the results

$$\boldsymbol{\phi}(t - t_0) = \left[\frac{4}{3}\epsilon^{-(t - t_0)} - \frac{1}{3}\epsilon^{-4(t - t_0)}\right]\mathbf{I} + \left[\frac{1}{3}\epsilon^{-(t - t_0)} - \frac{1}{3}\epsilon^{-4(t - t_0)}\right]\mathbf{A}$$

$$= \begin{bmatrix} \frac{1}{3}\epsilon^{-(t - t_0)} + \frac{2}{3}\epsilon^{-4(t - t_0)} & \frac{1}{3}\epsilon^{-(t - t_0)} - \frac{1}{3}\epsilon^{-4(t - t_0)} \\ \frac{2}{3}\epsilon^{-(t - t_0)} - \frac{2}{3}\epsilon^{-4(t - t_0)} & \frac{2}{3}\epsilon^{-(t - t_0)} + \frac{1}{3}\epsilon^{-4(t - t_0)} \end{bmatrix} \tag{8-32}$$

The foregoing procedures for evaluating the state-transition matrix are general in the sense that they can be carried out in almost every case, although it obviously becomes much more difficult if n is large. Another procedure, which may be very simple and straightforward in some cases (even for large n) but which may offer no simplification at all in other cases, is based on the physical interpretation of the state-transition matrix in terms of the impulse response of the state variables. In order to investigate this possibility, consider the zero-state response for the state vector given in (8-26) as

$$\mathbf{q}_i(t) = \int_{t_0}^{t} \boldsymbol{\phi}(t - \lambda)\,\mathbf{B}\mathbf{x}(\lambda)\,d\lambda \tag{8-26}$$

It is now desired to pick $\mathbf{B}$ and $\mathbf{x}(\lambda)$ so that they correspond to applying a unit impulse directly into the integrator associated with any one state variable, say the jth one. This can be done in several ways, but the easiest is to let the input vector be:

$$\mathbf{x}(\lambda) = \begin{bmatrix} \delta(\lambda - t_0) \\ 0 \\ \vdots \\ 0 \end{bmatrix} \qquad (m \times 1)$$

and let the **B**-matrix be all zeros except b_{j1}; that is,

$$B = \begin{bmatrix} 0 & \cdots & 0 \\ 0 & & \\ 0 & & \\ 1 & \cdots & 0 \\ 0 & & \\ \vdots & & \\ 0 & & 0 \end{bmatrix} \leftarrow j\text{th row} \quad (n \times m)$$

Then

$$\mathbf{Bx}(\lambda) = \begin{bmatrix} 0 & \cdots & 0 \\ & \vdots & \\ 1 & & \\ & \vdots & \\ 0 & \cdots & 0 \end{bmatrix} \begin{bmatrix} \delta(\lambda - t_0) \\ 0 \\ \vdots \\ \\ \vdots \\ 0 \end{bmatrix} = \begin{bmatrix} 0 \\ \vdots \\ \delta(\lambda - t_0) \\ \vdots \\ 0 \end{bmatrix} \leftarrow j\text{th element} \quad (n \times 1)$$

Multiplying by the state-transition matrix gives

$$\boldsymbol{\phi}(t - \lambda)\mathbf{Bx}(\lambda) = \begin{bmatrix} \phi_{11}(t - \lambda) & \cdots & \phi_{1n}(t - \lambda) \\ \vdots & & \\ \vdots & & \\ \phi_{n1}(t - \lambda) & \cdots & \phi_{nm}(t - \lambda) \end{bmatrix} \begin{bmatrix} 0 \\ \vdots \\ \delta(\lambda - t_0) \\ \vdots \\ 0 \end{bmatrix}$$

$$= \begin{bmatrix} \phi_{ij}(t - \lambda)\delta(\lambda - t_0) \\ \phi_{2j}(t - \lambda)\delta(\lambda - t_0) \\ \vdots \\ \phi_{nj}(t - \lambda)\delta(\lambda - t_0) \end{bmatrix} \tag{8-33}$$

Introducing (8-33) into (8-26) and integrating over the δ functions leads immediately to

$$\mathbf{q}_i(t) = \begin{bmatrix} \phi_{1j}(t - t_0) \\ \phi_{2j}(t - t_0) \\ \vdots \\ \phi_{nj}(t - t_0) \end{bmatrix} \tag{8-34}$$

The interpretation of the elements of the state-transition matrix is now clear. The element $\phi_{jk}(t - t_0)$ is the zero-state response for the kth state variable when a unit impulse occurs in the *derivative* of the jth state variable — that is, at the input to the jth integrator in the block diagram.

As an illustration of the procedure, consider the system represented by the block diagram of Fig. 8-11 and, in particular, the portion inside

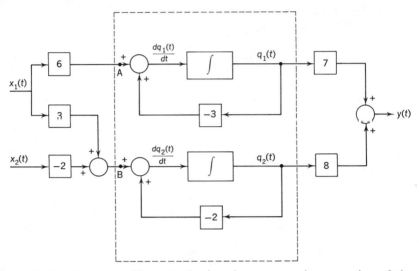

Figure 8-11 System to illustrate the impulse-response interpretation of the state-transition matrix.

the dotted lines. If a unit impulse, at $t = t_0$, is introduced at point A, the resulting $q_1(t)$ and $q_2(t)$ are clearly just

$$q_1(t) = \epsilon^{-3(t - t_0)} \qquad t \geq t_0$$
$$q_2(t) = 0 \qquad t \geq t_0$$

since there is no cross coupling between state variables in this example. Likewise, if a unit impulse at $t = t_0$ is introduced at point B, the state response is

$$q_1(t) = 0 \qquad t \geq t_0$$
$$q_2(t) = \epsilon^{-2(t - t_0)} \qquad t \geq t_0$$

Hence, the state-transition matrix can be written immediately as

$$\phi(t - t_0) = \begin{bmatrix} \epsilon^{-3(t - t_0)} & 0 \\ 0 & \epsilon^{-2(t - t_0)} \end{bmatrix} \tag{8-35}$$

For the case of time-invariant systems, the state-transition matrix can also be obtained quite straightforwardly, by use of the Laplace transform. This procedure will be discussed in Section 8-9.

There are a few properties of the state-transition matrix that are frequently useful in analysis or for the purpose of checking results. These are summarized as follows:

1. $\phi(0) = \mathbf{I}$
2. $\phi(t_2 - t_0) = \phi(t_2 - t_1)\phi(t_1 - t_0)$
3. $\phi(t_0 - t) = \phi^{-1}(t - t_0)$

The first property may be obtained either by setting $t = t_0$ in the series expansion (8-29) for $\phi(t - t_0)$ or from the uniqueness of the solution of the homogeneous state equation, as given in (8-23). That is, since

$$\mathbf{q}_s(t) = \phi(t - t_0)\mathbf{q}(t_0) \tag{8-23}$$

and

$$\mathbf{q}_s(t_0) = \mathbf{q}(t_0)$$

it follows that $\phi(0) = \mathbf{I}$. The second property can be obtained from the same equation since

$$\begin{aligned} \mathbf{q}_s(t_2) &= \phi(t_2 - t_0)\mathbf{q}(t_0) \\ &= \phi(t_2 - t_1)\mathbf{q}_s(t_1) \end{aligned}$$

But

$$\mathbf{q}(t_1) = \phi(t_1 - t_0)\mathbf{q}(t_0)$$

so

$$\mathbf{q}_s(t_2) = \phi(t_2 - t_1)\phi(t_1 - t_0)\mathbf{q}(t_0)$$

from which the second property is apparent.

The third property, concerning the inverse of the state transition matrix, is obtained by premultiplying (8-27) by $\phi^{-1}(t - t_0)$. Thus

$$\phi^{-1}(t - t_0)\mathbf{q}_s(t) = \phi^{-1}(t - t_0)\,\phi(t - t_0)\mathbf{q}(t_0) = \mathbf{q}(t_0)$$

But

$$\mathbf{q}(t_0) = \phi(t_0 - t)\mathbf{q}_s(t)$$

from which it follows that

$$\phi^{-1}(t - t_0) = \phi(t_0 - t) \tag{8-36}$$

An important consideration with regard to the inverse of the state transition matrix is whether or not it exists. It can be shown, by methods that are too lengthy to include here, that $\phi(t - t_0)$ is always nonsingular and, hence, its inverse will always exist. In addition, (8-24) is true for *all* values of t, not just $t \geq t_0$. The inverse can be interpreted as being the state-transition matrix for another system known as the *adjoint system*. The use of the adjoint system is an important aspect of system analysis but is beyond the scope of the present discussion.

8-8 The Impulse-Response Matrix

In the previous discussion of single-input, single-output linear systems, the impulse response was a convenient way of characterizing systems and could be used for determining the system output for any input by means of convolution. As a matter of convenience, the impulse response was defined to be the response to an impulse of unit area applied at time $t = 0$.

A similar concept can be applied to multiple-input, multiple-output systems by defining the *impulse-response matrix* for such a system. If there are m inputs and p outputs, the impulse-response matrix will be a $(p \times m)$ matrix whose (i, j) element is the zero-state response at the ith output due to a unit impulse at $t = 0$, applied at the jth input, with all other inputs zero. This matrix, which will be designated as $\mathcal{H}(t)$, can then be used in a multidimensional form of the convolution integral to obtain the system output for any input.

For purposes of obtaining the impulse-response matrix, it will be assumed that the system output equation is of the form

$$\mathbf{y}(t) = \mathbf{Cq}(t) \qquad (8\text{-}37)$$

thus assuming that there are no contributions of the form $\mathbf{Dx}(t)$ in $\mathbf{y}(t)$.[5] Since only the zero-state response is being considered, the state vector can be obtained from (8-26) with $t_0 = 0$. Then, the output vector becomes

$$\mathbf{y}(t) = \int_0^t \mathbf{C}\boldsymbol{\phi}(t - \lambda)\mathbf{Bx}(\lambda)\, d\lambda \qquad (8\text{-}38)$$

When a unit impulse is applied to the jth input only, then

$$\mathbf{Bx}(\lambda) = \begin{bmatrix} b_{11} & \cdots & b_{1n} \\ \vdots & & \\ & & \\ \vdots & & \\ b_{n1} & \cdots & b_{nm} \end{bmatrix} \begin{bmatrix} 0 \\ \vdots \\ \delta(\lambda) \\ \vdots \\ 0 \end{bmatrix} = \begin{bmatrix} b_{1j} \\ \vdots \\ \vdots \\ b_{nj} \end{bmatrix} \delta(\lambda) \qquad (8\text{-}39)$$

which is simply the jth column of $\mathbf{B}$ times the impulse. The corresponding output vector, which is the jth column of $\mathcal{H}(t)$, is, after integrating over the δ function, just

$$\mathbf{y}_j(t) = \begin{bmatrix} h_{1j}(t) \\ \vdots \\ h_{pj}(t) \end{bmatrix} = \mathbf{C}\boldsymbol{\phi}(t) \begin{bmatrix} b_{1j} \\ \vdots \\ b_{nj} \end{bmatrix} \qquad (8\text{-}40)$$

A similar result can be obtained for every $1 \leq j \leq m$, and this will give every column of $\mathcal{H}(t)$. Then the complete impulse-response matrix is given by

$$\mathcal{H}(t) = \mathbf{C}\boldsymbol{\phi}(t)\mathbf{B} \qquad t \geq 0 \qquad (8\text{-}41)$$

---

[5] The case in which $\mathbf{D}$ is not zero can be handled also by using additional state variables. It is being eliminated here simply for ease in discussion.

When the input vector $\mathbf{x}(t)$ is not an impulse but a set of general time functions, the output vector can be obtained by using (8-41) in (8-38) to give

$$\mathbf{y}(t) = \int_0^t \mathcal{H}(t - \lambda)\mathbf{x}(\lambda) \, d\lambda \qquad \text{(8-42)}$$

The similarity of this result to the previous convolution integral is apparent.

It may be useful to consider a simple example to illustrate these concepts. The system represented by the block diagram of Fig. 8-12

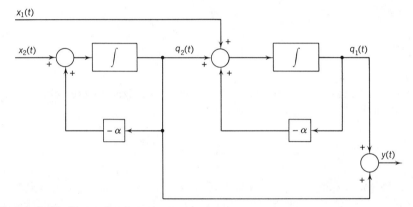

Figure 8-12 Example of system analysis.

will be used for this purpose. The various matrices that characterize this system are

$$\mathbf{A} = \begin{bmatrix} -\alpha & 1 \\ 0 & -\alpha \end{bmatrix} \quad \mathbf{B} = \begin{bmatrix} 1 & 0 \\ 0 & 1 \end{bmatrix}$$

$$\mathbf{C} = [1 \ 1]$$

The first step is to determine the state-transition matrix. For illustrative purposes, this will be done directly from the series expansion. The important thing that is needed here is a general expression for any power of $\mathbf{A}$; this will be determined by induction. Consider first

$$\mathbf{A}^2 = \begin{bmatrix} -\alpha & 1 \\ 0 & -\alpha \end{bmatrix}\begin{bmatrix} -\alpha & 1 \\ 0 & -\alpha \end{bmatrix} = \begin{bmatrix} \alpha^2 & -2\alpha \\ 0 & \alpha^2 \end{bmatrix}$$

and also

$$\mathbf{A}^3 = \begin{bmatrix} -\alpha & 1 \\ 0 & -\alpha \end{bmatrix}\begin{bmatrix} \alpha^2 & -2\alpha \\ 0 & \alpha^2 \end{bmatrix} = \begin{bmatrix} -\alpha^3 & 3\alpha^2 \\ 0 & -\alpha^3 \end{bmatrix}$$

From these it can be deduced that:

$$\mathbf{A}^k = \begin{bmatrix} (-\alpha)^k & k(-\alpha)^{k-1} \\ 0 & (-\alpha)^k \end{bmatrix}$$

Using this result in the series expansion

$$\phi(t - t_0) = \mathbf{I} + \mathbf{A}(t - t_0) + \mathbf{A}^2 \frac{(t - t_0)^2}{2!} + \cdots \qquad \text{(8-29)}$$

leads to

$$\phi(t - t_0) = \begin{bmatrix} \displaystyle\sum_{k=0}^{\infty} (-\alpha)^k \frac{(t - t_0)^k}{k!} & \displaystyle\sum_{k=0}^{\infty} k(-\alpha)^{k-1} \frac{(t - t_0)^k}{k!} \\ 0 & \displaystyle\sum_{k=0}^{\infty} (-\alpha)^k \frac{(t - t_0)^k}{k!} \end{bmatrix} \qquad \text{(8-43)}$$

Each of the summations in (8-43) can be recognized as the series for an exponential. Thus, it can be written as

$$\phi(t - t_0) = \begin{bmatrix} \epsilon^{-\alpha(t - t_0)} & (t - t_0)\, \epsilon^{-\alpha(t - t_0)} \\ 0 & \epsilon^{-\alpha(t - t_0)} \end{bmatrix} \qquad \text{(8-44)}$$

In this example it was a simple matter to recognize the closed-form summation of the series. In other cases a closed-form may not exist or may be too complicated to recognize easily. Hence the use of the series has only limited application in attempts to find state-transition matrices analytically.

Once the state-transition matrix is found, the impulse-response matrix can be found from (8-41). Thus, in this case,

$$\mathcal{H}(t) = \mathbf{C}\phi(t)\mathbf{B} = [1, 1] \begin{bmatrix} \epsilon^{-\alpha t} & t\epsilon^{-\alpha t} \\ 0 & \epsilon^{-\alpha t} \end{bmatrix} \begin{bmatrix} 1 & 0 \\ 0 & 1 \end{bmatrix}$$
$$= [\epsilon^{-\alpha t} \quad (t + 1)\epsilon^{-\alpha t}] \qquad t \geq 0 \qquad \text{(8-45)}$$

In order to illustrate a particular case of system analysis, let the input signals be

$$x_1(t) = u(t)$$
$$x_2(t) = \epsilon^{-t} u(t)$$

The integrand of (8-42) then becomes

$$\mathcal{H}(t - \lambda)\mathbf{x}(\lambda) = [\epsilon^{-\alpha(t - \lambda)} \quad (t - \lambda + 1)\epsilon^{-\alpha(t - \lambda)}] \begin{bmatrix} u(\lambda) \\ \epsilon^{-\lambda} u(\lambda) \end{bmatrix} \qquad \text{(8-46)}$$

$$= \epsilon^{-\alpha(t - \lambda)} u(\lambda) + (t - \lambda + 1)\epsilon^{-\alpha t} \epsilon^{(\alpha - 1)\lambda} u(\lambda)$$

Since there is only one output signal in this example, (8-46) represents a scalar. In general, it would be a $(p \times 1)$ vector and each component would have to be integrated to obtain the corresponding output component. In the present case, however,

$$y(t) = \int_0^t \left[\epsilon^{-\alpha(t-\lambda)} u(\lambda) + (t - \lambda + 1) \epsilon^{-\alpha t} \epsilon^{(\alpha-1)\lambda} u(\lambda) \right] d\lambda$$

$$= \epsilon^{-\alpha t} \frac{\epsilon^{\alpha\lambda}}{\alpha} \bigg|_0^t + (t + 1) \epsilon^{-\alpha t} \frac{\epsilon^{(\alpha-1)\lambda}}{\alpha - 1} \bigg|_0^t$$

$$- \epsilon^{-\alpha t} \frac{\epsilon^{(\alpha-1)\lambda} \left[(\alpha - 1)\lambda - 1 \right]}{(\alpha - 1)^2} \bigg|_0^t \qquad \text{(8-47)}$$

$$= \frac{u(t)}{\alpha} + \frac{\alpha}{(\alpha - 1)^2} \epsilon^{-t} u(t) - \left[\frac{t + 2}{\alpha - 1} + \frac{1}{\alpha(\alpha - 1)^2} \right] \epsilon^{-\alpha t} u(t)$$

8-9 Frequency-Domain Solution of the State Equations

The use of Fourier and Laplace transforms in linear, time-invariant system analysis has been discussed in previous chapters. It was found that the use of such transforms resulted in differential equations becoming algebraic equations and, thus, often simplifying the mechanics of carrying out a solution. It should be expected, therefore, that a similar simplification should result from using transform methods in connection with the state equations.

In order to examine this possibility, recall that the state equations for time-invariant systems had the form

$$\frac{d\mathbf{q}(t)}{dt} = \mathbf{A}\mathbf{q}(t) + \mathbf{B}\mathbf{x}(t) \qquad \text{(8-17)}$$

$$\mathbf{y}(t) = \mathbf{C}\mathbf{q}(t) + \mathbf{D}\mathbf{x}(t) \qquad \text{(8-18)}$$

Let the one-sided Laplace transform[6] of $q(t)$ be designated as

$$\mathbf{Q}(s) = \begin{bmatrix} Q_1(s) \\ Q_2(s) \\ \vdots \\ Q_n(s) \end{bmatrix} = \begin{bmatrix} \mathscr{L}\left[q_1(t)\right] \\ \mathscr{L}\left[q_2(t)\right] \\ \vdots \\ \mathscr{L}\left[q_n(t)\right] \end{bmatrix}$$

---

[6]The use of the one-sided Laplace transform is equivalent to setting $t_0 = 0$. It is possible to avoid this restriction by using the two-sided Laplace transform, but it is seldom necessary to do so.

and the Laplace transform of $\mathbf{x}(t)$ and $\mathbf{y}(t)$ be defined in a similar manner as $\mathbf{X}(s)$ and $\mathbf{Y}(s)$. Then the Laplace transform of (8-17) can be written as

$$s\mathbf{Q}(s) - \mathbf{q}(0) = \mathbf{A}\mathbf{Q}(s) + \mathbf{B}\mathbf{X}(s) \tag{8-48}$$

and the Laplace transform of (8-18) as

$$\mathbf{Y}(s) = \mathbf{C}\mathbf{Q}(s) + \mathbf{D}\mathbf{X}(s) \tag{8-49}$$

Equation (8-48) can be written as

$$(s\mathbf{I} - \mathbf{A})\mathbf{Q}(s) = \mathbf{q}(0) + \mathbf{B}\mathbf{X}(s)$$

when $\mathbf{I}$ is an $(n \times n)$ identity matrix. This can be solved for $\mathbf{Q}(s)$ by premultiplying by $(s\mathbf{I} - \mathbf{A})^{-1}$. Thus,

$$\mathbf{Q}(s) = (s\mathbf{I} - \mathbf{A})^{-1}\mathbf{q}(0) + (s\mathbf{I} - \mathbf{A})^{-1}\mathbf{B}\mathbf{X}(s) \tag{8-50}$$

The Laplace transform of the output can then be obtained by substituting into (8-49) to yield

$$\mathbf{Y}(s) = \mathbf{C}(s\mathbf{I} - \mathbf{A})^{-1}\mathbf{q}(0) + [\mathbf{C}(s\mathbf{I} - \mathbf{A})^{-1}\mathbf{B} + \mathbf{D}]\mathbf{X}(s) \tag{8-51}$$

This result can be used to determine the system response to any causal input when the initial state is known.

The transfer function for a linear system was previously defined as the ratio of the output and input transforms when the initial condition was zero. Thus, if $\mathbf{q}(0) = \mathbf{0}$, one can define a *transfer function matrix* by

$$\mathbf{Y}(s) = \mathbf{H}(s)\mathbf{X}(s)$$

Upon comparison with (8-51) it is clear that

$$\mathbf{H}(s) = \mathbf{C}(s\mathbf{I} - \mathbf{A})^{-1}\mathbf{B} + \mathbf{D} \tag{8-52}$$

The transfer function matrix is a $(p \times m)$ matrix whose (i, j) element is the transfer function relating the ith output and the jth input. Hence, this element must be the Laplace transform of the impulse response between these two terminals; that is,

$$H_{ij}(s) = \mathscr{L}[h_{ij}(t)]$$

or, more completely,

$$\begin{aligned} \mathbf{H}(s) &= \mathscr{L}[\boldsymbol{\mathscr{H}}(t)] \\ &= \int_0^\infty \boldsymbol{\mathscr{H}}(t)\epsilon^{-st}\,dt \end{aligned} \tag{8-53}$$

Thus, the transfer function matrix is just the Laplace transform of the impulse-response matrix.

It is also possible to obtain an explicit expression for the state-transition matrix. The total state response was shown in (8-27) to be given (for $t_0 = 0$) by:

$$\mathbf{q}(t) = \boldsymbol{\phi}(t)\mathbf{q}(0) + \int_0^t \boldsymbol{\phi}(t - \lambda)\, \mathbf{BX}(\lambda)\, d\lambda \tag{8-54}$$

Since the integral in (8-54) is a convolution integral, its Laplace transform is simply a product of transforms. Thus, the Laplace transform of (8-54) is

$$\mathbf{Q}(s) = \boldsymbol{\Phi}(s)\mathbf{q}(0) + \boldsymbol{\Phi}(s)\mathbf{BX}(s) \tag{8-55}$$

where $\boldsymbol{\Phi}(s)$ is the Laplace transform of the state-transition matrix, $\boldsymbol{\phi}(t)$, and is also an $(n \times n)$ matrix. Upon comparing (8-55) with (8-50), it is clear that

$$\boldsymbol{\Phi}(s) = (s\mathbf{I} - \mathbf{A})^{-1} \tag{8-56}$$

This result leads to another procedure for evaluating the state-transition matrix; namely, taking the inverse Laplace transform of (8-56). Thus,

$$\boldsymbol{\phi}(t) = \mathscr{L}^{-1}\left[(s\mathbf{I} - \mathbf{A})^{-1}\right] \tag{8-57}$$

Although this procedure is straightforward, finding the inverse may become cumbersome if n is large.

In order to illustrate the foregoing procedure for obtaining the state-transition matrix, consider the system shown in Fig. 8-12, for which the **A** matrix was

$$\mathbf{A} = \begin{bmatrix} -\alpha & 1 \\ 0 & -\alpha \end{bmatrix}$$

Hence

$$s\mathbf{I} - \mathbf{A} = \begin{bmatrix} s + \alpha & -1 \\ 0 & s + \alpha \end{bmatrix}$$

and its inverse is

$$\boldsymbol{\Phi}(s) = (s\mathbf{I} - \mathbf{A})^{-1} = \begin{bmatrix} s + \alpha & -1 \\ 0 & s + \alpha \end{bmatrix}^{-1}$$

$$= \begin{bmatrix} \dfrac{1}{s + \alpha} & \dfrac{1}{(s + \alpha)^2} \\ 0 & \dfrac{1}{s + \alpha} \end{bmatrix}$$

The inverse Laplace transform of $\boldsymbol{\Phi}(s)$ yields the state-transition matrix as

$$\boldsymbol{\phi}(t) = \mathscr{L}^{-1} \begin{bmatrix} \dfrac{1}{s + \alpha} & \dfrac{1}{(s + \alpha)^2} \\ 0 & \dfrac{1}{s + \alpha} \end{bmatrix} = \begin{bmatrix} \epsilon^{-\alpha t} & t\epsilon^{-\alpha t} \\ 0 & \epsilon^{-\alpha t} \end{bmatrix} \tag{8-58}$$

which is identical to the previous result, (8-44), when $t_0 = 0$.

The transfer function matrix for a system in the zero state can also be related to the Laplace transform of the state-transition matrix. It was shown in (8-41) that

$$\mathscr{H}(t) = \mathbf{C}\boldsymbol{\phi}(t)\mathbf{B} \tag{8-41}$$

when $\mathbf{D} = \mathbf{O}$. The Laplace transform of this immediately yields

$$\mathbf{H}(s) = \mathbf{C}\boldsymbol{\Phi}(s)\mathbf{B} \tag{8-59}$$

As an illustration of this result, return to the example considered above. For the system of Fig. 8-12 the $\mathbf{B}$ and $\mathbf{C}$ matrices were

$$\mathbf{B} = \begin{bmatrix} 1 & 0 \\ 0 & 1 \end{bmatrix} \quad \mathbf{C} = [1 \ 1]$$

Hence

$$
\begin{aligned}
\mathbf{H}(s) = \mathbf{C}\boldsymbol{\Phi}(s)\mathbf{B} &= [1 \ 1] \begin{bmatrix} \dfrac{1}{s+\alpha} & \dfrac{1}{(s+\alpha)^2} \\ 0 & \dfrac{1}{s+\alpha} \end{bmatrix} \begin{bmatrix} 1 & 0 \\ 0 & 1 \end{bmatrix} \\
&= \left[\dfrac{1}{s+\alpha} \quad \dfrac{1}{(s+\alpha)^2} + \dfrac{1}{s+\alpha} \right]
\end{aligned}
\tag{8-60}
$$

This also leads directly to the Laplace transform of the output since

$$\mathbf{Y}(s) = \mathbf{H}(s)\mathbf{X}(s)$$

In this example, the input vector is

$$\mathbf{x}(t) = \begin{bmatrix} u(t) \\ \epsilon^{-t}u(t) \end{bmatrix}$$

so that its Laplace transform is

$$\mathbf{X}(s) = \begin{bmatrix} \dfrac{1}{s} \\ \dfrac{1}{s+1} \end{bmatrix} \tag{8-61}$$

Hence

$$
\begin{aligned}
\mathbf{Y}(s) &= \left[\dfrac{1}{s+\alpha} \quad \dfrac{1}{(s+\alpha)^2} + \dfrac{1}{s+\alpha} \right] \begin{bmatrix} \dfrac{1}{s} \\ \dfrac{1}{s+1} \end{bmatrix} \\
&= \dfrac{1}{s(s+\alpha)} + \dfrac{1}{(s+1)(s+\alpha)^2} + \dfrac{1}{(s+1)(s+\alpha)} \\
&= \dfrac{2s^2 + 2(\alpha+1)s + \alpha}{s(s+1)(s+\alpha)^2}
\end{aligned}
\tag{8-62}
$$

The output time function may be obtained by first making a partial fraction expansion of (8-62). Thus,

$$\mathbf{Y}(s) = \frac{1}{\alpha s} + \frac{\alpha}{(\alpha - 1)^2(s + 1)} + \frac{1}{(1 - \alpha)(s + \alpha)^2}$$
$$- \left(\frac{2}{\alpha - 1} + \frac{1}{\alpha(\alpha - 1)^2}\right)\frac{1}{s + \alpha}$$

from which

$$\mathbf{y}(t) = \frac{u(t)}{\alpha} + \frac{1}{(\alpha - 1)^2}\,\epsilon^{-t}u(t) - \left(\frac{t + 2}{\alpha - 1} + \frac{1}{\alpha(\alpha - 1)^2}\right)\epsilon^{-\alpha t}u(t)$$

which agrees with the previous result (8-47).

8-10 Selection of State Variables for Network Analysis

Since this text is intended primarily as an introduction to general system analysis, it is not appropriate to consider network analysis in great detail. Nevertheless, it is of interest to have some idea as to how one would select an appropriate set of state variables in typical networks. This section briefly outlines a procedure which, while not infallible, will work in a majority of the cases.

Although it is not necessary that state variables represent physical quantities in the network, it is a great conceptual advantage to have them do so. Furthermore, from the block diagram representation of the normal equations, such as Fig. 8-8, it is clear that each state variable should also be the *integral* of another physical quantity, since it always appears as the output of an integrator. This implies that it might be reasonable to associate state variables with the energy-storage elements of the network; that is, with the inductances and capacitances.

In line with this discussion, therefore, it is appropriate to let the state variables consist of the capacitor voltages and the inductor currents. Note that a capacitor voltage is the integral of the corresponding capacitor current, and that an inductor current is the integral of the corresponding inductor voltage. In certain cases this simple procedure leads to too many state variables and some have to be eliminated. This occurs, for example, if there is a capacitance loop so that the sum of the capacitor voltages is constrained to be zero. It is also true if there is an inductance cut-set so that the sum of the inductor currents is constrained to be zero. In such cases, it is necessary to eliminate one capacitance voltage in each capacitance loop and one inductance current in each inductance cut-set.

Choosing state variables in this way also makes it relatively easy to determine the initial state of the system. In particular, the initial state vector will have as its elements the initial capacitor voltages and the initial inductor currents; these are the quantities that can most easily be determined by inspection of the circuit.

Although several different networks have been considered in previous examples, it may be desirable to consider still another network in order to emphasize some of the points mentioned above. Hence, consider the R-L-C network shown in Fig. 8-13, and designate the state variables as

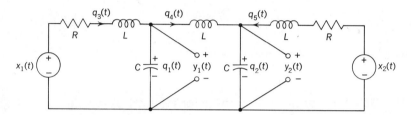

Figure 8-13   An R-L-C network with two inputs and two outputs.

the capacitor voltages and the inductor currents. The first step in the analysis is to determine the **A** matrix for the network. There are several standard procedures for doing this almost by inspection. However, since it is not appropriate in this brief discussion to develop the theoretical basis for such a procedure, we will resort to a less formal approach.

In the first place, it should be recalled that the first row of the **A** matrix comes from the relation between $q_1(t)$ and the other state variables; that is

$$\frac{dq_1(t)}{dt} = a_{11}q_1(t) + a_{12}q_2(t) + \cdots + a_{15}q_5(t) + \cdots \qquad \textbf{(8-63)}$$

In the present example, $C[dq_1(t)/dt]$ is the current in the left-hand capacitor, and this current must be related to the inductor currents $q_3(t)$ and $q_4(t)$ by

$$C\frac{dq_1(t)}{dt} = q_3(t) - q_4(t)$$

from which

$$\frac{dq_1(t)}{dt} = \frac{1}{C}q_3(t) - \frac{1}{C}q_4(t) \qquad \textbf{(8-64)}$$

It is clear from this that $a_{11} = a_{12} = a_{15} = 0$, $a_{13} = 1/C$, and $a_{14} = -1/C$.

The second row of **A** relates to the current in the right-hand capacitor, the third row relates to the voltage across the left-hand inductor, and the fourth and fifth rows relate to the other two inductor voltages. Thus, by using only elementary reasoning of this sort, it is possible to write down the **A** matrix immediately. It is

$$\mathbf{A} = \begin{bmatrix} 0 & 0 & 1/C & -1/C & 0 \\ 0 & 0 & 0 & 1/C & 1/C \\ -1/L & 0 & -R/L & 0 & 0 \\ 1/L & -1/L & 0 & 0 & 0 \\ 0 & -1/L & 0 & 0 & -R/L \end{bmatrix} \tag{8-65}$$

The **B** matrix, which is (5 × 2) in this case, can also be determined by inspection by noting that $x_1(t)$ enters only into the voltage relationship involving $q_3(t)$ and $x_2(t)$ enters only into the voltage relationship involving $q_5(t)$. Hence,

$$\mathbf{B} = \begin{bmatrix} 0 & 0 \\ 0 & 0 \\ 1 & 0 \\ 0 & 0 \\ 0 & 1 \end{bmatrix} \tag{8-66}$$

Likewise, the **C** matrix, which is (2 × 5) in this example, is obtained readily by noting that

$$y_1(t) = q_1(t)$$

and

$$y_2(t) = q_2(t)$$

Hence,

$$\mathbf{C} = \begin{bmatrix} 1 & 0 & 0 & 0 & 0 \\ 0 & 1 & 0 & 0 & 0 \end{bmatrix} \tag{8-67}$$

These relationships also make it clear that **D** = 0 in this case. Hence, the state equations can be written as

$$\frac{d\mathbf{q}(t)}{dt} = \mathbf{A}\mathbf{q}(t) + \mathbf{B}\mathbf{x}(t) \tag{8-68}$$

$$\mathbf{y}(t) = \mathbf{C}\mathbf{q}(t) \tag{8-69}$$

where

$$\mathbf{q}(t) = \begin{bmatrix} q_1(t) \\ q_2(t) \\ q_3(t) \\ q_4(t) \\ q_5(t) \end{bmatrix} \qquad \mathbf{x}(t) = \begin{bmatrix} x_1(t) \\ x_2(t) \end{bmatrix} \qquad \mathbf{y}(t) = \begin{bmatrix} y_1(t) \\ y_2(t) \end{bmatrix}$$

and the other matrices are as defined above.

For the circuit as shown in Fig. 8-13, the zero-state vector is

$$\mathbf{q}_0(t_0) = \mathbf{0}$$

The initial-state vector, on the other hand, need not be zero (although it may be), but the individual elements of this vector cannot be adjusted arbitrarily and independently unless additional inputs are permitted.

The foregoing discussion of state-variable selection avoids many subtle problems which may arise with some network configurations or in the case of active networks or networks with negative elements. These problems are discussed in the literature, however, and there are straightforward procedures for dealing with them. Some appropriate references are given at the end of this chapter for the interested reader.

8-11   Time-varying Systems

One of the outstanding advantages of the state-space approach to system analysis is the relative ease with which it can be extended to handle time-varying linear systems. A detailed discussion of this aspect is beyond the scope of the present treatment, but it is worthwhile to point out some of the similarities to, and differences from, the time-invariant case already discussed. In order to do this, the principal results of the previous section will be rewritten, without proof, for time-varying systems and will be discussed briefly.

In the first place, the matrices that describe the system will be functions of time instead of constants, so the state equations become

$$\frac{d\mathbf{q}(t)}{dt} = \mathbf{A}(t)\mathbf{q}(t) + \mathbf{B}(t)\,\mathbf{x}(t) \tag{8-70}$$

$$\mathbf{y}(t) = \mathbf{C}(t)\mathbf{q}(t) + \mathbf{D}(t)\mathbf{x}(t) \tag{8-71}$$

There is still a state-transition matrix that relates the state of the system at any time t to its initial state at time t_0 in the manner indicated by (8-35). In the time-varying case, however, the state-transition matrix cannot always be written as a function of the time difference $(t - t_0)$. Thus, it will be designated as $\phi(t, t_0)$, and (8-23) becomes

$$\mathbf{q}_s(t) = \phi(t, t_0)\mathbf{q}(t_0) \tag{8-72}$$

The state-transition matrix must still be a solution of the homogeneous equation

$$\frac{d\mathbf{q}(t)}{dt} = \mathbf{A}(t)\mathbf{q}(t)$$

If this were a scalar equation of the form

$$\frac{dq(t)}{dt} = A(t)q(t)$$

it would be an easy matter to show that the solution would be given by (8-72), where

$$\phi(t, t_0) = \exp\left[\int_{t_0}^{t} A(\lambda)\, d\lambda\right] \tag{8-73}$$

Unfortunately, the same result does not always carry over into the matrix form of the equation, because matrix multiplication is not always commutative. It can be shown, however, that this general result does apply under certain circumstances. Specifically, if and only if the matrix $\mathbf{A}(t)$ is commutative with the matrix

$$\int_{t_0}^{t} \mathbf{A}(\lambda)\, d\lambda$$

is the state-transition matrix given by

$$\phi(t, t_0) = \exp\left[\int_{t_0}^{t} \mathbf{A}(\lambda)\, d\lambda\right] \tag{8-74}$$

This commutativity always exists when $\mathbf{A}$ is constant, and (8-74) reduces immediately to the previous result given in (8-28).

The total state vector can be related to the input by a result analogous to (8-27). Specifically,

$$\mathbf{q}(t) = \phi(t, t_0)\mathbf{q}(t_0) + \int_{t_0}^{t} \phi(t, \lambda)\mathbf{B}(\lambda)\mathbf{x}(\lambda)\, d\lambda \tag{8-75}$$

The output of the system then becomes

$$\mathbf{y}(t) = \mathbf{C}(t)\phi(t, t_0)\mathbf{q}(t_0) + \mathbf{C}(t)\int_{t_0}^{t} \phi(t, \lambda)\mathbf{B}(\lambda)\mathbf{x}(\lambda)\, d\lambda \tag{8-76}$$

The impulse-response matrix for a time-varying system is a function of two variables and will be designated as $\mathcal{H}(t, \lambda)$. The (i, j) element of this matrix is the zero-state response at the ith output at time t resulting from a unit impulse applied to the jth input at time λ. By analogy to (8-41), the impulse-response matrix may be written as

$$\mathcal{H}(t, \lambda) = \mathbf{C}(t)\phi(t, \lambda)\mathbf{B}(\lambda) \qquad t \geq \lambda \tag{8-77}$$

The zero-state output resulting from a general input, $\mathbf{x}(t)$, can be expressed as:

$$\mathbf{y}(t) = \int_{t_0}^{t} \mathscr{H}(t, \lambda)\mathbf{x}(\lambda) \, d\lambda \qquad \text{(8-78)}$$

when $\mathbf{D}(t) = 0$. This result is the time-varying version of (8-42).

The foregoing discussion clearly indicates that most of the results obtained for time-invariant systems carry over to the time-varying case with simply a change in notation. The major exception is the state-transition matrix, which follows the previous result only in special cases. When (8-74) does not hold, there is no general procedure for finding the state-transition matrix. This poses the most serious obstacle to the analysis of general time-varying linear systems.

■ REFERENCES

Although there are several books now available that discuss state-space methods of system analysis, the level of discussion is usually too advanced for undergraduate students. Nevertheless, the interested student may find portions of the following books useful for answering specific questions or extending their knowledge.

1. De Russo, Paul M., Rob J. Roy, and Charles M. Close, *State Variables for Engineers*. New York: John Wiley & Sons, Inc., 1965.
2. Schwartz, Ralph J., and Bernard Friedland, *Linear Systems*. New York: McGraw-Hill Book Company, Inc., 1965.

■ PROBLEMS

8-1   a. Prove that the equivalent impulse response of two linear systems connected in cascade is the convolution of the individual impulse responses.

b. Prove that the equivalent transfer function of two linear systems connected in cascade is the product of the individual transfer functions.

8-2   a. Show that the equivalent system of two cascaded, *invariant* linear systems is independent of the sequence in which they are connected.

b. Show by means of a simple example that the statement in (a) does *not* hold for cascaded, time-varying linear systems.

8-3 Two systems having impulse responses of

$$h_1(t) = 10\epsilon^{-2t}u(t) \quad \text{and} \quad h_2(t) = 20\epsilon^{-t}u(t)$$

aŕe connected in cascade. Find the equivalent impulse response of the combination.

8-4 a. Prove that the equivalent impulse response of two linear systems connected in parallel is the sum of the individual impulse responses.
    b. Repeat part a for transfer functions.

8-5 Find the equivalent transfer function for each of the three block diagrams shown.

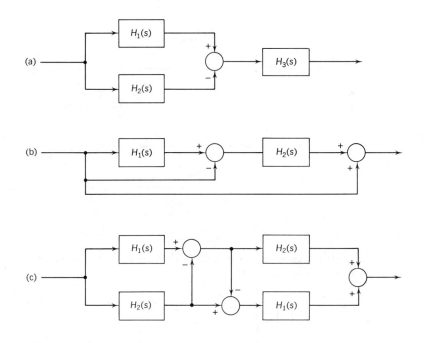

8-6 a. A linear system has an impulse response of

$$h(t) = 0.1\epsilon^{-2t}u(t)$$

Find the impulse response of the inverse system
    b. Is the inverse system causal?

8-7 Prove the results given for the equivalent of the feedback system shown in Fig. 8-3(d).

8-8 Find the equivalent transfer function for each of the three block diagrams shown.

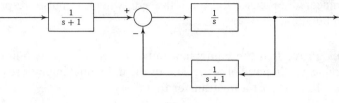

(a)

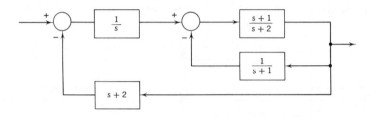

(b)

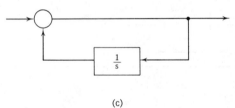

(c)

8-9 Write a single differential equation that relates the output $y(t)$ to the input $x(t)$, for the system shown.

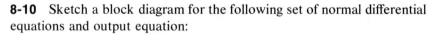

8-10 Sketch a block diagram for the following set of normal differential equations and output equation:

$$\frac{dq_1(t)}{dt} = -5q_1(t) + q_2(t)$$

$$\frac{dq_2(t)}{dt} = -3q_2(t) + x(t)$$

$$y(t) = q_1(t)$$

8-11   Write a set of normal differential equations and the output equation corresponding to the block diagram shown.

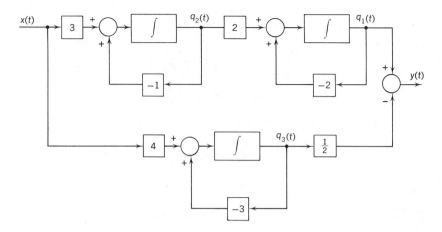

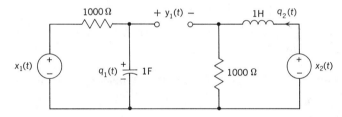

8-12   a.   Write the normal equations and output equation for the two-input, one-output network shown, using the state variables indicated.

b.   Sketch a block diagram for this network based on first-order feedback systems.

8-13   a.   Write the matrix form of the normal equations for the network of Problem 8-12 and specify the elements of all vectors and matrices.
b.   Sketch the matrix block diagram for this network.

8-14   Write the matrix equations for the block diagram shown. Specify the elements of all vectors and matrices.

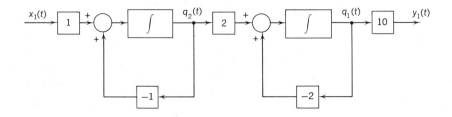

8-15

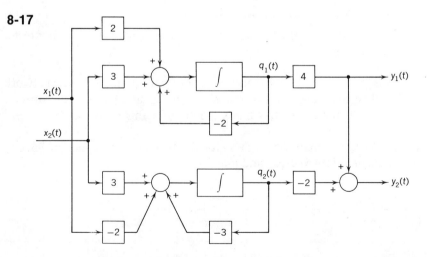

System 1 is defined by the matrix equations

$$\frac{dq_1(t)}{dt} = A_1(t)q_1(t) + B_1(t)x(t)$$

$$y(t) = C_1(t)q_1(t)$$

and system 2 by the equations

$$\frac{dq_2(t)}{dt} = A_2(t)q_2(t) + B_2(t)y(t)$$

$$z(t) = C_2 q_2(t)$$

If the cascaded combination of these two systems is defined by

$$\frac{dq(t)}{dt} \quad A(t)q(t) + B(t)x(t)$$

$$z(t) = C(t)q(t)$$

find $q(t)$, $A(t)$, $B(t)$, and $C(t)$ in terms of the similar quantities for the separate systems.

8-16 Repeat Problem 8-15 if the two systems are connected in parallel.

8-17

Write the matrix state equations for the system shown and specify the elements of all vectors and matrices.

8-18 A system is characterized by state equations with the following matrices:

$$A = \begin{bmatrix} -1 & 1 \\ 0 & -1 \end{bmatrix} \quad B = \begin{bmatrix} 1 & 0 & 1 \\ 0 & 1 & 0 \end{bmatrix}$$

$$C = \begin{bmatrix} -1 & 1 \end{bmatrix} \quad D = \begin{bmatrix} 1 & 0 & 0 \end{bmatrix}$$

Sketch the complete block diagram for this system.

8-19

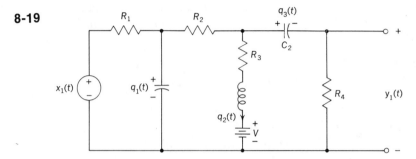

a. Find a zero-state vector for the system shown.
b. Is this system fully linear?

8-20 Use the series expansion for the exponential to show that

a. $\dfrac{d\epsilon^{At}}{dt} = A\epsilon^{At}$

b. $\epsilon^{At}\epsilon^{-At} = \epsilon^{-At}\epsilon^{At} = I$

8-21 A time-invariant system has a fundamental matrix of the form

$$\phi(t) = \begin{bmatrix} \epsilon^{-at} & t\epsilon^{-at} \\ 0 & \epsilon^{-at} \end{bmatrix}$$

a. Find the A matrix for the system.
b. If the initial state for the system is

$$q(t_0) = \begin{bmatrix} 10 \\ -5 \end{bmatrix}$$

write the zero-input response for the state vector for all $t \geq t_0$.

8-22 For the system of Problem 8-21, the B matrix is

$$B = \begin{bmatrix} 2 \\ -2 \end{bmatrix}$$

If the input is a δ function at $t = t_0 + 1$, write the total state vector for all $t > t_0$.

8-23 Use the series expansion for the exponential to determine the state-transition matrix for a system whose **A** matrix is $(n \times n)$ and has the form

$$\mathbf{A} = -\mathbf{I} \quad (n \times n)$$

8-24 A particular class of nth-order system has a block diagram consisting of n integrators with feedback connected in parallel with *no* cross connections from the output of one integrator to the input of another.
a.   Show that the **A** matrix for such a system has the form

$$\mathbf{A} = \begin{bmatrix} -\alpha_1 & 0 & \cdots\cdots & & & 0 \\ 0 & -\alpha_2 & 0 & \cdots & & 0 \\ 0 & 0 & -\alpha_3 & 0 \cdots & 0 \\ \cdot & & & & & \\ \cdot & & & & & 0 \\ 0 & \cdots\cdots & & 0 & -\alpha_n \end{bmatrix}$$

b.   Find the state-transition matrix for this class of system.

8-25 Use the eigenvalue method to evaluate the state-transition matrix for a system whose **A** matrix is

$$\mathbf{A} = \begin{bmatrix} -1 & 1 & 0 \\ 0 & -2 & 1 \\ 0 & 0 & -3 \end{bmatrix}$$

8-26 Using the impulse-response interpretation, find the state-transition matrix for the system of Problem 8-12.

8-27 Using the impulse-response method, find the state-transition matrix for the system shown.

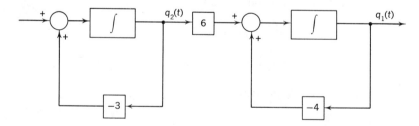

8-28 For each of the following matrices, specify whether or not it is a valid state-transition matrix for a linear, time-invariant system. If it is not, state the reason.

a. $\begin{bmatrix} 2\epsilon^{-2(t-t_0)} & 0 \\ 0 & \epsilon^{-3(t-t_0)} \end{bmatrix}$

b. $\begin{bmatrix} \epsilon^{-(t-t_0)} & \epsilon^{-2(t-t_0)} \\ \epsilon^{-3(t-t_0)} & \epsilon^{-4(t-t_0)} \end{bmatrix}$

c. $\begin{bmatrix} \epsilon^{-(t-t_0)} & (t-t_0)\,\epsilon^{-2(t-t_0)} \\ 0 & \epsilon^{-3(t-t_0)} \end{bmatrix}$

d. $\begin{bmatrix} 1 & 0 \\ 0 & 1 \end{bmatrix}$

8-29 a. Find the impulse-response matrix for the system of Problem 8-17.

      b. Find the output vector for this system if the input vector is

$$\mathbf{x}(t) = \begin{bmatrix} \epsilon^{-100t}u(t) \\ 5\delta(t) \end{bmatrix}$$

and the initial state is a zero state.

8-30 All of the impulse responses indicated in the block diagram shown are physically realizable.

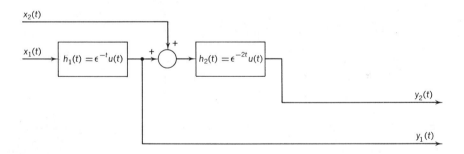

a. Find the impulse-response matrix for this system.
b. Find the zero-state response of this system if the input vector is

$$\mathbf{x}(t) = \begin{bmatrix} u(t) \\ u(t - 1/2) \end{bmatrix}$$

8-31 Find the state-transition matrix for the system of Problem 8-24 by using Laplace transform methods.

8-32 Find the state-transition matrix for the system of Problem 8-25 by using Laplace transform methods.

8-33 Find the transfer function matrix for the system of Problem 8-27.

8-34 a. Find the transfer function matrix for the system of Problem 8-30.

b. Find the zero-state response for the specified input by using frequency-domain methods.

8-35 Write the state equations for the network shown and define all matrices and vectors.

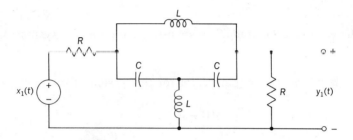

8-36 Find the impulse response of the network shown using state-space methods.

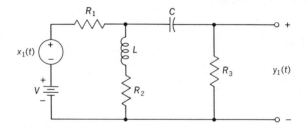

8-37 a. Find the state-transition matrix for the time-varying system shown.

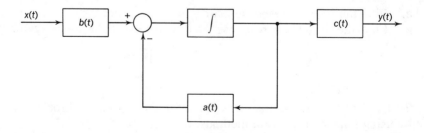

b. Find the impulse response for this system.

8-38 A time-varying linear system has an **A** matrix of the form

$$\mathbf{A} = \begin{bmatrix} 1 + 1/t & 0 \\ 0 & 2/t \end{bmatrix} \qquad t \geq t_0 = 1$$

Find the state-transition matrix for this system.

CHAPTER

9
Random Signals and Probability

9-1 System Analysis with Random Input Signals

The central problem of system analysis is to determine the response of a system to a known input forcing function. When this input is known explicitly, as a function of time, say, then the response can also be determined explicitly by methods that have already been discussed. Thus, it is possible to carry out system analysis in detail when the input has a simple form such as an impulse, step, ramp, exponential, sinusoid, or some combination of these. Analysis of this type is quite useful in gaining an understanding of the behavior of linear systems, but it is not very representative of the situations that arise in actual system operation.

   The signal waveforms arising in practical system operation are usually not describable by simple mathematical expressions that yield the value of the waveform explicitly at every instant of time. In many cases, the input signals are *random* functions of time and, hence, the system response will also be random. (The term random is being used loosely here to imply an irregular variation with time that cannot be predicted in advance. This concept is not quite correct, and the terminology will be made more precise in a later section.) This raises the important question as to whether any meaningful system analysis is possible when one cannot write precise mathematical expressions for the quantities of interest. In general, the answer to this question is that analysis is possible if one is willing to accept results that are less explicit than complete time functions. The purpose of the following discussion is to explore some of the possible results and to discover their significance.

In order to carry out the analysis for random signals, it is necessary to have suitable methods for representing these signals mathematically. Hence, most of the discussion will deal with this problem. Once a suitable mathematical representation is available, the actual system analysis is done in exactly the same way as in the case of explicit signals, since the input-output relationships of a linear system do not depend upon the actual form of the signal.

Although the study of random signals is primarily mathematical in nature, it is important to be able to relate the mathematics to physical quantities. Therefore, it is desirable to have in mind some physical situations in which random signals arise. Although there are many such situations involving engineering systems of various types, only a few will be noted here.

If, for example, the output of a high-gain amplifier is connected to a loudspeaker, one frequently hears a variety of snaps, crackles, and pops. This random *noise* arises from thermal motion of the conduction electrons in the amplifier input circuit or from random variations in the number of electrons (or holes) passing through the tubes and transistors. It is obvious that one could not hope to calculate the value of this noise at every instant of time since this value represents the combined effects of literally billions of individual moving charges. It *is* possible, however, to calculate the average power of this noise, its frequency spectrum, and even the probability of observing a noise value larger than some specified value. As a practical matter, these quantities are more important in determining the quality of the amplifier than is a knowledge of the instantaneous waveforms.

As a second example, consider a radio or television receiver. In addition to noise generated within the receiver by the mechanisms noted, there is random noise arriving at the antenna. This results from distant electrical storms, man-made disturbances, radiation from space, or thermal radiation from surrounding objects. Hence, even if perfect receivers and amplifiers were available, the received signal would be combined with random noise. Again, the calculation of such quantities as average power and frequency spectrum may be more significant than the determination of instantaneous value.

A different type of system is illustrated by a large radar antenna, which may be pointed in any direction by means of an automatic control system. The wind blowing on the antenna will produce random forces that must be compensated for by the control system. Since the compensation is never perfect there will always be some random fluctuation in the antenna direction; it is important to be able to calculate the effective value of this fluctuation.

A still different situation is illustrated by an airplane flying in turbulent air, a ship sailing in stormy seas, or an army truck traveling over rough terrain. In all these cases random forces acting on complex mechanical systems interfere with the proper control or guidance of the system. It is important to be able to determine how the system responds to these random input signals.

The foregoing examples were selected to illustrate the point that many different types of systems are subjected to a variety of different random inputs in normal operation. In fact, it would be difficult, if not impossible, to find any kind of dynamic system that does not have random inputs of significant magnitude. Hence, although the study of the response of these systems to random inputs involves somewhat more abstract mathematics, this study is actually the link needed to tie system analysis to physical reality. There are two general methods of describing random signals mathematically. The first, and most basic, is a probabilistic description in which the random quantity is characterized by a *probability model.* This method will be discussed in the remainder of the present chapter.

The probabilistic description of random signals cannot be used directly in system analysis since it tells very little about how the random signal varies with time or what its frequency spectrum is. It does, however, lead to the statistical description of random signals, which is useful in system analysis. In this case the random signal is characterized by a *statistical model,* which consists of an appropriate set of average values such as the mean, variance, correlation function, spectral density, and others. These averages represent a less precise description of the random signal than that offered by the probability model, but they are more useful for system analysis because they can be computed by using the analysis methods already discussed. Some of the statistical averages will be discussed in the present chapter and others will be considered in subsequent chapters.

9-2　Basic Concepts of Probability

The purpose of this section is to discuss some of the concepts of probability that are as needed as a basis for the applications which follow. It should be emphasized, however, that this very brief discussion of probability is no substitute for a more formal study of the subject. Since most system analysis is based on a statistical model of the random signal, the only purpose for a discussion of probability is to make more evident how this statistical model is obtained. Only a small fraction of the total body of probability theory is needed for this purpose, and is all that will be considered here. Hence, there are many important aspects of probability theory that will not be mentioned at all, but which should be familiar to the engineer. It is hoped that this introduction to probability and its subsequent applications will motivate the reader to undertake the more formal study essential to the modern engineer.

The concept of probability is closely linked with the frequency of occurrence of some particular event.[1] When dealing with random time functions, the event may be the observation of this function within a given range of values at a given time. The frequency of occurrence is obtained by considering all possible time functions that might have existed in a given physical situation and determining what fraction of these will be observed in the given range of values at the given time. This fraction is the *probability* of the given event. Obviously, this is not an experiment that can be performed in the laboratory, or anywhere else, since *all possible* time functions are not available. It can be imagined, however, and as such provides a physical picture for the concept of *random events*.

Although our major interest will eventually be in connection with random time functions having a continuous range of possible values, some of the basic concepts of probability can be introduced more easily and more understandably by considering situations in which only a finite number of different things can happen. This represents the special case of *discrete probability,* which usually provides the starting point for typical probability discussions. All of the terminology and methods of calculating average values can be derived for the discrete case and then carried over to the continuous case with only minor changes. However, since our objective is entirely concerned with the continuous case, we will not follow this procedure but will consider the discrete case only long enough to clarify the significance of the most important basic concept in probability; that of the *event*.

An event is something that may happen, or may not happen. For example, if a coin is tossed the result may be a "head" or a "tail" and each of these is an event. If a die is rolled, the result may be a "one," or a "two," or any other of the numbers up to six; each of these results is also an event. It is also possible to define more complicated events in connection with these simple experiments. In the case of rolling the die, for example, we may choose to define the event of obtaining a number

---

[1] Modern treatment of probability tends to regard it as an undefined concept. The probability of an event is simply a number associated with that event and operations with this number are carried out by means of a self-consistent set of axioms. The "frequency" concept employed here attempts to attach some physical significance to these operations and axioms but cannot be considered as a rigorously correct definition of probability.

greater than three, or the event of obtaining an even number, or any of a large number of other possible events.

It is also possible to conduct more complicated experiments with more complicated sets of events. For example, the experiment may consist of tossing ten coins, and it is apparent in this case that there are many different possible outcomes, each of which is an event. Another situation, which has more of an engineering flavor, is that of a telephone system having 10,000 telephones connected to it. At any given time, a possible event is that 2000 of these telephones are in use. Obviously, there are a great many other possible events.

Whenever the outcome of an experiment is uncertain, *before* the experiment is performed, the set of possible outcomes are *random events*. To each of these events it is possible to assign a number, called the *probability of that event*, and this number is a measure of how likely that event is. Usually, these numbers are *assumed,* the assumed values being based on our physical intuition about the experiment. For example, if we toss a coin, we would expect that the possible outcomes of "heads" and "tails" would be equally likely. Therefore, we would assume the probabilities of these two events to be the same.

It was noted earlier that probability could be related to the relative frequency with which an event occurred. Thus, in tossing a coin, we would expect a "head" to occur half the time and a "tail" half the time. Hence, we would assign a probability of one half to each of these events. More generally, if an experiment is performed N times and we *expect* event A to occur N_A times, then we would assume the probability of event A, $P(A)$, to be

$$P(A) = \frac{N_A}{N} \tag{9-1}$$

Note that N_A is not the *actual* number of times that event A occurs in N trials, but only the number we *assume* would occur on the basis of our physical intuition about the experiment. We could evaluate the validity of our assumption by actually performing the experiment and observing the number of times, N'_A, the event A occurs. If our assumption was correct, then the ratio N'_A/N should approach $P(A)$ as N becomes large. But making an evaluation of this sort is a problem of statistics rather than probability and need not concern us here.

The relative-frequency approach to probability does make evident a number of important properties of probability. Since both N_A and N are positive, real numbers and N_A must be less than or equal to N; it follows that a probability cannot be less than zero nor greater than unity. Furthermore, suppose the experiment has M possible outcomes, only *one* of which can occur on any given trial. The possible events are said to be *mutually exclusive.* If we expect event A to occur N_A times out of N

$$N_A + N_B + N_C + \cdots + N_M = N$$

or

$$\frac{N_A}{N} + \frac{N_B}{N} + \frac{N_C}{N} + \cdots + \frac{N_M}{N} = 1$$

From the relation given above, it follows that

$$P(A) + P(B) + P(C) + \cdots + P(M) = 1 \qquad \text{(9-2)}$$

and we can conclude that the sum of the probabilities of *all* of the mutually exclusive events associated with a given experiment must be unity.

These concepts can be summarized by the following set of statements:

1. $0 \leq P(A) \leq 1$
2. $P(A) + P(B) + P(C) + \cdots + P(M) = 1$, for a complete set of mutually exclusive events
3. An *impossible event* is represented by $P(A) = 0$
4. A *certain event* is represented by $P(A) = 1$

In order to make some of these ideas more concrete, consider the following hypothetical example. Assume that a large bin contains an assortment of resistors of different sizes, which are thoroughly mixed together. In particular, let there be 100 resistors having a marked value of 1 Ω, 500 resistors marked 10 Ω, 150 resistors marked 100 Ω, and 250 resistors marked 1000 Ω. Someone reaches into the bin and pulls out one resistor at random. There are now four possible outcomes corresponding to the value of the particular resistor selected. We would like to determine the probability of each of these events. In order to do this, we *assume* that the probability of each event is proportional to the number of resistors in the bin corresponding to that event. Since there are 1000 resistors in the bin all together, the resulting probabilities are:

$$P(1\ \Omega) = \frac{100}{1000} = 0.1 \qquad P(10\ \Omega) = \frac{500}{1000} = 0.5$$

$$P(100\ \Omega) = \frac{150}{1000} = 0.15 \qquad P(1000\ \Omega) = \frac{250}{1000} = 0.25$$

Note that these probabilities are all positive, less than 1.0, but do add up to 1.0.

Many times one is interested in more than one event at a time. For example, a coin may be tossed twice and one is interested in the probability that a "head" will occur on *both* tosses. Such a probability is referred to as a *joint probability*. In this particular case, one would *assume* that all four possible outcomes (HH, HT, TH, and TT) are equally likely and, hence, the probability of each would be one quarter. In a more general case the situation is not this simple, so it is necessary to look at a more complicated situation in order to deduce the true nature of joint probability. The notation to be employed is $P(A, B)$ and signifies the probability of the *joint* occurrence of events A and B.

Consider again the bin full of resistors and specify that in addition to having different resistance values, they also have different power ratings. Let the different power ratings be 1 watt, 2 watts, and 5 watts and indicate the number having each rating in Table 9-1.

Table 9-1

| POWER RATING | RESISTANCE VALUES | | | | |
	1 Ω	10 Ω	100 Ω	1000 Ω	TOTALS
1 W	50	300	90	0	440
2 W	50	50	0	100	200
5 W	0	150	60	150	360
Totals	100	500	150	250	1000

Before using this example to illustrate joint probabilities, consider the probability (now referred to as a *marginal probability*) of selecting a resistor having a given power rating without regard to its resistance value. From the totals given in the right-hand column, it is clear that these probabilities are

$$P(1 \text{ W}) = \frac{440}{1000} = 0.44 \qquad P(2 \text{ W}) = \frac{200}{1000} = 0.20$$

$$P(5 \text{ W}) = \frac{360}{1000} = 0.36$$

We now ask the question, "What is the joint probability of selecting a resistor of 10 ohms having a 5-watt power rating?" Since there are 150 such resistors in the bin, this joint probability is clearly

$$P(10 \text{ Ω}, 5 \text{ W}) = \frac{150}{1000} = 0.15$$

The eleven other joint probabilities can be determined in a similar way. Note that some of the joint probabilities are zero [for example, $P(1 \text{ Ω}, 5 \text{ W}) = 0$] simply because a particular combination of resistance and power does not exist.

It is necessary at this point to relate the joint probabilities to the marginal probabilities. In the example of tossing a coin two times, the relationship was simply a product. That is, for example,

$$P(H, H) = P(H)P(H) = \frac{1}{2} \times \frac{1}{2} = \frac{1}{4}$$

But this relationship is obviously not true for the resistor bin example. Note that

$$P(5 \text{ W}) = \frac{360}{1000} = 0.36$$

and it was previously shown that

$$P(10 \ \Omega) = 0.5$$

Thus

$$P(10 \ \Omega)P(5 \text{ W}) = 0.5 \times 0.36 = 0.18 \neq P(10 \ \Omega, 5 \text{ W}) = 0.15$$

and the joint probability is *not* the product of the marginal probabilities.

In order to clarify this point, it is necessary to introduce the concept of *conditional probability*. This is the probability of one event A, *given* that another event B has occurred; it will be designated as $P(A|B)$. In terms of the resistor bin, consider the conditional probability of selecting a 10 Ω resistor when it is already known that the chosen resistor is 5 W. Since there are 360 5-W resistors, and 150 of these are 10 Ω, the required conditional probability is

$$P(10 \ \Omega|5\text{W}) = \frac{150}{360} = 0.417$$

Now consider the product of this conditional probability and the marginal probability of selecting a 5-W resistor.

$$P(10 \ \Omega|5\text{W})P(5 \text{ W}) = 0.417 \times 0.36 = 0.15 = P(10 \ \Omega, 5 \text{ W})$$

It is seen that this product is indeed the joint probability.

The same result can also be obtained another way. Consider the conditional probability

$$P(5\text{W}|10 \ \Omega) = \frac{150}{500} = 0.30$$

since there are 150 5-W resistors out of the 500 10-Ω resistors. Then form the product

$$P(5\text{W}|10 \ \Omega) \ P(10 \ \Omega) = 0.30 \times 0.5 = 0.15 = P(10 \ \Omega, 5\text{W}) \qquad \text{(9-3)}$$

Again, the product is the joint probability.

The foregoing ideas concerning joint probability can be summarized in the general equation

$$P(A, B) = P(A|B)P(B) = P(B|A)P(A) \qquad \text{(9-4)}$$

which indicates that the joint probability of two events can always be expressed as the product of the marginal probability of one event and the conditional probability of the other event, given the first event.

We now return to the coin-tossing problem, in which it was indicated that the joint probability could be obtained as the product of two marginal probabilities. Under what conditions will this be true? From (9-4) it appears that this can be true if

$$P(A|B) = P(A) \quad \text{and} \quad P(B|A) = P(B)$$

These statements imply that the probability of event A does not depend upon whether event B has occurred or not. This is certainly true in coin tossing, since the outcome of the second toss cannot be influenced in any way by the outcome of the first toss. Such events are said to be *statistically independent*. More precisely, two random events are statistically independent if and only if

$$P(A, B) = P(A)P(B) \tag{9-5}$$

There are many other aspects of discrete probability that should be discussed in order for us to have a thorough understanding of probability theory, but the foregoing notions are the ones essential for the applications to be covered in this book. The next step, therefore, is to extend these notions to the case of continuous random variables. The essential difference between the continuous case and the discrete case is the manner in which events must be defined. Consider, for example, the probability of selecting a 20-Ω resistor from a bin full of resistors all marked 20 Ω. Because of manufacturing tolerances, each of the resistors in the bin will have a slightly different resistance. Even if all of the resistance values actually lie between 19.99 Ω and 20.01 Ω, there is an infinite number of such values in this region. Hence the probability that the selected resistor will have a resistance of exactly 20.00 $\cdots$ Ω will be zero, and it makes no sense to talk about this event. As an alternative, one could talk about the event that the selected resistor will have a resistance between any two specified values such as 19.9999 Ω and 20.0001 Ω. This event will occur with a nonzero probability.

9-3 Random Variables

For purposes of system analysis, the random variables are associated with random functions of time. There are many other physical quantities that may also be random variables but do not depend upon time. In the preceding example, for instance, the value of the resistance is a random variable that does not depend upon time. However, our major interest is in random time functions and thus, unless otherwise specified, all random variables will be assumed to be associated with such a time function.

A typical random time function, shown in Fig. 9-1, is designated as

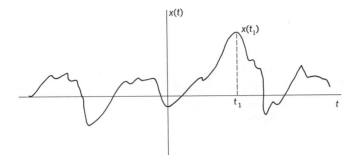

Figure 9-1 A random time function.

$x(t)$. In a given physical situation, this particular time function is only one of an infinite number of time functions that *might* have occurred. The collection of all possible time functions that might have been observed belong to a *random process,* which will be designated as $\{x(t)\}$, for example. When the probability functions are also specified, this collection is referred to as an *ensemble*. Any particular member of the ensemble, say $x(t)$, is a *sample function* and the value of a sample function at some particular time is a *random variable;* for example, $X_1 = x(t_1)$.

A random variable associated with a random process is a considerably more involved concept than the random variable associated with the resistor in the preceding section. In the first place, there is a different random variable for each instant of time, although there usually is some relation between two random variables corresponding to two different time instants. In the second place, the randomness we are concerned with is the randomness that exists from sample function to sample function throughout the complete ensemble. There may also be randomness from time instant to time instant, but this is *not* an essential ingredient of a random process. Therefore, the probability description of the random variables being considered here is also the probability description of the random process. However, our initial discussion will concentrate on the random variables and will be extended later to the process.

If a random variable can assume *any* value within a specified range (possibly infinite), then it will be designated as a *continuous* random variable. In the following discussion all random variables will be assumed to be continuous unless stated otherwise. It will be shown, however, that *discrete* random variables (that is, those assuming one of a countable set of values) can also be treated by exactly the same methods.

9-4 Distribution Functions

Let X be a random variable as defined above and x be any allowed value of this random variable. The *probability distribution function* is defined to be the probability of the event that the observed random variable X is less than or equal to the allowed value x. That is,

$$P(x) = \text{Prob } (X \leq x)$$

The symbol $P(\;)$, which was used previously to designate the probability of any event, will now be restricted to the particular event associated with the probability distribution function.[2]

Since the probability of an event must be positive and less than or equal to unity, the probability distribution function has the following general properties:

1. $0 \leq P(x) \leq 1$ $-\infty < x < \infty$
2. $P(-\infty) = 0$ $P(\infty) = 1$
3. $P(x)$ is *nondecreasing* as x increases
4. Prob $(x_1 < X \leq x_2) = P(x_2) - P(x_1)$

Some possible distribution functions are shown in Fig. 9-2. The

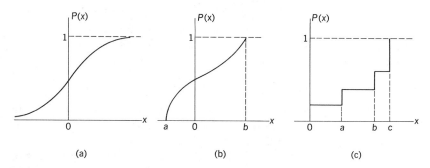

Figure 9-2   Some possible probability distribution functions.

sketch in (a) indicates a continuous random variable having possible values ranging from $-\infty$ to ∞ while (b) shows a continuous random variable for which the possible values lie between a and b. The sketch in (c) shows the probability distribution function for a discrete random variable which can assume only 4 possible values (that is, 0, a, b, or c).

---

[2] There are many different notations in common use in the engineering and mathematical literature, and the same symbol may mean different things for different authors. It is advisable to check the definitions in each case.

9-5 Density Functions

Although the distribution function is a complete description of the probability model for a single random variable, it is not the most convenient
form for many calculations of interest. Instead, it may be preferable to
use the derivative of $P(x)$ rather than $P(x)$ itself. This derivative is called
the *probability density function* and, when it exists, is defined by

$$p(x) = \lim_{\epsilon \to 0} \frac{P(x + \epsilon) - P(x)}{\epsilon} = \frac{dP(x)}{dx}$$

The physical significance of the probability density function is best described in terms of the *probability element, p(x) dx*. This may be interpreted as

$$p(x)\, dx = \text{Prob } (x < X \le x + dx) \tag{9-6}$$

Equation (9-6) simply states that the probability element, $p(x)\, dx$, is the
probability of the event that the random variable X lies in the range of
possible values between x and $x + dx$.

Since $p(x)$ is a density function and not a probability, it is not necessary that its value be less than 1; it may have any non-negative value.
Its general properties may be summarized as follows:

1. $p(x) \ge 0 \qquad -\infty < x < \infty$

2. $\displaystyle\int_{-\infty}^{\infty} p(x)\, dx = 1$

3. $\displaystyle P(x) = \int_{-\infty}^{x} p(u)\, du$

4. $\displaystyle\int_{x_1}^{x_2} p(x)\, dx = \text{Prob } (x_1 < X \le x_2)$

As examples of probability density functions, those corresponding to
the distribution functions of Fig. 9-2 are shown in Fig. 9-3. Note particu-

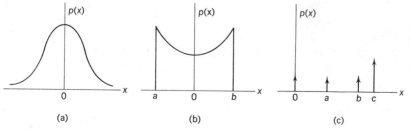

Figure 9-3 Probability density functions corresponding to the distribution functions of Fig. 9-2.

larly that the density function for a discrete random variable consists of a set of delta functions. It is also possible to have density functions which contain both a continuous part and one or more delta functions.

There are many different mathematical forms that might be probability density functions, but only a very few of these arise in the analysis of engineering systems to any significant extent. Some of these are shown in Table 9-2.

Table 9-2 SOME COMMON PROBABILITY DENSITY FUNCTIONS.

NAME	DENSITY FUNCTION, $p(x)$	RANGE OF VARIABLE
Gaussian (Normal)	$\dfrac{1}{\sqrt{2\pi}\,\sigma}\epsilon^{-(x-\bar{x})^2/2\sigma^2}$	$-\infty < x < \infty$
Rayleigh	$\dfrac{x}{\eta^2}\epsilon^{-x^2/2\eta^2}$	$0 \leq x < \infty$
Exponential	$\alpha\epsilon^{-\alpha x}$	$0 \leq x < \infty$
Uniform	$\dfrac{1}{x_2 - x_1}$	$x_1 \leq x \leq x_2$

9-6 Mean Values and Moments

One of the most important and most fundamental concepts associated with statistical methods is that of finding average values of random variables or functions of random variables. The concepts of finding average values for time functions by integrating over some time interval is a familiar one to electrical engineers, since operations of this sort are used to find the dc component, the root-mean-square value, or the average power of the time function. Such time averages may also be important for random functions of time, but, of course, have no meaning when considering a single random variable, which is defined as the value of the time function at a single instant of time. Instead, it is necessary to find the average value by integrating over the range of possible values that the random variable may assume. Such an operation is referred to as "ensemble averaging," and the result is the *mean value*.

Several different notations are in standard use for the mean value but the most common ones in the engineering literature[3] are

$$\bar{x} = E[x] = \int_{-\infty}^{\infty} xp(x)\,dx \tag{9-7}$$

[3] It is customary in engineering literature to make no distinction between a random variable X and the values x that it may assume. Although this custom is not mathematically correct, it will be employed in much of the following discussion as a means of simplifying notation in situations which will not lead to ambiguity.

The symbol $E[x]$ is usually read "the expected value of x" or "the mathematical expectation of x." It will be shown later that in many cases of practical interest the mean value of a random variable is identical to the time average of any sample function from the random process to which the random variable belongs. In such cases, finding the mean value of a random voltage or current is equivalent to finding its dc component; this interpretation will be employed here for purposes of illustration.

The expected value of any function of x can also be obtained by a similar calculation. Thus,

$$E[f(x)] = \int_{-\infty}^{\infty} f(x)p(x) \, dx \tag{9-8}$$

A function of particular importance is $f(x) = x^n$, since this leads to the general *moments* of the random variable. Thus,

$$\overline{x^n} = E[x^n] = \int_{-\infty}^{\infty} x^n p(x) \, dx \tag{9-9}$$

By far the most important moments of x are those given by $n = 1$, which is the mean value discussed above, and by $n = 2$, which leads to the *mean-square value*.

$$\overline{x^2} = E[x^2] = \int_{-\infty}^{\infty} x^2 p(x) \, dx \tag{9-10}$$

The importance of the mean-square value lies in the fact that it may often be interpreted as being equal to the time average of the square of a random voltage or current. In such cases, the mean-square value is proportional to the *average power* (in a resistor) and its square root is equal to the *rms* or *effective* value of the random voltage or current.

It is also possible to define *central moments,* which are simply the moments of the *difference* between a random variable and its mean value. Thus, the nth central moment is

$$\overline{(x - \bar{x})^n} = E[(x - \bar{x})^n] = \int_{-\infty}^{\infty} (x - \bar{x})^n p(x) \, dx \tag{9-11}$$

The central moment for $n = 1$ is, of course, zero, while the central moment for $n = 2$ is so important that it carries a special name, the *variance,* and is usually symbolized by σ^2. Thus,

$$\sigma^2 = \overline{(x - \bar{x})^2} = \int_{-\infty}^{\infty} (x - \bar{x})^2 p(x) \, dx \tag{9-12}$$

The variance can also be expressed in an alternative form by using the rules for the expectations of sums; that is,

$$E[x_1 + x_2 + \cdots + x_m] = E[x_1] + E[x_2] + \cdots + E[x_m]$$

Thus

$$\sigma^2 = E[(x - \bar{x})^2] = E[x^2 - 2x\bar{x} + \bar{x}^2]$$
$$= E[x^2] - 2E[x]\bar{x} + \bar{x}^2$$
$$= \overline{x^2} - 2\bar{x}\bar{x} + \bar{x}^2 = \overline{x^2} - \bar{x}^2$$

(9-13)

and it is seen that the variance is the difference between the mean-square value and the square of the mean value.

In electrical circuits the variance can often be related to the average power (in a resistance) of the ac components of a voltage or current. The square root of the variance would be the value indicated by an ac voltmeter or ammeter of the rms type which does not respond to direct current (because of capacitive coupling, for example).

In order to illustrate some of the above ideas concerning mean values and moments consider a random variable having a uniform probability density function as shown in Fig. 9-4. A voltage waveform that would

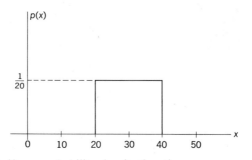

Figure 9-4 A uniform probability density function.

have such a probability density function might be a sawtooth waveform which varied linearly between 20 and 40 volts. The appropriate mathematical representation for this density function is

$$p(x) = 0 \qquad -\infty < x < 20$$

$$= \frac{1}{20} \qquad 20 \leq x \leq 40$$

$$= 0 \qquad 40 < x < \infty$$

The mean value of this random variable is obtained by using (9-7). Thus,

$$\bar{x} = \int_{20}^{40} x\left(\frac{1}{20}\right) dx = \frac{1}{20} \cdot \frac{x^2}{2}\bigg]_{20}^{40} = \frac{1}{40}(1600 - 400) = 30$$

This value is intuitively the average value of the sawtooth waveform just described. The mean-square value is obtained from (9-10) as:

$$\overline{x^2} = \int_{20}^{40} x^2 \left(\frac{1}{20}\right) dx = \frac{1}{20} \frac{x^3}{3} \Bigg]_{20}^{40} = \frac{1}{60} (64 - 8)10^3 = 933.3$$

The variance of the random variable can be obtained from either (9-12) or (9-13). From the latter,

$$\sigma^2 = \overline{x^2} - (\overline{x})^2 = 933.3 - (30)^2 = 33.3$$

On the basis of the assumptions that will be made concerning random processes, if the sawtooth voltage were measured with a dc voltmeter, the reading would be 30 volts. If it were measured with an rms-reading ac voltmeter (which did not respond to dc), the reading would be $\sqrt{33.3}$ volts.

9-7 The Gaussian Random Variable

Of the various density functions listed in Table 9-2, the most important by far is the Gaussian or normal density function. There are many reasons for this importance, some of which are:

1. It provides a good mathematical model for a great many different physically observed random phenomena. Furthermore, the fact that it should be a good model can be justified theoretically in many cases.

2. It is one of the few density functions that can be extended to handle an arbitrarily large number of random variables conveniently.

3. Linear combinations of Gaussian random variables lead to new random variables that are also Gaussian. This is not true for most other density functions.

4. The random process from which Gaussian random variables are derived can be *completely* specified, in a statistical sense, from a knowledge of all first and second moments only. This is not true for other processes.

5. In system analysis, the Gaussian process is often the only one for which a complete statistical analysis can be carried through in either the linear or nonlinear situation.

From Table 9-2 it is seen that the Gaussian density function is given by

$$p(x) = \frac{1}{\sqrt{2\pi}\,\sigma} \exp \left[\frac{-(x - \bar{x})^2}{2\sigma^2}\right] \qquad -\infty < x < \infty \qquad \textbf{(9-14)}$$

where $\bar{x}$ and σ^2 are the mean and variance, respectively. The corresponding distribution function cannot be written in closed form. The shapes of the density function and distribution function are shown in Fig. 9-5.

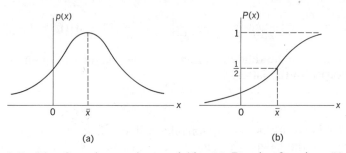

Figure 9-5 The Gaussian random variable. **(a)** Density function. **(b)** Distribution function.

Although most of the results to be obtained in the analysis of linear systems do not depend upon the type of density function assumed, a few of them do. In these cases, the Gaussian random variable will be assumed.

9-8 Two Random Variables

In analyzing the response of linear systems to random inputs one must be able to specify the relationship between two random variables. These random variables may come from different random processes, or they may come from the same process at different instants of time. The first situation would arise, for example, when one attempts to relate the output of a system to its input. The second situation arises if one attempts to relate present or future values of a sample function to past values. In either case it is necessary to establish a probability model for the joint occurrence of two random events.

Let the two random variables be designated as X and Y, with the understanding that they may be either from two different processes or from the same process at different times. In later usage, the distinction between these two situations will be made clear by the notation, but for the present discussion a general notation is more convenient. It is now possible to define a *joint probability distribution function* as

$$P(x, y) = \text{Prob} \left(X \leq x, Y \leq y \right) \tag{9-15}$$

In words, this says that $P(x, y)$ is the probability associated with the joint occurrence of the event that the random variable X is less than or equal to a possible value x *and* the event that the random variable Y is less than or equal to a possible value y.

As an example of the physical significance of this function, let $X = x(t_1)$ be the voltage at the input of the system at time t_1 and $Y = y(t_1)$ be the voltage at the output of the system at the same time. Then $P(10, 5)$, say, would be the probability of the event that the input voltage is less than or equal to 10 volts *and* that the output voltage is less than or equal to 5 volts at the same time.

The properties of the joint distribution function may be summarized as follows:

  1. $0 \le P(x, y) \le 1 \quad -\infty < x < \infty, \quad -\infty < y < \infty$
  2. $P(-\infty, y) = P(x, -\infty) = P(-\infty, -\infty) = 0$
  3. $P(\infty, \infty) = 1$
  4. $P(x, y)$ is a nondecreasing function as either x or y, or both, increase
  5. $P(\infty, y) = P_y(y), \quad P(x, \infty) = P_x(x)$

In item 5 above, the subscripts on $P_y(y)$ and $P_x(x)$ are introduced to indicate that these are not necessarily the *same* function of their respective arguments. These distribution functions are in all respects the same as the distribution function discussed in Section 9-4 for a single random variable. However, when obtained from a joint distribution function they are frequently designated as the *marginal distribution functions*.

Joint probability density functions can also be defined as

$$p(x, y) = \frac{\partial^2 P(x, y)}{\partial x \, \partial y} \tag{9-16}$$

and have the physical significance that the probability element is

$$p(x, y) \, dx \, dy = \text{Prob} \, [x < X \le x + dx, \, y < Y \le y + dy] \tag{9-17}$$

The properties of the joint density function are:

  1. $p(x, y) \ge 0 \quad -\infty < x < \infty, \quad -\infty < y < \infty$

  2. $\displaystyle\int_{-\infty}^{\infty} dx \int_{-\infty}^{\infty} p(x, y) \, dy = 1$

  3. $P(x, y) = \displaystyle\int_{-\infty}^{x} du \int_{-\infty}^{y} p(u, v) \, dv$

  4. $p_x(x) = \displaystyle\int_{-\infty}^{\infty} p(x, y) \, dy, \quad p_y(y) = \int_{-\infty}^{\infty} p(x, y) \, dx$

  5. $\displaystyle\int_{x_1}^{x_2} dx \int_{y_1}^{y_2} p(x, y) \, dy = \text{Prob} \, (x_1 < X \le x_2, \, y_1 < Y \le y_2)$

The joint distribution and density functions can be represented pictorially as surfaces over an x-y plane. As a simple illustration of this, consider a pair of random variables having a uniform joint density function; that is,

$$p(x, y) = \frac{1}{(x_2 - x_1)(y_2 - y_1)} \quad \begin{matrix} x_1 \le x \le x_2 \\ \\ y_1 \le y \le y_2 \end{matrix} \tag{9-18}$$
$$= 0 \qquad\qquad\qquad\qquad \text{elsewhere}$$

This density function and the corresponding distribution function are shown in Fig. 9-6.

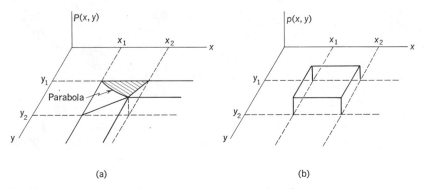

(a)   (b)

Figure 9-6   (a) Joint distribution and (b) density functions.

The joint probability density function can be used to find the expected value of functions of the two random variables. One such expected value, which will be discussed in much more detail later, is

$$E[xy] = \int_{-\infty}^{\infty} dx \int_{-\infty}^{\infty} xy p(x, y) \, dy \qquad \text{(9-19)}$$

As a simple example of this calculation, consider the joint density function given by (9-18). Since it is zero everywhere except in the specified region, (9-19) may be written as

$$E[xy] = \int_{x_1}^{x_2} dx \int_{y_1}^{y_2} xy \left[\frac{1}{(x_2 - x_1)(y_2 - y_1)} \right] dy$$

$$= \frac{1}{(x_2 - x_1)(y_2 - y_1)} \left[\frac{x^2}{2} \Big|_{x_1}^{x_2} \right] \left[\frac{y^2}{2} \Big|_{y_1}^{y_2} \right] \qquad \text{(9-20)}$$

$$= \tfrac{1}{4}(x_2 + x_1)(y_2 + y_1)$$

It is of interest to note that in this particular case the expected value is simply the *product* of the *mean values* of the two random variables. This is a consequence of the fact that these two random variables are *statistically independent*. The concept of statistical independence is considered in more detail in the following section.

9-9   Statistical Independence

A special condition that frequently arises when we are dealing with two random variables is that they do not depend upon each other in any way. This is almost always true when the random variables come from different sources. For example, the random thermal voltage generated by one resistor in a circuit is in no way related to the thermal voltage generated by another resistor. It may also be true when the random variables come from the same source but are defined at greatly different times. For example, the thermal voltage generated in a resistor tomorrow almost certainly does not depend upon the voltage today. One property of random variables which assures that they are unrelated is that they be *statistically independent*. When two random variables are statistically independent, a knowledge of one random variable gives no information about the value of the other.

The joint probability density function for statistically independent random variables can always be factored into the two marginal density functions. Thus, the relationship

$$p(x, y) = p_x(x)p_y(y) \tag{9-21}$$

can be used as a definition for statistical independence, since it can be shown that this factorization is both a necessary and sufficient condition. As an example, this condition is satisfied by the joint density function given in (9-18). Hence, these two random variables are statistically independent.

An important special case which arises is that of statistically independent Gaussian random variables. If these random variables have mean values of $\bar{x}$ and $\bar{y}$ and variances of σ_x^2 and σ_y^2, then from (9-14) and (9-21) the joint density function can be written as

$$p(x, y) = \frac{1}{2\pi\sigma_x\sigma_y} \exp\left\{ -\frac{1}{2}\left[\frac{(x - \bar{x})^2}{\sigma_x^2} + \frac{(y - \bar{y})^2}{\sigma_y^2} \right] \right\} \tag{9-22}$$

Another important property that statistically independent random variables possess concerns the expected value of their product. Thus, from (9-19)

$$E[xy] = \int_{-\infty}^{\infty} dx \int_{-\infty}^{\infty} xyp(x, y)\, dy = \int_{-\infty}^{\infty} dx \int_{-\infty}^{\infty} xyp_x(x)p_y(y)\, dy \tag{9-23}$$

$$= \int_{-\infty}^{\infty} xp_x(x)\, dx \int_{-\infty}^{\infty} yp_y(y)\, dy = \bar{x}\,\bar{y}$$

In words, this result says that the expected value of the product of two statistically independent random variables is just the product of their mean values. The result will be zero, of course, if *either* random variable has zero mean.

9-10 Random Processes

A *random process* was previously stated to be a collection of time functions that becomes an ensemble if there is a suitable probability description by which we may determine the probability that any one member of the ensemble has certain observable properties. So far the discussion has been limited to considering random variables that are point functions of the process at specified time instants. It will be shown later, that in the analysis of linear systems it is often necessary to consider only two random variables (that is, the process at only two instants of time) *provided* that the time interval between these instants is arbitrary. Hence, the extension of the concepts of random variables to that of random processes is fairly simple insofar as the mechanics of doing it is concerned; in fact, all of the essential ideas have already been considered.

A much more difficult step, however, is the conceptual one of relating the mathematical representations for random variables to the physical properties of the process. First it is necessary to define some more terminology and to illustrate it by means of examples. In discussing the terminology it is convenient to consider a set of names, arranged in pairs, and to select one name from each pair to describe the process. Those pairs of names that are appropriate to the present discussion are:

1. Continuous; discrete
2. Deterministic; nondeterministic
3. Stationary; nonstationary
4. Ergodic; nonergodic

9-11   Continuous and Discrete Random Processes

These terms normally apply to the possible values of the random variables. A *continuous random process* is one in which random variables such as $x(t_1)$, $x(t_2)$, and so on, can assume *any* value within a specified range of possible values. This range may be finite, infinite, or semi-infinite. Such things as thermal agitation noise in conductors, shot noise in electron tubes or transistors, and wind velocity are examples of continuous random processes. A sketch of a typical sample function and the corresponding probability density function are shown in Fig. 9-7. In this example, the range of possible values is semi-infinite.

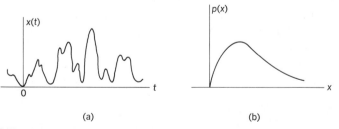

(a)   (b)

Figure 9-7   A continuous random process. **(a)** Typical sample function. **(b)** Probability density function.

A more precise definition for continuous random processes would be that the probability distribution function is continuous. This would also imply that the density function has no δ functions in it.

A *discrete random process* is one in which the random variables can assume only certain specified values (possibly infinite in number) and no other values. For example, a voltage that is either 0 or 100 because of randomly opening and closing a switch would be a sample function from a discrete random process. This example is illustrated in Fig. 9-8. Note that the probability density function contains *only* δ functions.

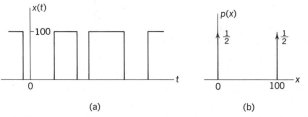

(a)   (b)

Figure 9-8 A discrete random process. **(a)** Typical sample function. **(b)** Probability density function.

It is also possible to have *mixed* processes, which have both continuous and discrete components. For example, the current flowing in an ideal rectifier may be zero for one half the time, as shown in Fig. 9-9. The corresponding probability density has both a continuous part and a δ function.

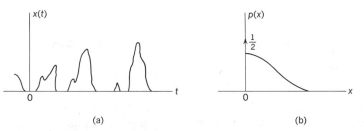

(a)   (b)

Figure 9-9 A mixed random process. **(a)** Typical sample function. **(b)** Probability density function.

In all of the cases just mentioned, the sample functions are continuous in *time*; that is, a random variable may be defined for any time. Situations in which the random variables exist for certain discrete times only (referred to as *point processes* or *time series*) will not be discussed here.

9-12 Deterministic and Nondeterministic Random Processes

In most of the discussion so far, it has been implied that each sample function is a random function of time and, as such, its future values cannot be exactly predicted from the observed past values. Such a random process is said to be *nondeterministic*. Almost all natural random processes are nondeterministic, because the basic mechanism that generates them is either unobservable or extremely complex. All of the examples presented in Section 9-11 are nondeterministic.

It is possible, however, to define random processes for which the future values of any sample function can be exactly predicted from a knowledge of all past values. Such a process is said to be *deterministic*. As an example, consider a random process for which each sample function of the process is of the form

$$x(t) = A \cos (\omega t + \theta) \qquad \text{(9-24)}$$

where A and ω are constants and θ is a random variable with a specified probability distribution. That is, for any one sample function, θ has a given value for all t, but it has different values for the other members of the ensemble. In this case, the only random variation is over the ensemble — not with respect to time. It is still possible to define random variables $x(t_1)$, $x(t_2)$, etc., and to determine probability density functions for them.

Although the concept of deterministic random processes may seem a little artificial, it often is convenient to employ it as a means of obtaining a probability model for signals that are known except for one or two parameters. The process described by (9-24), for example, may be suitable to represent a radio signal in which the magnitude and frequency are known but the phase is unknown because the precise distance between transmitter and receiver is not known to within a fraction of a wavelength.

9-13   Stationary and Nonstationary Random Processes

It has been noted that one can define a probability density function for random variables of the form $x(t_1)$ but so far no mention has been made of the dependence of this density function on the value of time t_1. If all marginal and joint density functions of the process do not depend upon the choice of time origin, the process is said to be *stationary*. In this case, all of the mean values and moments discussed previously are constants which do not depend upon the absolute value of time.

If any of the probability density functions do change with the choice of time origin, the process is *nonstationary*. In this case, one or more of the mean values or moments will also depend on time. Since the analysis of systems responding to nonstationary random inputs is much more involved than in the stationary case, all future discussion will be limited to the stationary case unless it is specifically stated to the contrary.

In a rigorous sense, there are no stationary random processes that actually exist physically, since any process must have started at some finite time in the past and must presumably stop at some finite time in the future. However, there are many physical situations in which the process does not change appreciably during the time it is being observed. In these cases the stationary assumption leads to a convenient mathematical model, which closely approximates reality.

Determining whether or not the stationary assumption is reasonable for any given situation may not be easy. For nondeterministic processes it depends upon the mechanism of generating the process and upon the time duration over which the process is observed. As a rule of thumb, it is customary to assume stationarity unless there is some obvious change in the source or unless logic dictates otherwise. For example, the thermal noise generated by the random motion of electrons in a resistor might reasonably be considered stationary under normal conditions. However, if this resistor were being intermittently heated with a blow torch, the stationary assumption is obviously false. As another example, it might be reasonable to assume that random wind velocity comes from a stationary source over a period of one hour, say, but logic indicates that applying this same assumption to a period of one week might be unreasonable.

Deterministic processes are usually stationary only under certain very special conditions. It is customary to assume that these conditions exist, but one must be aware that this is a deliberate choice and not necessarily a natural occurrence. For example, in the case of the random process defined by (9-24), the reader may easily show (by calculating the mean value) that the process may be (and, in fact, is) stationary when θ is uniformly distributed over a range from 0 to 2π, but that it is definitely not stationary when θ is uniformly distributed over a range from 0 to π.

9-14 Ergodic and Nonergodic Random Processes

Some stationary random processes possess the property that almost every member of the ensemble exhibits the same statistical behavior that the whole ensemble has. Thus, it is possible to determine this statistical behavior by examining only one typical sample function. Such processes are said to be *ergodic*.

For ergodic processes, the mean values and moments can be determined by time averages as well as by ensemble averages. Thus, for example, the nth moment is given by

$$\overline{x^n} = \int_{-\infty}^{\infty} x^n p(x) \, dx = \lim_{T \to \infty} \frac{1}{2T} \int_{-T}^{T} x^n(t) \, dt \qquad \text{(9-25)}$$

It should be emphasized, however, that this condition cannot exist unless the process is stationary. Thus, ergodic processes are also stationary processes.

A process that does not possess this property is *nonergodic*. All nonstationary processes are nonergodic, but it is also possible for stationary processes to be nonergodic. For example, consider sample functions of the form

$$x(t) = A \cos (\omega t + \theta) \tag{9-26}$$

where ω is a constant, A is a random variable (with respect to the ensemble), and θ is a random variable that is uniformly distributed over 0 to 2π, with θ and A being statistically independent. This process can be shown to be stationary, but it is nonergodic since A is a constant in any one sample function but is different for different sample functions.

It is generally difficult, if not impossible, to prove that ergodicity is a reasonable assumption for any physical process, since only one sample function of the process can be observed. Nevertheless, it is customary to assume ergodicity unless there are compelling physical reasons for not doing so. This custom will be followed here.

■ REFERENCES

A great many books have been written on probability theory at many different levels of difficulty. The following books are appropriate for undergraduates:

1. Gnedenko, B. V., and A. Y. Khinchin, *An Elementary Introduction to the Theory of Probability.* San Francisco: W. H. Freeman and Company, 1961.

2. McCord, James R., and Richard M. Moroney, Jr., *Introduction to Probability Theory.* New York: The Macmillan Company, 1964.

■ PROBLEMS

9-1   If a single dice is rolled, determine the probability of each of the following events:
a.   Obtaining the number 5.
b.   Obtaining an even number.
c.   Obtaining a number *greater* than 2.

9-2   If two dice are rolled, determine the probability of each of the following events:
a.   Obtaining a sum of 2.
b.   Obtaining a sum of 7.
c.   Obtaining an even sum.

9-3 A company manufactures radios which have either six, eight, or ten transistors, and come in cases that are either ivory, black, or green. Their warehouse contains 10,000 of these radios distributed as in the table shown.

	IVORY	BLACK	GREEN	TOTALS
6	1000	3000	2000	6000
8	600	1000	1000	2600
10	400	1000	0	1400
Totals	2000	5000	3000	10000

An illiterate thief breaks into the warehouse and steals one radio in a box. Determine the probability of each of the following events:
a. That the thief got a green radio.
b. That the thief got a 10-transistor radio.
c. That the thief got a green 10-transistor radio.
d. That the thief got a black 6-transistor radio.

9-4 In Problem 9-3, 10 percent of the 6-transistor radios don't work, 5 percent of the 8-transistor radios don't work, and 1 percent of the 10-transistor radios don't work.
a. What is the probability that the thief got a green radio that didn't work?
b. What is the probability that the thief got a radio, of any kind, that didn't work?

9-5 If five coins are tossed, determine the probability of each of the following events:
a. That three heads will occur.
b. That only one head will occur.
c. That five heads will occur.

9-6 In the system shown, the switch is initially in position 1.

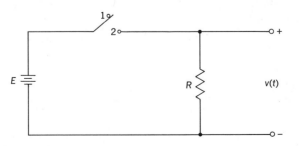

At $t = 0$, a coin is flipped and the switch is moved to position 2 if a head results and is left on 1 if a tail results. At $t = 1$ the coin is flipped again and the switch positioned according to the same rule. This process is repeated at $t = 2$. At $t = 3$ the switch is assigned to position 1 and remains there. As an example, if the three coin tosses result in H H T, the corresponding *sample function* would be as shown.

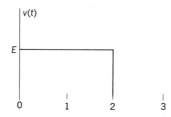

a. Sketch all possible sample functions that belong to the random process described above.
b. What is the probability that any particular sample function will occur?
c. Does the set of all possible sample functions constitute an ensemble?
d. Let a random variable V_1 be defined as $v(0.5)$. What are the possible values that this random variable can assume? Is this a continuous random variable?

9-7 A probability distribution function for a random variable X has the form shown.

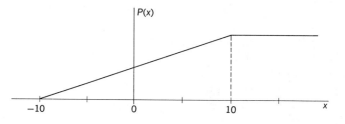

a. What is $P(8)$?
b. What is the probability that the random variable X will lie in the range $0 < X < \infty$?
c. What is the probability that the random variable X will lie in the range $4 < X \leq 8$?

9-8 A random variable X has a probability density function given by

$$p(x) = A\epsilon^{-bx} \qquad x > 0$$
$$= 0 \qquad x \leq 0$$

a. Determine the relationship between the constants A and b.
b. What is the probability that the random variable X is in the range $0 < X \leq 1$ if $A = 1$?
c. Determine and sketch the distribution function.

9-9 For the random variable of Problem 9-8, with $A = 0.1$, find
a. The mean value, $\bar{x}$.
b. The mean-square value, $\overline{x^2}$.
c. The variance, σ^2.

9-10 A Gaussian random variable X has a mean value of 2.0 and a variance of 1.0.
a. Write the probability density function, $p(x)$.
b. What is the value of the density function at $x = 0$? At $x = 2$?
c. What is the probability that the random variable X will have a value greater than zero?
d. What is the probability that the random variable X will lie in the range $(\bar{x} - \sigma) < X \leq (\bar{x} + \sigma)$?

9-11 Two random variables, X and Y, have a joint probability density function given by

$$p(x, y) = K, \qquad 0 < x < 1$$
$$-x < y < x$$
$$= 0 \qquad \text{elsewhere}$$

a. Sketch the density and distribution functions.
b. What value of K is permissible?
c. What is the joint probability of the event that $X > 0$ and the event that $Y > 0$?
d. What is the marginal density function $p_x(x)$?

9-12 a. Are the two random variables of Problem 9-11 statistically independent?
b. For these two random variables, find $E[xy]$.

9-13 Classify *each* of the following random processes according to the four pairs of names listed in Section 9-10. The basis for each classification should be whether it provides a *useful approximate probability model* for the process and not whether it is rigorously correct.
a. Thermal noise voltage across a resistor being held at a constant temperature.
b. Thermal noise voltage across a light bulb during the interval from one second before it is turned on to one second after it is turned on.
c. A process for which the random variable is the number of telephone

calls going through a telephone exchange at any one time and observed over a time interval of ten minutes.

d.   The same process as (c) but observed over a time interval of one day.

e.   A process having sample functions of the form

$$x(t) = at + b$$

where a is a constant and b is a random variable.

f.   A process having sample functions of the form

$$x(t) = X_0$$

where X_0 is a random variable.

9-14   Consider a random process having *periodic* sample functions as shown, in which t_0 is a random variable that is uniformly distributed between 0 and T. Both A and T are constants.

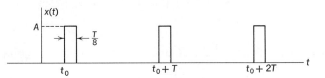

a.   Classify this process according to the four pairs of descriptors.

b.   Write a probability density function, $p(x)$, for this process.

c.   Calculate the mean value, $\bar{x}$, as an ensemble average.

d.   Calculate the variance, σ^2, as an ensemble average.

e.   Repeat parts c and d using time averages.

9-15   A sample function from an ergodic random process is observed over a time interval from 0 to T, where T is finite, and a time average is computed from

$$x_{avg} = \frac{1}{T} \int_0^T x(t) \, dt$$

a.   Is x_{avg} a constant, with respect to the ensemble, or a random variable?

b.   What relationship does x_{avg} have to the mean value of the process, $\bar{x}$? Why are they not equal?

c.   If x_{avg} is a constant, what is its value? If x_{avg} is a random variable, what is its mean value? (Note: You may assume that it is possible to interchange the sequence in which time averages and ensemble averages are taken. This point will be discussed in more detail later.)

10

Correlation Functions

10-1 Introduction

The last two sections have considered in some detail the probabilistic description of random signals and noise. This description is the most complete one, since it incorporates all the knowledge that is available about a random process. There are many engineering situations, however, in which this degree of completeness is either not needed or not possible. If the major interest in a random quantity is in its average power, or the way in which that power is distributed with frequency, then the entire probability model is not needed. If the probability distributions of the random quantities are not known, use of the probability model is not even possible. In either case, a partial statistical description, in terms of certain average values, may provide an acceptable substitute for the probability description.

The mean values and moments for single random variables were discussed in Chapter 9. However, it is not sufficient to consider only single random variables if the time rate of change of sample functions is of concern — as it always is in the analysis of systems with energy storage.

A statistical parameter which involves *two* random variables, and is useful in the analysis of linear systems, is the correlation function. In general, a correlation function is the expected value of the *product* of two random variables.

When the two random variables come from the same random process, this quantity is called the *autocorrelation function*. If $x(t)$ is a sample function from this process, and the random variables are defined to be

$$x_1 = x(t_1)$$
$$x_2 = x(t_2)$$

then the autocorrelation function is defined to be

$$R_x(t_1, t_2) = E[x_1 x_2] = \int_{-\infty}^{\infty} dx_1 \int_{-\infty}^{\infty} x_1 x_2 p(x_1, x_2)\, dx_2 \qquad \text{(10-1)}$$

This definition is valid for both stationary and nonstationary random processes. However, our interest is primarily in stationary processes, for which further simplification of (10-1) is possible. It will be recalled from the previous chapter that for a stationary process all ensemble averages are independent of the time origin. Accordingly, for a stationary process,

$$R_x(t_1, t_2) = R_x(t_1 + T, t_2 + T)$$
$$= E[x(t_1 + T)x(t_2 + T)]$$

Since this expression is independent of the time origin, we can set $T = -t_1$ to give

$$R_x(t_1, t_2) = R_x(0, t_2 - t_1) = E[x(0)x(t_2 - t_1)]$$

It is seen that this expression depends only on the time difference $t_2 - t_1$. Setting this time difference equal to $\tau = t_2 - t_1$, and suppressing the zero in the argument of $R_x(0, t_2 - t_1)$ we can rewrite (10-1) as

$$R_x(\tau) = E[x(t_1)x(t_1 + \tau)] \qquad \text{(10-2)}$$

This is the expression for the autocorrelation function of a stationary process and depends only on τ and not on the value of t_1. Because of this lack of dependence on the particular time t_1 at which the ensemble averages are taken, it is common practice to write (10-2) without the subscript; thus,

$$R_x(\tau) = E[x(t)x(t + \tau)]$$

Whenever correlation functions relate to nonstationary processes, they must be written as $R_x(t_1, t_2)$ or $R_x(t_1, \tau)$ since they are dependent on the particular time t_1 at which the ensemble average is taken as well as on the time difference between samples. In all cases in this and subsequent chapters, it should be assumed that all correlation functions relate to stationary random processes unless specifically stated otherwise.

It is also possible to define a *time autocorrelation* function as[1]

$$\mathcal{R}_x(\tau) = \lim_{T \to \infty} \frac{1}{2T} \int_{-T}^{T} x(t)x(t + \tau)\, dt = \;<x(t)x(t + \tau)> \qquad (10\text{-}3)$$

For the special case of an *ergodic process* these two functions are the same; that is,

$$\mathcal{R}_x(\tau) = R_x(\tau) \qquad \text{for an ergodic process} \qquad (10\text{-}4)$$

The assumption of ergodicity, where it is not obviously invalid, often simplifies the computation of correlation functions.

From (10-2) it is seen readily that for $\tau = 0$, the autocorrelation function is equal to the mean-square value of the process since in this case $R_x(0) = E[x(t_1)x(t_1)]$. For values of τ other than $\tau = 0$, the autocorrelation function $R_x(\tau)$ can be thought of as a measure of the similarity of the waveform $x(t)$ and the waveform $x(t + \tau)$. In order to illustrate this point further, let $x(t)$ be a sample function from a zero-mean stationary random process and form the new function

$$y(t) = x(t) - \rho x(t + \tau)$$

By determining the value of ρ that minimizes the mean-square value of $y(t)$ we will have a measure of how much of the waveform $x(t + \tau)$ is contained in the waveform $x(t)$. The determination of ρ is made by computing the variance of $y(t)$, setting the derivative of the variance with respect to ρ equal to zero, and solving for ρ. The operations are as follows:

$$\begin{aligned} E\{[y(t)]^2\} &= E\{[x(t) - \rho x(t_2 + \tau)]^2\} \\ &= E\{x^2(t) - 2\rho x(t)x(t + \tau) + \rho^2 x^2(t + \tau)\} \\ \sigma_y^2 &= \sigma_x^2 - 2\rho R_x(\tau) + \rho^2 \sigma_x^2 \end{aligned}$$

$$\frac{d\sigma_y^2}{d\rho} = -2R_x(\tau) + 2\rho\sigma_x^2 = 0 \qquad\qquad (10\text{-}5)$$

$$\rho = \frac{R_x(\tau)}{\sigma_x^2}$$

It is seen from (10-5) that ρ is directly related to $R_x(\tau)$; in fact, ρ is called the *correlation coefficient* or *normalized correlation function*. The coefficient ρ can be thought of as the fraction of the waveshape of $x(t)$ remaining after τ seconds have elapsed. It must be remembered that ρ was calculated on a statistical basis and that it is the average retention of

---

[1] The symbol $<\;>$ is used to denote time averaging just as $-$ is used to denote ensemble averaging.

waveshape over the ensemble, and not this property in any particular sample function, that is important. The correlation coefficient ρ can vary from $+1$ to -1. For a value of $\rho = 1$, the waveshapes would be identical — that is, completely correlated. For $\rho = 0$, the waveforms would be completely uncorrelated; that is, no part of the waveform $x(t + \tau)$ is contained in $x(t)$. For $\rho = -1$, the waveshapes would be identical except for opposite signs; that is, the waveform $x(t + \tau)$ would be the negative of $x(t)$.

For an ergodic process or for nonrandom signals, the foregoing interpretation can be made in terms of average power instead of variance and in terms of the time correlation function instead of the (ensemble) correlation function.

Since $R_x(\tau)$ is dependent both on the amount of correlation ρ and the variance of the process, σ_x^2, it is not possible to estimate the significance of some particular value of $R_x(\tau)$ without knowing one or the other of these quantities. For example, if the random process has a zero mean and the autocorrelation function has a positive value, the most that can be said is that it is likely that the random variables $x(t_1)$ and $x(t_1 + \tau)$ have the same sign.[2] If it has a negative value, it is likely that the random variables have opposite signs. If it is nearly zero, the random variables are about as likely to have opposite signs as they are to have the same sign.

These ideas may be made somewhat clearer by considering, as a special example, a random process having a very simple autocorrelation function. Figure 10-1 shows a typical sample function from a discrete,

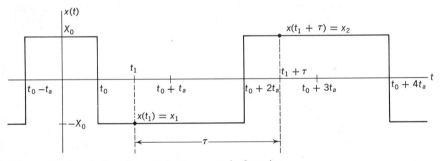

Figure 10-1   A discrete, stationary sample function.

stationary, zero-mean random process in which only two values, $\pm X_0$, are possible. The sample function either can change from one value to the other every t_a seconds or remain the same, with equal probability. The time t_0 is a random variable with respect to the ensemble of possible time functions and is uniformly distributed over an interval of t_a. This means, so far as the ensemble is concerned, that changes in value can

---

[2] This is strictly true only if $p(x_1)$ is symmetrical about the axis $x = 0$.

occur at any time with equal probability. It is also assumed that the value of $x(t)$ in any interval is statistically independent of its value in any other interval.

The autocorrelation function of this process will be determined by heuristic arguments rather than by rigorous derivation. In the first place, when $|\tau|$ is larger than t_a, then t_1 and $t_1 + \tau$ cannot lie in the same interval and x_1 and x_2 are statistically independent. Since x_1 and x_2 have zero mean, the expected value of their product must be zero, as shown by (9-23): that is,

$$R_x(\tau) = E[x_1 x_2] = \bar{x}_1 \bar{x}_2 = 0 \qquad |\tau| > t_a$$

since $\bar{x}_1 = \bar{x}_2 = 0$. When $|\tau|$ is less than t_a, then t_1 and $t_1 + \tau$ may or may not be in the same interval, depending upon the value of t_0. Since t_0 can be anywhere, with equal probability, then the probability that they do lie in the same interval is proportional to the *difference* between t_a and τ. In particular, for $\tau \geq 0$,

Prob (t_1 and $t_1 + \tau$ are in the same interval)
$$= \text{Prob}\left[(t_1 + \tau - t_a < t_0 \leq t_1)\right]$$
$$= \frac{1}{t_a}\left[t_1 - (t_1 + \tau - t_a)\right] = \frac{t_a - \tau}{t_a}$$

since the probability density function for t_0 is just $1/t_a$. When $\tau < 0$,

Prob (t_1 and $t_1 + \tau$ are in the same interval)
$$= \text{Prob}\left[(t_1 - t_a) < t_0 \leq (t_1 + \tau)\right]$$
$$= \frac{1}{t_a}\left[t_1 + \tau - (t_1 - t_a)\right] = \frac{t_a + \tau}{t_a}$$

Hence, in general,

$$\text{Prob } (t_1 \text{ and } t_1 + \tau \text{ are in same interval}) = \frac{t_a - |\tau|}{t_a}$$

When they are in the same interval, the product of x_1 and x_2 is always X_0^2; when they are not, the expected value of this product is zero. Hence,

$$R_x(\tau) = X_0^2 \left[\frac{t_a - |\tau|}{t_a}\right] = X_0^2 \left[1 - \frac{|\tau|}{t_a}\right] \qquad 0 \leq |\tau| \leq t_a$$
$$= 0 \qquad\qquad\qquad\qquad |\tau| \geq t_a$$

(10-6)

This function is sketched in Fig. 10-2.

It is of interest to consider the physical interpretation of this auto-correlation function in the light of the previous discussion. Note that when $|\tau|$ is small (less than t_a) there is an increased probability that $x(t_1)$ and $x(t_1 + \tau)$ will have the same value, and the autocorrelation function is positive. When $|\tau|$ is greater than t_a, it is equally probable that

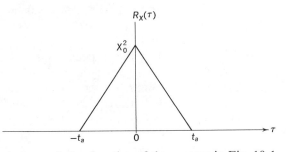

Figure 10-2   Autocorrelation function of the process in Fig. 10-1.

$x(t_1)$ and $x(t_1 + \tau)$ will have the same value as that they will have opposite values, and the autocorrelation function is zero. For $\tau = 0$, the auto-correlation function yields the mean-square value of X_0^2.

10-2   Properties of Autocorrelation Functions

There are a few important general properties that are possessed by all autocorrelation functions. These may be summarized as follows:

1. $R_x(0) = \overline{x^2}$. Hence, the mean-square value of the random process can always be obtained simply by setting $\tau = 0$.

2. $R_x(\tau) = R_x(-\tau)$. The autocorrelation function is an *even* function of τ. It is even because the same set of product values is averaged regardless of the direction of translation.

3. $|R_x(\tau)| \leq R_x(0)$. The largest value of the autocorrelation function always occurs at $\tau = 0$. There may be other values of τ for which it is just as big (for example, see the periodic case below), but it cannot be larger. This is easily shown by considering

$$E[(x_1 + x_2)^2] = E[x_1^2 + x_2^2 \pm 2x_1x_2] \geq 0$$
$$E[x_1^2 + x_2^2] = 2R_x(0) \geq |E(2x_1x_2)| = |2R_x(\tau)|$$

and thus,

$$R_x(0) \geq |R_x(\tau)|$$

4. If $x(t)$ has a dc component, then $R_x(\tau)$ will also have a constant component. Thus, if $x(t) = X_0$, then

$$R_x(\tau) = E[x(t_1)x(t_1 + \tau)] = E[X_0X_0] = X_0^2$$

More generally, if $x(t)$ has a dc component *and* a zero mean component, $n(t)$, so that

$$x(t) = X_0 + n(t)$$

then

$$R_x(\tau) = E\{[X_0 + n(t_1)] [X_0 + n(t_1 + \tau)]\}$$
$$= E[X_0^2 + X_0 n(t_1) + X_0 n(t_1 + \tau) + n(t_1)n(t_1 + \tau)]$$
$$= X_0^2 + R_n(\tau)$$

since

$$E[n(t_1)] = E[n(t_1 + \tau)] = 0$$

Thus, even in this case, $R_x(\tau)$ contains a constant component.

5.   If $x(t)$ has a periodic component, then $R_x(t)$ will also have a periodic component with the same period. For example, let

$$x(t) = X_0 \cos (\omega t + \theta)$$

where X_0 and ω are constants and θ is a random variable uniformly distributed over a range of 2π. That is,

$$p(\theta) = \frac{1}{2\pi} \qquad 0 \le \theta \le 2\pi$$
$$= 0 \qquad \text{elsewhere}$$

Then

$$R_x(\tau) = E[X_0 \cos (\omega t_1 + \theta) X_0 \cos (\omega t_1 + \omega\tau + \theta)]$$
$$= E\left[\frac{X_0^2}{2} \cos (2\omega t_1 + \omega\tau + 2\theta) + \frac{X_0^2}{2} \cos \omega\tau\right]$$
$$= \frac{X_0^2}{2} \int_0^{2\pi} \frac{1}{2\pi} [\cos (2\omega t_1 + \omega\tau + 2\theta) + \cos \omega\tau]\, d\theta$$
$$= \frac{X_0^2}{2} \cos \omega\tau$$

In the more general case in which

$$x(t) = X_0 \cos (\omega\tau + \theta) + n(t)$$

where θ and $n(t_1)$ are statistically independent for all t_1, by the method used in property 4 it is easy to show that

$$R_x(\tau) = \frac{X_0^2}{2} \cos \omega\tau + R_n(\tau)$$

Hence, the autocorrelation function still contains a periodic component.

6.   If $x(t)$ has no periodic or dc components, then

$$\lim_{|\tau| \to \infty} R_x(\tau) = 0$$

For large values of τ, the random variables tend to become statistically independent since the effect of past values tends to die out as time progresses.

There is one further point that should be emphasized in connection with autocorrelation functions. Although a knowledge of the joint probability density functions of the random process is sufficient to obtain a unique autocorrelation function, the converse is not true. There may be many different random processes that can yield the same autocorrelation function. Furthermore, as will be shown later, the effect of linear systems on the autocorrelation function of the input can be computed *without* knowing anything about the probability density functions. Hence, the specification of the correlation function of a random process is not equivalent to specifying the probability density functions and, in fact, represents a considerably smaller amount of information.

10-3   Measurement of Autocorrelation Functions

Since the autocorrelation function plays an important role in the analysis of linear systems with random inputs, an important practical problem is that of determining these functions for experimentally observed random processes. In general, they cannot be calculated from the joint density functions, since these density functions are seldom known. Likewise, an ensemble average cannot be made, because there is usually only one sample function from the ensemble available. Under these circumstances, the only procedure available is to calculate a time autocorrelation function for a finite time interval.

In order to illustrate this, assume that a voltage or current $x(t)$ has been observed over a time interval from 0 to T seconds. It is then possible to define an *estimated* correlation function as

$$\hat{R}_x(\tau) = \frac{1}{T - \tau} \int_0^{T - \tau} x(t)x(t + \tau)\, dt \qquad \tau \ll T \qquad \text{(10-7)}$$

Because the averaging time is finite, the estimated correlation function will be in error by some random amount. In order to make this error have an rms value less than 10 percent of $R_x(0)$, it is necessary to make T about 200 times greater than the approximate width of the autocorrelation function.

Because of the large amount of data needed to determine correlation functions by the foregoing method, the most practical approach is to use a digital computer. This would be done by sampling the continuous time function, $x(t)$, at discrete instants of time $(0, \Delta t, 2\Delta t, \cdots, N\Delta t)$ to obtain a set of numbers x_0, x_1, x_2, $\cdots$, x_N. This operation is performed automatically by an analog-to-digital converter and the resulting numbers are punched out on computer cards or put on tape. The computer would then perform the discrete equivalent to (10-7); that is, it would calculate

$$\hat{R}_x(n\Delta t) = \frac{1}{N - n} \sum_{k=0}^{N-n} x_k x_{k+n} \qquad \begin{array}{l} n = 0, 1, 2, \cdots, M \\ M \ll N \end{array} \qquad \textbf{(10-8)}$$

In order to obtain 50 points on the autocorrelation function ($M = 50$), with about 10 percent rms error, about 5000 to 10,000 samples of $x(t)$ would be required ($5000 < N < 10{,}000$).

It will be shown later that system analysis based on the autocorrelation function of the input is not very difficult once a suitable mathematical model for that autocorrelation function has been obtained. The above discussion should illustrate that obtaining the mathematical model may be a much more difficult problem than using it. Throughout the following discussion, in which the *use* of the mathematical models is emphasized, it is important not to lose sight of the practical problems of obtaining these models.

10-4 Cross-correlation Functions

It is also possible to consider the correlation between two random variables from different random processes. This situation arises when there is more than one random signal being applied to a system or when one wishes to compare random voltages or currents occurring at different points in the system. If the random processes are jointly stationary (that is, the joint distributions depend only on time differences) and if sample functions from these processes are designated as $x(t)$ and $y(t)$, then for two random variables

$$x_1 = x(t_1)$$
$$y_2 = y(t_1 + \tau)$$

it is possible to define the *cross-correlation function*

$$R_{xy}(\tau) = E[x_1 y_2] = \int_{-\infty}^{\infty} dx_1 \int_{-\infty}^{\infty} x_1 y_2 p(x_1, y_2) \, dy_2 \qquad \textbf{(10-9)}$$

The order of subscripts is significant; the second subscript refers to the random variable taken at $(t_1 + \tau)$.[3]

---

[3] This is an arbitrary convention, which is by no means universal with all authors. The definitions should be checked in every case.

There is also another cross-correlation function that can be defined for the same two instants. Thus, let

$$y_1 = y(t_1)$$
$$x_2 = x(t_1 + \tau)$$

and define

$$R_{yx}(\tau) = E[y_1 x_2] = \int_{-\infty}^{\infty} dy_1 \int_{-\infty}^{\infty} y_1 x_2 p(y_1, x_1) \, dx_2 \qquad \text{(10-10)}$$

Note also that because both random processes were assumed to be *jointly* stationary, these cross-correlation functions depend only upon the time difference τ.

The *time cross-correlation functions* may be defined as before by

$$\mathcal{R}_{xy}(\tau) = \lim_{T \to \infty} \frac{1}{2T} \int_{-T}^{T} x(t) y(t + \tau) \, dt \qquad \text{(10-11)}$$

and

$$\mathcal{R}_{yx}(\tau) = \lim_{T \to \infty} \frac{1}{2T} \int_{-T}^{T} y(t) x(t + \tau) \, dt \qquad \text{(10-12)}$$

If the random processes are jointly ergodic, then

$$\mathcal{R}_{xy}(\tau) = R_{xy}(\tau) \qquad \text{(10-13)}$$

$$\mathcal{R}_{yx}(\tau) = R_{yx}(\tau) \qquad \text{(10-14)}$$

In general, the physical interpretation of cross-correlation functions is no more concrete than that of autocorrelation functions. It is simply a measure of how much these two random variables depend upon one another. In the later study of system analysis, however, the specific cross-correlation function between system input and output will take on a very definite and important physical significance.

10-5 Properties of Cross-correlation Functions

The general properties of all cross-correlation functions are quite different from those of autocorrelation functions. They may be summarized as follows:

    1. The quantities $R_{xy}(0)$ and $R_{yx}(0)$ have *no* particular physical significance and do *not* represent mean-square values. It is true, however, that $R_{xy}(0) = R_{yx}(0)$.

    2. Cross-correlation functions are not generally even functions of τ. There is a type of symmetry, however, as indicated by the relations

$$R_{yx}(\tau) = R_{xy}(-\tau) \qquad \text{(10-15)}$$

These results follow from the fact that a shift of $y(t)$ in one direction is equivalent to a shift of $x(t)$ in the other direction.

3. The cross-correlation function does not necessarily have its maximum value at $\tau = 0$. It can be shown, however, that

$$|R_{xy}(\tau)| \leq [R_x(0)R_y(0)]^{1/2} \qquad \text{(10-16)}$$

with a similar relationship for $R_{yx}(\tau)$. The maximum of the cross-correlation function can occur anywhere, but it cannot exceed the above values.

4. If the two random processes are statistically independent, then

$$\begin{aligned} R_{xy}(\tau) &= E[x_1, y_2] = E[x_1]E[y_2] = \bar{x}\,\bar{y} \\ &= R_{yx}(\tau) \end{aligned} \qquad \text{(10-17)}$$

If *either* process has zero mean, then the cross-correlation function vanishes for all τ. The converse of this is not necessarily true, however. The fact that the cross-correlation function is zero and that one process has zero mean does *not* imply that the random processes are statistically independent, except for jointly Gaussian random variables.

10-6 Sums of Random Processes

It was noted previously that one of the applications of cross-correlation functions was in connection with systems with two or more random inputs. In order to explore this in more detail, consider a random process whose sample functions are of the form

$$z(t) = x(t) \pm y(t) \qquad \text{(10-18)}$$

in which $x(t)$ and $y(t)$ are also sample functions of random processes. Then defining the random variables as

$$\begin{aligned} z_1 &= x_1 \pm y_1 = x(t_1) \pm y(t_1) \\ z_2 &= x_2 \pm y_2 = x(t_1 + \tau) \pm y(t_1 + \tau) \end{aligned} \qquad \text{(10-19)}$$

the autocorrelation function of z is

$$\begin{aligned} R_z(\tau) &= E[z_1 z_2] = E[(x_1 \pm y_1)(x_2 \pm y_2)] \\ &= E[x_1 x_2 + y_1 y_2 \pm x_1 y_2 \pm y_1 x_2] \\ &= R_x(\tau) + R_y(\tau) \pm R_{xy}(\tau) \pm R_{yx}(\tau) \end{aligned} \qquad \text{(10-20)}$$

This result is easily extended to the sum of any number of random variables. In general, the autocorrelation function of such a sum will be the sum of *all* the autocorrelation functions plus the sum of *all* cross-correlation functions.

If the two random processes being considered are statistically independent, and one of them has zero mean, then both of the cross-correlation functions in (10-20) vanish and the autocorrelation function of the sum is just the sum of the autocorrelation functions. An example of the importance of this result arises in connection with the extraction of periodic signals from random noise. Let $x(t)$ be a desired signal sample function of the form

$$x(t) = X_0 \cos (\omega t + \theta) \tag{10-21}$$

where θ is a random variable. It was shown previously that the autocorrelation function of this process is

$$R_x(\tau) = 1/2 \, X_0^2 \cos \omega\tau \tag{10-22}$$

Next, let $y(t)$ be a sample function of random noise that is independent of the signal and specify that it has an autocorrelation function of the form

$$R_y(\tau) = Y_0^2 \, \epsilon^{-\alpha|\tau|} \tag{10-23}$$

The observed quantity is $z(t)$, which from (10-20) has an autocorrelation function of

$$\begin{aligned} R_z(\tau) &= R_x(\tau) + R_y(\tau) \\ &= 1/2 \, X_0^2 \cos \omega\tau + Y_0^2 \, \epsilon^{-\alpha|\tau|} \end{aligned} \tag{10-24}$$

This function is sketched in Fig. 10-3 for a case in which the average

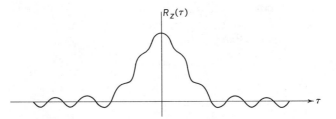

Figure 10-3   Autocorrelation function of sinusoidal signal plus noise.

noise power, Y_0^2, is much larger than the average signal power, $1/2 \, X_0^2$. It is clear from the sketch that for large values of τ, the autocorrelation function depends mostly upon the signal, since the noise autocorrelation function tends to zero. Thus, it should be possible to extract tiny amounts of sinusoidal signal from large amounts of noise by using an appropriate method for measuring the autocorrelation function of the received signal plus noise.

10-7 Correlation Functions for Random Vectors

The use of vector notation to represent a collection of time functions was introduced in Chapter 8 in connection with systems having several inputs and several outputs. Thus, for example, a set of m input signals can be represented by an $(m \times 1)$ vector of the form

$$\mathbf{x}(t) = \begin{bmatrix} x_1(t) \\ x_2(t) \\ \vdots \\ x_m(t) \end{bmatrix}$$

If these signals are all sample functions from random processes, then it is necessary to be able to represent the autocorrelation function of $\mathbf{x}(t)$ in a form that reveals the autocorrelation function of each of the processes and also the cross-correlation function of all pairs of random processes. Hence, there are m^2 correlation functions associated with $\mathbf{x}(t)$ and these can be displayed in an $(m \times m)$ matrix.

As in the case of single processes, the autocorrelation function will be defined as an ensemble average of the product of the sample functions for two different time instants. Thus, let

$$\mathbf{R}_x(t_1, t_2) = E\left[\mathbf{x}(t_1)\, \mathbf{x}^T(t_2)\right] \tag{10-25}$$

where the $\mathbf{x}^T$ indicates the transpose. Note that the use of the transpose is necessary to make the two vectors conformable and that the resulting product is an $(m \times m)$ matrix. In particular,

$$\mathbf{R}_x(t_1, t_2) = E\begin{bmatrix} x_1(t_1)x_1(t_2) & x_1(t_1)x_2(t_2) & \cdots & x_1(t_1)x_m(t_2) \\ x_2(t_1)x_1(t_2) & x_2(t_1)x_2(t_2) & & \\ \vdots & \vdots & & \vdots \\ x_m(t_1)x_1(t_2) & \cdots & & x_m(t_1)x_m(t_2) \end{bmatrix}$$

Since the expected value operation is an integral operation, it can be applied to *each* element within the matrix, and each of these yields an autocorrelation function or cross-correlation function exactly as defined previously. There is a notational problem, however, so in order to avoid subscripts on subscripts, we will make the following definitions:

$$R_{ii}(t_1, t_2) = E\left[x_i(t_1)x_i(t_2)\right] \tag{10-26}$$

$$R_{ij}(t_1, t_2) = E\left[x_i(t_1)x_j(t_2)\right] \tag{10-27}$$

Hence, the correlation matrix for $\mathbf{x}(t)$ can be expressed as

$$\mathbf{R}_x\,(t_1,\,t_2) = \begin{bmatrix} R_{11}(t_1,\,t_2) & R_{12}(t_1,\,t_2) & \cdots & R_{1m}(t_1,\,t_2) \\ R_{21}(t_1,\,t_2) & R_{22}(t_1,\,t_2) & & \\ \vdots & & & \vdots \\ R_{m1}(t_1,\,t_2) & & \cdots & R_{mm}(t_1,\,t_2) \end{bmatrix}$$

(10-28)

Note that the matrix contains all the autocorrelation functions and all the cross-correlation functions for the elements of $\mathbf{x}(t)$ as stated previously.

The random vector $\mathbf{x}(t)$ is said to come from a stationary vector process if all of its components come from stationary processes that are also joint stationary. In this case, just as for a single process, the correlation matrix becomes a function of time difference only. Thus, if

$$t_2 = t_1 + \tau$$

the correlation matrix becomes

$$\mathbf{R}_x(\tau) = \begin{bmatrix} R_{11}(\tau) & R_{12}(\tau) & \cdots & R_{1m}(\tau) \\ R_{21}(\tau) & R_{22}(\tau) & & \cdot \\ \cdot & & & \cdot \\ \cdot & & & \cdot \\ \cdot & & & \cdot \\ R_{m1}(\tau) & & \cdots & R_{mm}(\tau) \end{bmatrix}$$

(10-29)

The properties of $\mathbf{R}_x(\tau)$ can be deduced from the properties of its components since these are all normal autocorrelation and cross-correlation functions. In particular it should be noted that the $R_{ii}(\tau)$, where $i = 1, 2, \cdots, m$, are all *even* functions of τ with their maximum values at $t = 0$. The cross-correlation functions $R_{ij}(\tau)$, where $i \neq j$, are not necessarily even functions of τ, nor do they necessarily have their maximum values at $\tau = 0$. It is true, however, that

$$R_{ij}(\tau) = R_{ji}(-\tau)$$

(10-30)

and that

$$R_{ij}(0) = R_{ji}(0)$$

(10-31)

A situation of special interest is that in which all the components of the $\mathbf{x}(t)$ process have zero means and every pair of components is statistically independent. In this case, all the cross-correlation functions vanish and the correlation matrix becomes diagonal. Thus,

$$\mathbf{R}_x(\tau) = \begin{bmatrix} R_{11}(\tau) & 0 & \cdots & 0 \\ 0 & R_{22}(\tau) & & \\ \cdot & & & \\ \cdot & & & \\ \cdot & & & \\ 0 & & \cdots & R_{mm}(\tau) \end{bmatrix}$$

(10-32)

The foregoing discussion has considered only the autocorrelation function of a single random vector process. It is possible, however, to express the cross-correlation function between two random vector processes in a similar way. Suppose, for example, that $y(t)$ is a $(p \times 1)$ random vector described by

$$\mathbf{y}(t) = \begin{bmatrix} y_1(t) \\ y_2(t) \\ \vdots \\ y_p(t) \end{bmatrix}$$

The cross-correlation matrix for this process and that of $\mathbf{x}(t)$ can be defined by

$$\mathbf{R}_{xy}(t_1, t_2) = E[\mathbf{x}(t_1)\,\mathbf{y}^T(t_2)] \tag{10-33}$$

and is an $(m \times p)$ matrix whose elements are

$$\mathbf{R}_{xy}(t_1, t_2) = \begin{bmatrix} R_{x_1 y_1}(t_1, t_2) & R_{x_1 y_2}(t_1, t_2) & \cdots & R_{x_1 y_p}(t_1, t_2) \\ R_{x_2 y_1}(t_1, t_2) & R_{x_2 y_2}(t_1, t_2) & & \\ \vdots & & & \\ R_{x_m y_1}(t_1, t_2) & & \cdots & R_{x_m y_p}(t_1, t_2) \end{bmatrix} \tag{10-34}$$

The multiple subscript notation is used here to avoid the notation ambiguity that would otherwise arise. If $\mathbf{x}(t)$ and $\mathbf{y}(t)$ are jointly stationary, then the above correlation matrix can be expressed as a function of the time difference τ only. If *either* $\mathbf{x}(t)$ and $\mathbf{y}(t)$ have zero mean and if they are statistically independent, then *all* the elements of the correlation matrix vanish.

10-8   Correlation Matrices for Sampled Functions

Another situation in which vector notation is useful in representing a signal arises in the case of a single time function that is sampled at periodic time instants. If only a finite number of such samples are to be considered, say N, then each sample value can become a component of an $(N \times 1)$ vector. Thus, if the sampling times are $t_1, t_2, \cdots, t_N$, the vector representing the time function $x(t)$ may be expressed as

$$\mathbf{x} = \begin{bmatrix} x(t_1) \\ x(t_2) \\ \vdots \\ x(t_N) \end{bmatrix}$$

Note that in this case the vector **x** is *not* a function of the continuous time variable t and that each component of **x** is a single number instead of a complete time function. If $x(t)$ is a sample function from a random process, then each component is also a random variable.

It is still possible to define a correlation matrix, however, and in this case it becomes $(N \times N)$. Thus,

$$\mathbf{R}_X = E[\mathbf{xx}^T] = E \begin{bmatrix} x(t_1)x(t_1) & x(t_1)x(t_2) & \cdots & x(t_1)x(t_N) \\ x(t_2)x(t_1) & x(t_2)x(t_2) & & \\ \vdots & & & \\ x(t_N)x(t_1) & & \cdots & x(t_N)x(t_N) \end{bmatrix}$$

When the expected value of each element of the matrix is taken, that element becomes a particular value of the autocorrelation function of the random process from which $x(t)$ came. Thus,

$$\mathbf{R}_X = \begin{bmatrix} R_x(t_1, t_1) & R_x(t_1, t_2) & \cdots & R_x(t_1, t_N) \\ R_x(t_2, t_1) & R_x(t_2, t_2) & & \\ \vdots & & & \\ R_x(t_N, t_1) & & \cdots & R_x(t_N, t_N) \end{bmatrix} \tag{10-35}$$

When the random process from which $x(t)$ came is stationary, then all the components of $\mathbf{R}_X$ become functions of time difference only. If the interval between sample values is Δt, then

$$t_2 = t_1 + \Delta t$$
$$t_3 = t_1 + 2\Delta t$$
$$\vdots$$
$$t_N = t_1 + (N - 1)\Delta t$$

and

$$\mathbf{R}_X = \begin{bmatrix} R_x[0] & R_x[\Delta t] & \cdots & R_x[(N - 1)\Delta t] \\ R_x[\Delta t] & R_x[0] & & \\ \cdot & & & \\ \cdot & & & \\ \cdot & & & \\ R_x[(N - 1)\Delta t] & \cdots & & R_x[0] \end{bmatrix} \tag{10-36}$$

where use has been made of the symmetry of the autocorrelation function; that is, $R_x[i\Delta t] = R_x[-i\Delta t]$. Note that as a consequence of the symmetry $\mathbf{R}_x$ is a symmetric matrix (even in the nonstationary case), and that as a consequence of stationarity the major diagonal (and all diagonals parallel to it) have identical elements.

Although the $\mathbf{R}_x$ just defined is a logical consequence of previous definitions, it is not the most customary way of designating the correlation matrix of a random vector consisting of sample values. A more common procedure is to define a *covariance matrix,* which contains the variances and covariances of the random variables. The general covariance between two random variables is defined as

$$E\{[x(t_i) - \bar{x}(t_i)]\ [x(t_j) - \bar{x}(t_j)]\} = \sigma_i \sigma_j \rho_{ij} \tag{10-37}$$

where

$$\begin{aligned}
\bar{x}(t_i) &= \text{mean value of } x(t_i)\\
\bar{x}(t_j) &= \text{mean value of } x(t_j)\\
\sigma_i^2 &= \text{variance of } x(t_i)\\
\sigma_j^2 &= \text{variance of } x(t_j)\\
\rho_{ij} &= \text{normalized covariance coefficient of } x(t_i) \text{ and } x(t_j)\\
&= 1, \text{ when } i = j
\end{aligned}$$

The covariance matrix is defined as

$$\Lambda_x = E\,[\mathbf{x} - \bar{\mathbf{x}})\,(\mathbf{x}^T - \bar{\mathbf{x}}^T)\,|\,] \tag{10-38}$$

where $\bar{\mathbf{x}}$ is the mean value of $\mathbf{x}$. Using the covariance definitions leads immediately to

$$\Lambda_x = \begin{bmatrix} \sigma_1^2 & \sigma_1\sigma_2\rho_{12} & \cdots & \sigma_1\sigma_N\rho_{1N} \\ \sigma_2\sigma_1\rho_{21} & \sigma_2^2 & & \\ \vdots & & & \\ \sigma_N\sigma_1\rho_{N1} & \cdots & & \sigma_N^2 \end{bmatrix} \tag{10-39}$$

since $\rho_{ii} = 1$, for $i = 1, 2, \cdots, N$. By expanding (10-39) it is easy to show that Λ_x is related to $\mathbf{R}_x$ by

$$\Lambda_x = \mathbf{R}_x - \bar{\mathbf{x}}\bar{\mathbf{x}}^T \tag{10-40}$$

If the random process has a zero mean, then the two are identical.

The above representation for the covariance matrix is valid for both stationary and nonstationary processes. In the case of a stationary process, however, all the variances are the same and the correlation coefficients in a given diagonal are the same. Thus,

$$\begin{aligned}
\sigma_i^2 &= \sigma_j^2 = \sigma^2 & i, j &= 1, 2, \cdots, N\\
\rho_{ij} &= \rho_{|i-j|} & i, j &= 1, 2, \cdots, N
\end{aligned}$$

and

$$\Lambda_x = \sigma^2 \begin{bmatrix} 1 & \rho_1 & \rho_2 & \cdots & & \rho_{N-1} \\ \rho_1 & 1 & \rho_1 & \cdots & & \rho_{N-2} \\ \rho_2 & \rho_1 & 1 & \rho_1 & & \\ \vdots & & & \ddots & 1 & \rho_1 \\ & & & & \ddots & \rho_1 \\ \rho_{N-1} & \cdots & & & \rho_1 & 1 \end{bmatrix}$$

(10-41)

Before we leave the subject of covariance matrices, it is worth noting the important role that these matrices play in connection with the joint probability density function for N random variables from a Gaussian process. It was noted earlier that the Gaussian process was one of the few for which it is possible to write a joint probability density function for any number of random variables. The derivation of this joint density function is beyond the scope of this discussion, but it can be shown that it becomes

$$P(\mathbf{x}) = P\left[x(t_1), x(t_2), \cdots x(t_N) \right]$$
$$= \frac{1}{(2\pi)^{N/2} |\Lambda_x|^{1/2}} \exp\left[-\frac{1}{2} (\mathbf{x}^T - \bar{\mathbf{x}}^T) \Lambda_x^{-1} (\mathbf{x} - \bar{\mathbf{x}}) \right]$$

(10-42)

where $|\Lambda_x|$ is the determinant of Λ_x and Λ_x^{-1} is its inverse.

■ REFERENCES

See Chapter 12.

■ PROBLEMS

10-1 Consider a stationary random process having sample functions of the form shown. At periodic time instants of $t_0 \pm nt_a$ there is a rectan-

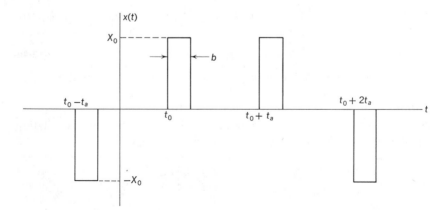

gular pulse of width b and having a magnitude of $\pm X_0$ with equal probability. The time t_0 is a random variable, independent of pulse amplitude,
and uniformly distributed over an interval of t_a.
a.   Find the autocorrelation function $R_x(\tau)$.
b.   Find the time autocorrelation function $\mathscr{R}_x(\tau)$.
c.   Can this process be ergodic?
d.   What is the mean-square value of the process?

10-2   A stationary random process has an autocorrelation function of
the form

$$R_x(\tau) = 100\epsilon^{-|\tau|} \cos 10\pi\tau$$

a.   Sketch the autocorrelation function.
b.   What is the mean-square value of the process?
c.   What does this correlation function imply about random variables
separated in time by $|\tau| = 1/20$ second?
d.   What does it imply about random variables separated by $|\tau| =$
1/10 second?
e.   What is the mean value of the process?

10-3   A stationary random process has an autocorrelation function of
the form

$$R_x(\tau) = 25\epsilon^{-|\tau|} + 100$$

a.   What is the mean-square value of the process?
b.   What is the mean value of the process?
c.   What is the variance of the process?

10-4   A stationary random process has an autocorrelation function of
the form

$$R_x(\tau) = 16\epsilon^{-|\tau|} \cos \pi\tau + 4 \cos 2\pi\tau$$

a.   What is the mean value of the process?
b.   What discrete frequency components are present?
c.   If any sinusoidal component is considered to be a signal and the rest
noise, what is the signal-to-noise power ratio?

10-5   Consider two signals $x(t)$ and $y(t)$ that are sample functions from
zero mean stationary random processes. Form a new function by subtracting a constant ρ_{xy} times the displaced waveform $y(t + \tau)$ for $x(t)$.
Thus

$$z(t) = x(t) - \rho_{xy} y(t + \tau)$$

a.   Find the value of ρ_{xy} that minimizes σ_z^2.

b. Over what range of values can ρ_{xy} vary?

c. For an ergodic process what physical interpretation can be given to ρ_{xy} when $\tau = 0$?

10-6 Two random processes have sample functions of the form

$$x(t) = A \cos (\omega_0 t + \theta) \quad \text{and} \quad y(t) = B \sin (\omega_0 t + \theta)$$

where θ is a random variable uniformly distributed between 0 and 2π and A and B are constants.

a. What are the cross-correlation functions $R_{xy}(t)$ and $R_{yx}(t)$?

b. What is the significance of the values of these cross-correlation functions at $\tau = 0$?

10-7 A sample function from a stationary random process $x(t)$ is cross-correlated with its derivative $x'(t)$. Find the expression for the cross-correlation function $R_{xx'}(\tau)$ in terms of $R_x(\tau)$. Find the expression for $R_{x'x'}(\tau)$ in terms of $R_x(\tau)$.

10-8 Prove the inequality shown in Equation (10-17). (Hint: Look at property 4 in Section 10-2.)

10-9 Sample functions from two statistically independent, stationary random processes $\{x(t)\}$ and $\{y(t)\}$, are used to form two new random processes having sample functions of the form

$$z(t) = x(t) - y(t)$$
$$w(t) = x(t) + y(t)$$

Find the following correlation functions in terms of the autocorrelation functions of $\{x(t)\}$ and $\{y(t)\}$:

a. $R_z(\tau)$ **c.** $R_{zw}(\tau)$

b. $R_w(\tau)$ **d.** $R_{wz}(\tau)$

10-10 Sample functions from the random process discussed in Problem 10-1 are applied to an ideal diode as shown. Find:

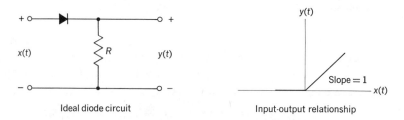

Ideal diode circuit   Input-output relationship

a. The autocorrelation function of the output, $R_y(\tau)$

b. The cross-correlation function, $R_{xy}(\tau)$
c. The cross-correlation function, $R_{yx}(\tau)$

10-11 Values of a sample function from an ergodic random process are given in the accompanying table.
a. Plot the portion of the sample function given in the table.
b. Compute estimates of the mean and variance of the signal. Determine the amplitude and frequency of any periodic component present.

t	0.0	0.2	0.4	0.6	0.8
0	0.200	2.143	0.580	−0.553	0.091
1	1.161	0.282	−1.001	−0.006	0.931
2	0.586	−0.027	0.498	0.919	−2.066
3	0.142	0.665	1.869	−0.184	−0.313
4	0.952	−0.820	3.473	−0.120	0.515
5	−0.586	1.808	0.032	0.223	−1.218
6	1.157	1.950	0.485	−0.048	−1.553
7	−0.443	0.395	0.078	−1.781	−1.008
8	−0.391	2.749	1.202	−1.948	1.543
9	0.832	1.378	−0.301	−0.171	−1.802
10	0.978	0.183	1.484	−0.073	−1.667
11	0.408	1.068	1.026	−0.373	−0.704
12	0.251	1.096	0.481	0.928	−1.065
13	−0.615	−0.709	1.238	−1.726	−1.030
14	2.196	1.788	1.421	−0.504	−0.394
15	0.596	−0.006	0.136	1.126	−0.834
16	0.888	2.391	0.421	1.401	0.440
17	1.360	1.577	1.365	−1.059	−2.878
18	0.396	1.268	1.894	1.187	−1.734
19	1.400	0.410	0.237	−0.492	−2.249

10-12 Compute the cross-correlation function of the signal given in the table in Problem 10-11 and each of the following signals:

$$y(t) = \cos\left[2\pi\,(^1\!/_4)T\right]$$
$$z(t) = \cos\left[2\pi t\right]$$

What conclusions can you draw from the results of this calculation?

10-13 A random vector $z(t)$ is composed of combinations of sample functions from two jointly stationary, statistically independent, random processes $\{x(t)\}$ and $\{y(t)\}$. In particular, let

$$\mathbf{z}(t) = \begin{bmatrix} \mathbf{x}(t) + \mathbf{y}(t) \\ \mathbf{x}(t) - \mathbf{y}(t) \end{bmatrix}$$

If

$$R_x(\tau) = 10\epsilon^{-|\tau|} + 25$$
$$R_y(\tau) = 10 \cos 2\pi\tau - 16$$

find the correlation matrix $\mathbf{R}_z(\tau)$.

10-14   A stationary random process, having an autocorrelation function of

$$R_x(\tau) = 10\epsilon^{-|\tau|}$$

is sampled at periodic time instants separated by $\Delta t = 0.5$ second.
a.   Write the complete covariance matrix, $\mathbf{\Lambda}_z$, for a set of three samples taken from this process.
b.   Write the general covariance matrix for N samples.

11

Spectral Density

11-1 Introduction

The use of Fourier transforms and Laplace transforms in the analysis of linear systems is widespread and frequently leads to much saving in labor. The principal reason for this simplification is that the convolution integral of time-domain methods is replaced by simple multiplication when frequency-domain methods are used.

In view of the widespread use of frequency-domain methods in system analysis it is natural to ask if such methods are still useful when the inputs to the system are random. The answer to this question is that they *are* still useful but that some modifications are required and that a little more care is necessary in order to avoid pitfalls. However, when properly used, frequency-domain methods offer essentially the same advantages in dealing with random signals as they do with nonrandom signals.

Before we begin this discussion, it is desirable to review briefly frequency-domain representation of a nonrandom time function. The most natural representation of this sort is the Fourier transform which leads to the concept of frequency spectrum. Thus, the Fourier transform of some nonrandom time function, $f(t)$, is defined to be

$$F(j\omega) = \int_{-\infty}^{\infty} f(t)\, \epsilon^{-j\omega t}\, dt \tag{11-1}$$

If $f(t)$ is a voltage, say, then $F(j\omega)$ has the units of volts per hertz and represents the *relative* magnitude and phase of steady-state sinusoids (of frequency ω) that can be summed to produce the original $f(t)$. Thus, the magnitude of the Fourier transform has the physical significance of being the *amplitude density* as a function of frequency and as such gives a clear indication of how the energy of $f(t)$ is distributed with respect to frequency.

It might seem reasonable to use exactly the same procedure in dealing with *random* signals — that is, to use the Fourier transform of any sample function $x(t)$, defined by

$$X(j\omega) = \int_{-\infty}^{\infty} x(t)\epsilon^{-j\omega t}\, dt$$

as the frequency-domain representation of the random process. This is not possible, however, for at least two reasons. In the first place, $X(j\omega)$ will be a random variable (for any fixed ω) since it will have a different value for each member of the ensemble of possible sample functions. Hence, it cannot be a frequency representation of the process, but only of one member of the process. However, it might still be possible to use this function by finding its expected value (or mean) over the ensemble if it were not for the second reason. The second, and more basic, reason for not using the $X(j\omega)$ just defined is that — for stationary processes, at least — it almost never exists! It may be recalled that one of the conditions for a time function to be Fourier transformable is that it be absolutely integrable; that is,

$$\int_{-\infty}^{\infty} |x(t)|\, dt < \infty \tag{11-2}$$

This condition can never be satisfied by any sample function from a stationary random process. The Fourier transform in the ordinary sense will never exist in this case, although it may occasionally exist in the sense of generalized functions, including impulses, and so forth.

Now that the usual Fourier transform has been ruled out as a means of obtaining a frequency-domain representation for a random process, the next thought is to use the Laplace transform, since this contains a built-in convergence factor. Of course, the usual one-sided transform, which requires that $f(t) = 0$ for $t < 0$, is not applicable for a stationary process; however, this is no real difficulty. It is quite possible to define a two-sided Laplace transform that is good'for negative values of time as well as positive. Once this is done, the Laplace transform for almost any sample function from a stationary random process will exist.

It turns out, however, that this approach is not so promising as it looks since it merely transfers the existence problems from the transform to the inverse transform. A study of these problems requires a knowledge of complex variable theory that is beyond the scope of the present discussion. Hence, it appears that the simplest, mathematically acceptable approach is to return to the Fourier transform and employ an artifice that will insure existence. Even in this case it will not be possible to justify rigorously all the steps, and a certain amount of the procedure will have to be accepted on faith.

The artifice to be employed is to define a new sample function of finite duration as

$$x_T(t) = x(t) \qquad |t| \leq T < \infty$$
$$= 0 \qquad |t| > T \tag{11-3}$$

If the stationary random process from which $x(t)$ is taken has a finite mean-square value, then the truncated sample function $x_T(t)$ will have finite energy and, hence, will be Fourier transformable. In fact, it will satisfy the condition for integrable square functions; that is,

$$\int_{-\infty}^{\infty} |x_T(t)|^2 \, dt < \infty \tag{11-4}$$

The Fourier transform may now be written as

$$X_T(j\omega) = \int_{-\infty}^{\infty} x_T(t)\epsilon^{-j\omega t} \, dt \tag{11-5}$$

and will exist for all $T < \infty$.

At this point it is necessary to digress from the main discussion and derive a more general form for Parseval's theorem. This will be done for two different time functions, $f(t)$ and $g(t)$. Although the immediate application is one in which $f(t) = g(t)$, the more general case will be needed later in this section. The two time functions will be assumed to be Fourier transformable with transforms of $F(j\omega)$ and $G(j\omega)$, respectively. The inverse transform for one of them, say $g(t)$, is

$$g(t) = \frac{1}{2\pi} \int_{-\infty}^{\infty} G(j\omega)\epsilon^{j\omega t} \, d\omega \tag{11-6}$$

Now consider the integral

$$\int_{-\infty}^{\infty} f(t)g(t) \, dt = \int_{-\infty}^{\infty} f(t) \left[\frac{1}{2\pi} \int_{-\infty}^{\infty} G(j\omega)\epsilon^{j\omega t} \, d\omega \right] dt$$
$$= \frac{1}{2\pi} \int_{-\infty}^{\infty} G(j\omega) \left[\int_{-\infty}^{\infty} f(t)\epsilon^{j\omega t} \, dt \right] d\omega \tag{11-7}$$

In the last integral of (11-7) the quantity in brackets is just the Fourier transform of $f(t)$ with ω replaced by $-\omega$. This leads immediately to the desired result, namely

$$\int_{-\infty}^{\infty} f(t)g(t)\, dt = \frac{1}{2\pi} \int_{-\infty}^{\infty} G(j\omega)F(-j\omega)\, d\omega \tag{11-8}$$

If (11-6) had been written for $f(t)$, an equally correct result would be

$$\int_{-\infty}^{\infty} f(t)g(t)\, dt = \frac{1}{2\pi} \int_{-\infty}^{\infty} F(j\omega)G(-j\omega)\, d\omega \tag{11-9}$$

The special case which will be used immediately is for $f(t) = g(t)$. In this case,

$$\begin{aligned}
\int_{-\infty}^{\infty} f^2(t)\, dt &= \frac{1}{2\pi} \int_{-\infty}^{\infty} F(j\omega)F(-j\omega)\, d\omega \\
&= \frac{1}{2\pi} \int_{-\infty}^{\infty} |F(j\omega)|^2\, d\omega
\end{aligned} \tag{11-10}$$

The last form follows if we remember that $F(-j\omega)$ is the complex conjugate of $F(j\omega)$. This form also emphasizes a physical interpretation of Parseval's theorem. If $f(t)$ is a voltage across a resistance of one ohm, then the left side of (11-10) is simply the energy dissipated by $f(t)$ as computed in the time domain, whereas the right-hand side is the energy as computed in the frequency domain. Obviously they must be equal.

Returning now to the main discussion, it is possible to use (11-10) to write

$$\int_{-\infty}^{\infty} x_T^2(t)\, dt = \frac{1}{2\pi} \int_{-\infty}^{\infty} |X_T(j\omega)|^2\, d\omega \tag{11-11}$$

Dividing both sides by $2T$ gives

$$\frac{1}{2T} \int_{-\infty}^{\infty} x_T^2(t)\, dt = \frac{1}{4\pi T} \int_{-\infty}^{\infty} |X_T(j\omega)|^2\, d\omega \tag{11-12}$$

The left side of (11-12) has the physical significance of being proportional to the average power of the sample function in the time interval $-T$ to T if $x_T(t)$ is a voltage or current associated with a resistance. More exactly, it is the square of the *effective* value of $x_T(t)$. Furthermore, for an ergodic process, this quantity would approach the mean-square value of the process as T approached infinity.

However, it is not possible at this stage to let T approach infinity since $X_T(j\omega)$ simply does not exist in the limit. It should be remembered, though, that $X_T(j\omega)$ is a random variable with respect to the ensemble of sample functions from which $x(t)$ was taken. It is reasonable to suppose (and can be rigorously proved) that the limit of the *expected value of* $(1/T)|X_T(j\omega)|^2$ does exist since the integral of this "always positive" quantity certainly does exist, as shown by (11-12). Hence, taking the expectation of both sides of (11-12), interchanging the expectation and integration and then taking the limit as $T \to \infty$ we obtain

$$E\left\{\frac{1}{2T}\int_{-\infty}^{\infty} x_T^2(t)\ dt\right\} = E\left\{\frac{1}{4\pi T}\int_{-\infty}^{\infty} |X_T(j\omega)|^2\ d\omega\right\}$$

$$\lim_{T \to \infty}\frac{1}{2T}\int_{-\infty}^{\infty} \overline{x^2}\ dt = \lim_{T \to \infty}\frac{1}{4\pi T}\int_{-\infty}^{\infty} E\{|X_T(j\omega)|^2\}\ d\omega \qquad \textbf{(11-13)}$$

$$<\overline{x^2}> = \frac{1}{2\pi}\int_{-\infty}^{\infty} \lim_{T \to \infty}\frac{E\{|X_T(j\omega)|^2\}}{2T}\ d\omega$$

For a stationary process, the time average of the mean-square value is equal to the mean-square value and (11-13) can be written as

$$\overline{x^2} = \frac{1}{2\pi}\int_{-\infty}^{\infty} \lim_{T \to \infty}\frac{E\{|X_T(j\omega)|^2\}}{2T}\ d\omega \qquad \textbf{(11-14)}$$

The integrand of the right side of (11-14), which will be designated by the symbol $S_x(\omega)$, is called the *spectral density* of the random process. Thus,

$$S_x(\omega) = \lim_{T \to \infty}\frac{E[|X_T(j\omega)|^2]}{2T} \qquad \textbf{(11-15)}$$

and it must be remembered that it is not possible to let $T \to \infty$ *before* taking the expectation. If $x(t)$ is a voltage, say, then $S_x(\omega)$ has the units of volts² per hertz and its integral, as shown by (11-14) leads to the mean-square value; that is,

$$\overline{x^2} = \frac{1}{2\pi}\int_{-\infty}^{\infty} S_x(\omega)\ d\omega \qquad \textbf{(11-16)}$$

The physical interpretation of spectral density can be made somewhat clearer by thinking in terms of average power, although this is a fairly specialized way of looking at it. If $x(t)$ is a voltage or current associated with a one-ohm resistance, then $\overline{x^2}$ is just the average power dissipated in that resistance. The spectral density, $S_x(\omega)$, can then be interpreted as the average power associated with a bandwidth of one hertz centered at $\omega/2\pi$ hertz. [Note that the unit of bandwidth is the hertz (or cycle per second) and not the radian per second, because of the factor of $1/2\pi$ in the integral of (11-16).]

The foregoing analysis of spectral density has been carried out in somewhat more detail than is customary in an introductory discussion. The reason for this is an attempt to avoid some of the mathematical pitfalls that a more superficial approach might gloss over. There is no doubt that this method makes the initial study of spectral density more difficult for the reader, but it is felt that the additional rigor is well worth the effort in this instance. Furthermore, even if all of the implications of the discussion are not fully understood, it should serve to make the reader aware of the existence of some of the less obvious difficulties of frequency-domain methods.

Before we turn to a more detailed discussion of the properties of spectral densities, it may be noted that in system analysis the spectral density of the input random process will play the same role as does the transform of the input in the case of nonrandom signals. The major difference is that spectral density represents a *power* density rather than a *voltage* density. Thus, it will be necessary to define a *power transfer function* for the system rather than a *voltage transfer function*.

11-2 Properties of Spectral Density

Most of the important properties of spectral density are summarized by the simple statement that it is a *real, positive, even* function of ω. It is known from previous study of Fourier transforms that their magnitude is certainly real and positive. Hence, the expected value will also possess the same properties.

A special class of spectral densities, which is more commonly used than any other, is said to be *rational*, since it is composed of a ratio of polynomials involving only even powers of ω. Thus, it might be represented by

$$S_x(\omega) = \frac{S_0(\omega^{2n} + a_{2n-2}\omega^{2n-2} + \cdots + a_2\omega^2 + a_0)}{\omega^{2m} + b_{2m-2}\omega^{2m-2} + \cdots + b_2\omega^2 + b_0} \tag{11-17}$$

If the mean-square value of the random process is finite, then the area under $S_x(\omega)$ must also be finite, from (11-16). In this case it is necessary that $m > n$. This condition will always be assumed here except for a very special case of *white noise*. White noise is a term applied to a random process for which the spectral density is constant for all ω; that is, $S_x(\omega) = S_0$. Although such a process cannot exist physically (since it has infinite mean-square value) it is a convenient mathematical fiction, which greatly simplifies many computations that would otherwise be very difficult. The justification and illustration of the use of this concept will be discussed in more detail later.

Spectral densities of this type are continuous and, as such, cannot represent random processes having dc or periodic components. The reason is not difficult to understand when spectral density is interpreted as average power per unit bandwidth. Any dc component in a random process represents a finite average power in *zero* bandwidth, since this component has a discrete frequency spectrum. Finite power in zero bandwidth is equivalent to an infinite power density. Hence, we would expect the spectral density in this case to be infinite at zero frequency but finite elsewhere; that is, it would contain a δ function at $\omega = 0$. A similar argument for periodic components would justify the existence of δ functions at these discrete frequencies. A rigorous derivation of these results will serve to make the argument more precise and, at the same time, illustrate the use of the defining equation, (11-15), in the calculation of spectral densities.

In order to carry out the desired derivation, consider a stationary random process having sample functions of the form

$$x(t) = X_0 + X_1 \cos (\omega_1 t + \theta) \tag{11-18}$$

where X_0, X_1, and ω_1 are constants and θ is a random variable uniformly distributed from 0 to 2π; that is,

$$p(\theta) = \frac{1}{2\pi} \qquad 0 \le \theta \le 2\pi$$

$$= 0 \qquad \text{elsewhere}$$

The Fourier transform of the truncated sample function, $x_T(t)$, is

$$X_T(j\omega) = \int_{-T}^{T} [X_0 + X_1 \cos (\omega_1 t + \theta)] \epsilon^{-j\omega t} \, dt$$

$$= X_0 \frac{\epsilon^{-j\omega t}}{-j\omega} \Big]_{-T}^{T} + \frac{X_1}{2} \frac{\epsilon^{j[(\omega_1 - \omega)t + \theta]}}{j(\omega_1 - \omega)} \Big]_{-T}^{T} + \frac{X_1}{2} \frac{\epsilon^{-j[(\omega_1 + \omega)t + \theta]}}{-j(\omega_1 + \omega)} \Big]_{-T}^{T}$$

Substituting in the limits and simplifying leads immediately to

$$X_T(j\omega) = \frac{2X_0 \sin \omega T}{\omega} + X_1 \left[\frac{\epsilon^{j\theta} \sin (\omega - \omega_1)T}{(\omega - \omega_1)} + \frac{\epsilon^{-j\theta} \sin (\omega + \omega_1)T}{(\omega + \omega_1)} \right] \tag{11-19}$$

The square of the magnitude of $X_T(j\omega)$ will have nine terms, some of which are independent of the random variable θ, and the rest involving either $\epsilon^{\pm j\theta}$ or $\epsilon^{\pm j2\theta}$. In anticipation of the result that the expectation of all terms involving θ will vanish, it is convenient to write the squared magnitude in symbolic form without bothering to determine all the co-efficients. Thus,

$$|X_T(j\omega)|^2 = \frac{4X_0^2 \sin^2 \omega T}{\omega^2} + X_1^2 \left[\frac{\sin^2 (\omega - \omega_1)T}{(\omega - \omega_1)^2} + \frac{\sin^2 (\omega + \omega_1)T}{(\omega + \omega_1)^2} \right]$$

$$+ A(\omega)\epsilon^{j\theta} + B(\omega)\epsilon^{-j\theta} + C(\omega)\epsilon^{j2\theta} + D(\omega)\epsilon^{-j2\theta} \tag{11-20}$$

Now consider the expected value of any term involving θ. These are all of the form $G(\omega)\epsilon^{jn\theta}$, and the expected value is:

$$E[G(\omega)\epsilon^{jn\theta}] = G(\omega) \int_0^{2\pi} \frac{1}{2\pi} \epsilon^{jn\theta} \, d\theta = \frac{G(\omega)}{2\pi} \left. \frac{\epsilon^{jn\theta}}{jn} \right]_0^{2\pi}$$ (11-21)

$$= 0 \qquad n = \pm 1, \pm 2, \cdots$$

Thus, the last four terms of (11-20) will vanish and the expected value becomes

$$E[|X_T(j\omega)|^2] = 4X_0^2 \left[\frac{\sin^2 \omega T}{\omega^2} \right] + X_1^2 \left[\frac{\sin^2 (\omega - \omega_1)T}{(\omega - \omega_1)^2} + \frac{\sin^2 (\omega + \omega_1)T}{(\omega + \omega_1)^2} \right]$$

(11-22)

From (11-15), the spectral density is

$$S_x(\omega) = \lim_{T \to \infty} \left\{ 2X_0^2 T \left[\frac{\sin \omega T}{\omega T} \right]^2 + \frac{X_1^2 T}{2} \left[\frac{\sin (\omega - \omega_1)T}{(\omega - \omega_1)T} \right]^2 \right.$$
$$\left. + \frac{X_1^2 T}{2} \left[\frac{\sin (\omega + \omega_1)T}{(\omega + \omega_1)T} \right]^2 \right\}$$

(11-23)

In order to investigate the limit, consider the essential part of the first term; that is,

$$\lim_{T \to \infty} T \left[\frac{\sin \omega T}{\omega T} \right]^2 = ?$$

This limit is clearly zero when ω is *not* zero since $\sin^2 \omega T$ cannot exceed 1 and the denominator increases as T. When $\omega = 0$, however,

$$\left. \frac{\sin \omega T}{\omega T} \right|_{\omega = 0} = 1$$

and the limit is infinite. Hence, one can write

$$\lim_{T \to \infty} T \left[\frac{\sin \omega T}{\omega T} \right]^2 = K \delta(\omega)$$ (11-24)

where K represents the area of the δ function and has not yet been evaluated. The value of K can be found by equating the areas of both sides of (11-24); that is,

$$\lim_{T \to \infty} \int_{-\infty}^{\infty} T \left[\frac{\sin \omega T}{\omega T} \right]^2 \, d\omega = \int_{-\infty}^{\infty} K \delta(\omega) \, d\omega$$ (11-25)

The integral on the left is tabulated and has a value of π for *all* values of T. Thus, the limiting operation becomes trivial, and (11-25) leads to

$$\pi = K$$

An exactly similar procedure can be used for the other terms in (11-23). It is left as an exercise for the reader to show that the final result becomes

$$S_x(\omega) = 2\pi X_0^2 \delta(\omega) + \frac{\pi}{2} X_1^2 \delta(\omega - \omega_1) + \frac{\pi}{2} X_1^2 \delta(\omega + \omega_1) \quad \textbf{(11-26)}$$

This spectral density is shown in Fig. 11-1.

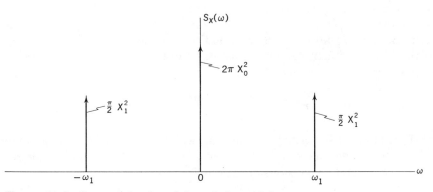

Figure 11-1   Spectral density of dc and sinusoidal components.

It is of interest to determine the area of the spectral density in order to verify that (11-26) does in fact lead to the proper mean-square value. Thus, according to (11-16)

$$\overline{x^2} = \frac{1}{2\pi} \int_{-\infty}^{\infty} \left[2\pi X_0^2 \delta(\omega) + \frac{\pi}{2} X_1^2 \delta(\omega - \omega_1) + \frac{\pi}{2} X_1^2 \delta(\omega + \omega_1) \right] d\omega$$

$$\quad \textbf{(11-27)}$$

$$= \frac{1}{2\pi} \left[2\pi X_0^2 + \frac{\pi}{2} X_1^2 + \frac{\pi}{2} X_1^2 \right] = X_0^2 + \frac{1}{2} X_1^2$$

The reader can verify easily that this same result would be obtained from ensemble averaging of $x^2(t)$.

It is also possible to have spectral densities with both a continuous component and discrete components. An example of this sort that arises frequently in connection with communication systems or sampled-data control systems is the random-amplitude pulse sequence shown in Fig. 11-2. It is assumed here that all of the pulses have the same shape

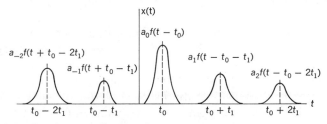

Figure 11-2   Random amplitude pulse sequence.

but that their amplitude is a random variable, which is independent from pulse to pulse. However, all the amplitude variables have the same mean, $\bar{a}$, and the same variance, σ_a^2. The repetition period for the pulses is t_1, a constant, and the reference time for any sample function is t_0, which is a random variable uniformly distributed over an interval of t_1.

The complete derivation of the spectral density is too lengthy to be included here, but the final result indicates some interesting points. This result may be expressed in terms of the Fourier transform $F(j\omega)$ of the basic pulse shape $f(t)$, and is

$$S_x(\omega) = |F(j\omega)|^2 \left[\frac{\sigma_a^2}{t_1} + \frac{2\pi(\bar{a})^2}{t_1^2} \sum_{n=-\infty}^{\infty} \delta\left(\omega - \frac{2\pi n}{t_1} \right) \right] \qquad \text{(11-28)}$$

If the basic pulse shape is rectangular, with a width of t_2, the corresponding spectral density will be as shown in Fig. 11-3. From (11-28) the following general conclusions are possible:

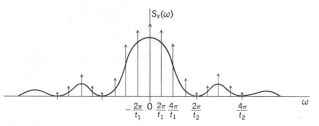

Figure 11-3 Spectral density for rectangular pulse sequence with random amplitudes.

    1. Both the continuous spectrum and the δ functions are proportional to the squared magnitude of the Fourier transform of the basic pulse shape.
    2. If the mean value of the pulse amplitude is zero, there will be *no discrete spectrum* even though the pulses occur periodically.
    3. If the variance of the pulse amplitude is zero, there will be *no* continuous spectrum.

11-3   Spectral Density and the Complex Frequency Plane

In the discussion so far the spectral density has been expressed as a function of the real angular frequency ω. However, for applications to system analysis, it is very convenient to express it in terms of the complex frequency s, since system transfer functions are more convenient in this form. This change can be made very simply by replacing $(j\omega)$ with s. Hence, along the $j\omega$-axis of the complex frequency plane the spectral density will be the same as that already discussed.

For the special case of rational spectral densities, in which only even powers of ω occur, this substitution is equivalent to replacing ω^2 by $-s^2$. For example, consider the rational spectrum

$$S_x(\omega) = \frac{10(\omega^2 + 5)}{\omega^4 + 10\omega^2 + 24} \qquad \text{(11-29)}$$

When expressed as a function of s, this becomes[1]

$$S_x(s) = S_x(-j\omega) = \frac{10(-s^2 + 5)}{s^4 - 10s^2 + 24} \qquad \text{(11-30)}$$

Any spectral density can also be represented in terms of its pole-zero configuration in the complex frequency plane. Such a representation is often convenient in carrying out certain calculations which will be discussed in the following sections. For purposes of illustration, consider the spectral density of (11-30). This may be factored as

$$S_x(s) = \frac{-10(s + \sqrt{5})(s - \sqrt{5})}{(s + 2)(s - 2)(s + \sqrt{6})(s - \sqrt{6})} \qquad \text{(11-31)}$$

and the pole-zero configuration plotted as shown in Fig. 11-4. This plot

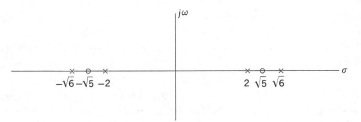

Figure 11-4   Pole-zero configuration for a spectral density.

also illustrates the important point that such configurations are always symmetrical about the $j\omega$ axis. When the spectral density is not rational, the substitution is the same but may not be quite so straightforward. For example, the spectral density given by (11-28) could be expressed in the complex frequency plane as

$$S_x(s) = F(s)F(-s)\left[\frac{\sigma_a^2}{t_1} + \frac{2\pi(\bar{a})^2}{t_1^2}\sum_{n=-\infty}^{\infty}\delta\left(s - j\frac{2\pi n}{t_1}\right)\right] \qquad \text{(11-32)}$$

where $F(s)$ is the *Laplace* transform of the basic pulse shape $f(t)$.

---

[1] The formal conversion from $S_x(\omega)$ to $S_x(s)$ is accomplished by replacing ω by $-js$ in the expression for $S_x(\omega)$. To go from $S_x(s)$ to $S_x(\omega)$, we make the substitution $\omega = js$. It is evident that $S_x(s)$ and $S_x(\omega)$ are somewhat different functions of their arguments; however, it is convenient to use the same notation just as in the case of the Fourier transform $F(j\omega)$ and $F(f)$.

In addition to making spectral densities more convenient for system analysis, the use of the complex frequency s also makes it more convenient to evaluate mean-square values. This application is discussed in the following section.

11-4 Mean-Square Values from Spectral Density

It was shown in the course of defining the spectral density that the mean-square value of the random process was given by

$$\overline{x^2} = \frac{1}{2\pi} \int_{-\infty}^{\infty} S_x(\omega) \, d\omega \tag{11-33}$$

Hence, the mean-square value is proportional to the *area* of the spectral density.

The evaluation of an integral such as the one occurring in (11-33) may be very difficult if the spectral density has a complicated form or if it involves high powers of ω. A classical way of carrying out such integration is to convert the variable of integration to a complex variable (by substituting s for $j\omega$) and then utilize some powerful theorems concerning integration around closed paths in the complex plane. This is probably the easiest and most satisfactory way of obtaining mean-square values but, unfortunately, requires a knowledge of complex variables that the reader is assumed not to possess. The *mechanics* of the procedure are discussed in the Appendix, however, for those interested in this method.

An alternative method, which will be discussed in this section, is to utilize some tabulated results for spectral densities that are rational. These have been tabulated in general form for polynomials of various degrees and their use is simply a matter of substituting in the appropriate numbers. The existence of such general forms is primarily a consequence of the symmetry of the spectral density. As a result of this symmetry, it is always possible to factor rational spectral densities into the form

$$S_x(s) = \frac{c(s)c(-s)}{d(s)d(-s)} \tag{11-34}$$

where $c(s)$ contains the left-half-plane zeros, $c(-s)$ the right-half-plane zeros, $d(s)$ the LHP poles, and $d(-s)$ the RHP poles.

When the real integration of Equation (11-33) is expressed in terms of the complex variable s, the mean-square value becomes

$$\overline{x^2} = \frac{1}{2\pi j} \int_{-j\infty}^{j\infty} S_x(s) \, ds = \frac{1}{2\pi j} \int_{-j\infty}^{j\infty} \frac{c(s)c(-s)}{d(s)d(-s)} \, ds \tag{11-35}$$

For the special case of rational spectral densities, $c(s)$ and $d(s)$ are polynomials in s and may be written as

$$c(s) = c_{n-1}s^{n-1} + c_{n-2}s^{n-2} + \cdots + c_0$$
$$d(s) = d_n s^n - d_{n-1}s^{n-1} + \cdots + d_0$$

Some of the coefficients may be zero, but $d(s)$ must be of higher degree than $c(s)$.

Integrals of the form in (11-35) have been tabulated for values of n up to 10, although beyond $n = 3$ or 4 the general results are so complicated as to be of doubtful value. An abbreviated table is given in Table 11-1.

Table 11-1   TABLE OF INTEGRALS

$$I_n = \frac{1}{2\pi j} \int_{-j\infty}^{j\infty} \frac{c(s)c(-s)}{d(s)d(-s)} \, ds$$

$$c(s) = c_{n-1}s^{n-1} + c_{n-2}s^{n-2} + \cdots + c_0$$
$$d(s) = d_n s^n + d_{n-1}s^{n-1} + \cdots + d_0$$

$$I_1 = \frac{c_0^2}{2d_0 d_1}$$

$$I_2 = \frac{c_1^2 d_0 + c_0^2 d_2}{2d_0 d_1 d_2}$$

$$I_3 = \frac{c_2^2 d_0 d_1 + (c_1^2 - 2c_0 c_2)d_0 d_3 + c_0^2 d_2 d_3}{2d_0 d_3 (d_1 d_2 - d_0 d_3)}$$

As an example of this calculation, consider the spectral density

$$S_x(\omega) = \frac{\omega^2 + 4}{\omega^4 + 10\omega^2 + 9} \tag{11-36}$$

When $j\omega$ is replaced by s, this becomes

$$S_x(s) = \frac{-(s^2 - 4)}{s^4 - 10s^2 + 9} = \frac{-(s^2 - 4)}{(s^2 - 1)(s^2 - 9)} \tag{11-37}$$

This can be factored into

$$S_x(s) = \frac{(s + 2)(-s + 2)}{(s + 1)(s + 3)(-s + 1)(-s + 3)} \tag{11-38}$$

from which it is seen that

$$c(s) = s + 2$$
$$d(s) = (s + 1)(s + 3) = s^2 + 4s + 3$$

This is a case in which $n = 2$ and

$$c_1 = 1$$
$$c_0 = 2$$
$$d_2 = 1$$
$$d_1 = 4$$
$$d_0 = 3$$

From Table 11-1, I_2 is given by

$$I_2 = \frac{c_1^2 d_0 + c_0^2 d_2}{2 d_0 d_1 d_2} = \frac{(1)^2(3) + (2)^2(1)}{2(3)(4)(1)} = \frac{3 + 4}{24} = \frac{7}{24}$$

However, $\overline{x^2} = I_2$, so that

$$\overline{x^2} = \frac{7}{24}$$

The procedure just presented is a mechanical one and does not require any deep understanding of the theory in order to be a useful tool. Some precautions are necessary, however. In the first place, as noted above, it is necessary that $c(s)$ be of lower degree than $d(s)$. Second, it is necessary that $c(s)$ and $d(s)$ have roots *only* in the left half plane. Finally, it is necessary that $d(s)$ have *no* roots on the $j\omega$-axis.

11-5   Relation of Spectral Density to the Autocorrelation Function

The autocorrelation function was shown in Chapter 10 to be the expected value of the product of time functions. In this chapter, it has been shown that the spectral density is related to the expected value of the product of Fourier transforms. It would appear, therefore, that there should be some direct relationship between these two expected values. Almost intuitively one would expect the spectral density to be the Fourier (or Laplace) tranform of the autocorrelation function, and this turns out to be the case.

We will consider first the case of a nonstationary random process and then specialize the result to a stationary process. In (11-15) the spectral density was defined as

$$S_x(\omega) = \lim_{T \to \infty} \frac{E[|X_T(j\omega)|^2]}{2T} \tag{11-39}$$

where $X_T(j\omega)$ was the Fourier transform of the truncated sample function. Thus,

$$X_T(j\omega) = \int_{-\infty}^{\infty} x_T(t) \, \epsilon^{-j\omega t} \, dt \qquad T < \infty \tag{11-40}$$

Substituting (11-40) into (11-39) yields

$$S_x(\omega) = \lim_{T \to \infty} \frac{1}{2T} E \left[\int_{-\infty}^{\infty} x_T(t_1) \, \epsilon^{+j\omega t_1} \, dt_1 \int_{-\infty}^{\infty} x_T(t_2) \, \epsilon^{-j\omega t_2} \, dt_2 \right] \tag{11-41}$$

since $|X_T(j\omega)|^2 = X_T(j\omega)X_T(-j\omega)$. The subscripts on t_1 and t_2 have been introduced so that we can distinguish the variables of integration when the *product* of integrals is rewritten as an *iterated double integral*. Thus, write (11-41) as

$$S_x(\omega) = \lim_{T \to \infty} \frac{1}{2T} E\left[\int_{-\infty}^{\infty} dt_2 \int_{-\infty}^{\infty} \epsilon^{-j\omega(t_2 - t_1)} x_T(t_1) x_T(t_2)\, dt_1\right]$$

$$= \lim_{T \to \infty} \frac{1}{2T} \int_{-\infty}^{\infty} dt_2 \int_{-\infty}^{\infty} \epsilon^{-j\omega(t_2 - t_1)} E\left[x_T(t_1) x_T(t_2)\right] dt_1$$

(11-42)

Moving the expectation operation inside the double integral can be shown to be valid in this case, but the details will not be discussed here. Further discussion of this type of interchange is given in the Appendix.

The expectation in the integrand of (11-42) is recognized as the autocorrelation function of the truncated process. Thus,

$$E\left[x_T(t_1)x_T(t_2)\right] = R_x(t_1, t_2) \qquad |t_1|, |t_2| \leq T$$
$$= 0 \qquad\qquad \text{elsewhere.}$$

(11-43)

Making the substitution

$$t_2 - t_1 = \tau$$
$$dt_2 = d\tau$$

we can write (11-42) as

$$S_x(\omega) = \lim_{T \to \infty} \frac{1}{2T} \int_{-\infty}^{\infty} d\tau \int_{-T}^{T} \epsilon^{-j\omega\tau} R_x(t_1, t_1 + \tau)\, dt_1$$

when the limits on t_1 are imposed by (11-43). Interchanging the order of integration and limiting gives

$$S_x(\omega) = \int_{-\infty}^{\infty} \left\{\lim_{T \to \infty} \frac{1}{2T} \int_{-T}^{T} R_x(t_1, t_1 + \tau)\, dt_1\right\} \epsilon^{-j\omega\tau}\, d\tau \qquad \text{(11-44)}$$

From (11-44) it is apparent that the spectral density is the Fourier transform of the time average of the autocorrelation function. This may be expressed in shorter notation as follows:

$$S_x(\omega) = \mathcal{F}\left\{< R_x(t, t + \tau) >\right\} \qquad \text{(11-45)}$$

The relationship given in (11-45) is valid for nonstationary processes.

If the process in question is a stationary random process, the autocorrelation function is independent of time; therefore,

$$< R_x(t_1, t_1 + \tau) > = R_x(\tau)$$

Accordingly, the spectral density of a stationary random process is just the Fourier transform of the autocorrelation function; that is,

$$S_x(\omega) = \int_{-\infty}^{\infty} R_x(\tau)\epsilon^{-j\omega\tau}\, d\tau$$

(11-46)

$$= \mathcal{F}\left\{R_x(\tau)\right\}$$

The relationship given in (11-46) is of fundamental importance in analyzing random signals because it provides the link between the time domain (correlation function) and the frequency domain (spectral density). Because of the uniqueness of the Fourier transform it follows that the autocorrelation function of a stationary random process is the inverse transform of the spectral density. In the case of a nonstationary process the autocorrelation function cannot be recovered from the spectral density — only the time average of the correlation function, as seen from (11-45). In subsequent discussions we will be dealing only with stationary random processes for which (11-46) is valid.

As a simple example of this result, consider an autocorrelation function of the form

$$R_x(\tau) = A \epsilon^{-\beta|\tau|} \tag{11-47}$$

The absolute value sign on τ is required by the symmetry of the autocorrelation function. This function is shown in Fig. 11-5(a) and is seen to

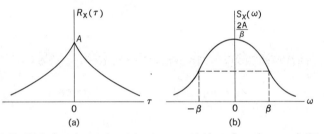

Figure 11-5 Relation between **(a)** autocorrelation function and **(b)** spectral density.

have a discontinuous derivative at $\tau = 0$. Hence, it is necessary to write (11-46) as the sum of two integrals — one for negative values of τ and one for positive values of τ. Thus,

$$S_x(\omega) = \int_{-\infty}^{0} A \epsilon^{\beta\tau} \epsilon^{-j\omega\tau} \, d\tau + \int_{0}^{\infty} A \epsilon^{-\beta\tau} \epsilon^{-j\omega\tau} \, d\tau$$

$$= A \frac{\epsilon^{(\beta - j\omega)\tau}}{\beta - j\omega} \Bigg]_{-\infty}^{0} + A \frac{\epsilon^{-(\beta + j\omega)\tau}}{-(\beta + j\omega)} \Bigg]_{0}^{\infty} \tag{11-48}$$

$$= A \left[\frac{1}{\beta - j\omega} + \frac{1}{\beta + j\omega} \right] = \frac{2A\beta}{\omega^2 + \beta^2}$$

This spectral density is shown in Fig. 11-5(b).

In the stationary case it is also possible to find the autocorrelation function corresponding to a given spectral density by using the inverse Fourier transform. Thus,

$$R_x(\tau) = \frac{1}{2\pi} \int_{-\infty}^{\infty} S_x(\omega) \epsilon^{j\omega\tau} \, d\omega \tag{11-49}$$

An example of the application of this result will be given in the next article.

It was noted earlier that the relationship between spectral density and correlation function could also be expressed in terms of the Laplace transform. However, it should be recalled that the form of Laplace transform used most often in system analysis requires that the time function being transformed be zero for negative values of time. Autocorrelation functions can never be zero for negative values of τ since they are always even functions of τ. Hence, it is necessary to use a *two-sided Laplace transform* for this application. Although the two-sided Laplace transform is a straightforward extension of the normal one-sided transform, and has been discussed previously, it will not be needed sufficiently in the present elementary discussion to justify its inclusion. Instead, the Fourier transform will be used for converting correlation functions to spectral densities and vice versa.

11-6   White Noise

The concept of *white noise* was mentioned previously. This term is applied to a spectral density that is constant for all values of ω; that is, $S_x(\omega) = S_0$. It is of interest to determine the correlation function for such a process. This is best done by giving the result and verifying its correctness. Consider an autocorrelation function that is a δ function of the form

$$R_x(\tau) = S_0 \delta(\tau)$$

Using this form in (11-44) leads to

$$S_x(\omega) = \int_{-\infty}^{\infty} R_x(\tau) \epsilon^{-j\omega\tau} \, d\tau = \int_{-\infty}^{\infty} S_0 \delta(\tau) \epsilon^{-j\omega\tau} \, d\tau = S_0 \qquad \text{(11-50)}$$

which is the result for white noise. It is clear, therefore, that the autocorrelation function for white noise is just a δ function with *an area equal to the spectral density.*

It was noted previously that the concept of white noise is fictitious because such a process would have infinite mean-square value since the area of the spectral density is infinite. This same conclusion is also apparent from the correlation function. It may be recalled that the mean-square value is equal to the value of the autocorrelation function at $\tau = 0$. For a δ function at the origin, this is also infinite.

Another concept that is frequently used is that of *band-limited white noise.* This implies a spectral density that is constant over a finite bandwidth and zero outside this frequency range. For example,

$$S_x(\omega) = S_0 \qquad |\omega| \le 2\pi W$$
$$ = 0 \qquad |\omega| > 2\pi W \tag{11-51}$$

as shown in Fig. 11-6(a). This spectral density is also fictitious even

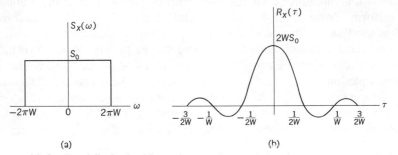

(a)   (h)

Figure 11-6   Band-limited white noise. **(a)** Spectral density. **(b)** Autocorrelation function.

though the mean-square value is finite (in fact, $\overline{x^2} = 2WS_0$). Why? It can be approached arbitrarily closely, however, and is a convenient form for many analysis problems.

The autocorrelation function for such a process is easily obtained from (11-49). Thus,

$$R_x(\tau) = \frac{1}{2\pi} \int_{-\infty}^{\infty} S_x(\omega)\epsilon^{j\omega\tau}\, d\omega = \frac{1}{2\pi} \int_{-2\pi W}^{2\pi W} S_0 \epsilon^{j\omega\tau}\, d\omega = \frac{S_0}{2\pi} \left[\frac{\epsilon^{j\omega\tau}}{j\tau}\right]_{-2\pi W}^{2\pi W}$$

$$= \frac{S_0}{2\pi}\frac{\epsilon^{j2\pi W\tau} - \epsilon^{-j2\pi W\tau}}{j\tau} = \frac{S_0}{\pi\tau}\sin 2\pi W\tau \tag{11-52}$$

$$= 2WS_0\left[\frac{\sin 2\pi W\tau}{2\pi W\tau}\right]$$

This is shown in Fig. 11-6(b). Note that in the limit as W approaches infinity, this approaches a δ function.

11-7   Cross Spectral Density

When two correlated random processes are being considered, such as the input and output of a linear system, it is possible to define a pair of quantities known as the cross spectral density. For purposes of the present discussion, it is sufficient to simply define them and note a few of their properties without undertaking any formal proofs.

If $X_T(j\omega)$ is the Fourier transform of a truncated sample function from one process and $Y_T(j\omega)$ is a similar transform for the other process, then the two cross spectral densities may be defined as

$$S_{xy}(\omega) = \lim_{T\to\infty} \frac{E\left[X_T(-j\omega)Y_T(j\omega)\right]}{2T} \tag{11-53}$$

$$S_{yx}(\omega) = \lim_{T \to \infty} \frac{E[Y_T(-j\omega)X_T(j\omega)]}{2T} \tag{11-54}$$

Unlike normal spectral densities, cross spectral densities need not be real, positive, or even functions of ω. They do have the following properties, however:

1. $S_{xy}(\omega) = S_{yx}{}^*(\omega)$ (* implies complex conjugate)
2. Re $[S_{xy}(\omega)]$ is an even function of ω. Also true for $S_{yx}(\omega)$.
3. Im $[S_{xy}(\omega)]$ is an odd function of ω. Also true for $S_{yx}(\omega)$.

Cross spectral densities can also be related to cross-correlation functions by the Fourier transform. Thus, for jointly stationary processes,

$$S_{xy}(\omega) = \int_{-\infty}^{\infty} R_{xy}(\tau)\epsilon^{-j\omega\tau}\, d\tau \tag{11-55}$$

$$R_{xy}(\tau) = \frac{1}{2\pi} \int_{-\infty}^{\infty} S_{xy}(\omega)\epsilon^{j\,\omega\tau}\, d\omega \tag{11-56}$$

$$S_{yx}(\omega) = \int_{-\infty}^{\infty} R_{yx}(\tau)\epsilon^{-j\omega\tau}\, d\tau \tag{11-57}$$

$$R_{yx}(\tau) = \frac{1}{2\pi} \int_{-\infty}^{\infty} S_{yx}(\omega)\epsilon^{j\omega\tau}\, d\omega \tag{11-58}$$

Other properties of cross spectral densities will be developed as the need arises.

11-8 Spectral Density for Random Vectors

If a random vector $\mathbf{x}(t)$ is composed of sample functions from stationary random processes, that is,

$$\mathbf{x}(t) = \begin{bmatrix} x_1(t) \\ x_2(t) \\ \vdots \\ x_n(t) \end{bmatrix}$$

then it is possible to define a spectral density matrix for the vector process by simply taking the Fourier transform of the correlation matrix defined in the previous chapter. This correlation matrix was given as

$$\mathbf{R_x}(\tau) = \begin{vmatrix} R_{11}(\tau) & R_{12}(\tau) & \cdots & R_{1m}(\tau) \\ R_{21}(\tau) & R_{22}(\tau) & \cdots & \cdot \\ \vdots & \vdots & & \vdots \\ R_{m1}(\tau) & \cdots & & R_{mm}(\tau) \end{vmatrix} \tag{11-59}$$

where

$$R_{ij}(\tau) = E[x_i(t)x_j(t+\tau)] \qquad i, j = 1, 2, \cdots, m$$

Taking a Fourier transform of the matrix would lead to a matrix of the Fourier transforms of the individual components. This leads to the spectral densities and cross spectral densities of the separate processes; that is, let

$$S_{ij}(\omega) = \mathscr{F}[R_{ij}(\tau)] \qquad i, j = 1, 2, \cdots, m$$

Hence, the spectral density matrix for a stationary $\mathbf{x}(t)$ is

$$\mathbf{S_x}(\omega) = \mathscr{F}[\mathbf{R_x}(\tau)] = \begin{vmatrix} S_{11}(\omega) & S_{12}(\omega) & \cdots & S_{1m}(\omega) \\ S_{21}(\omega) & S_{22}(\omega) & & \\ \vdots & & & \vdots \\ S_{m1}(\omega) & \cdots & & S_{mm}(\omega) \end{vmatrix}$$

If all pairs of processes in $\mathbf{x}(t)$ are statistically independent and have zero mean, this matrix will also become diagonal.

Note that a similar result for the random vector composed of sample values from a single time function does *not* exist. The covariance matrix for such a set of sample values does not have elements that are continuous functions of τ, but are instead simply constants. Hence, there is no spectral density matrix for this situation.

■ REFERENCES

See Chapter 12.

■ PROBLEMS

11-1 The spectral density defined in Section 11-1 is sometimes referred to as the "two-sided spectral density," since it exists for both positive and negative values of ω. However, some authors prefer to define a "one-sided spectral density," which is expressed as a function of $f = \omega/2\pi$ and exists for positive values of f. If this one-sided spectral density is designated as $G_x(f)$, then the mean-square value of the random process is given by

$$\overline{x^2} = \int_0^\infty G_x(f)\, df$$

a. Write a defining equation for $G_x(f)$ that is analogous to Equation (11-15).
b. What is the relationship between the magnitude of $G_x(f)$ and $S_x(\omega)$ for any value of $\omega = 2\pi f$?
c. A random process has a two-sided spectral density of

$$S_x(\omega) = \frac{10\omega^2}{\omega^4 + 2\omega^2 + 4}$$

What is the corresponding one-sided spectral density $G_x(f)$?

d. Write the one-sided spectral density that would correspond to the $S_x(\omega)$ given by Equation (11-26).

11-2 For each of the following functions of ω, state whether it can or cannot be a valid expression for the spectral density of a random process. If it cannot, state why.

a. $\dfrac{\omega^2 + 9}{\omega^4 - 3\omega^2 + 2}$

d. $\dfrac{\sqrt{\omega^4 - 2}}{\omega^2 + 10\omega^4 + 2\omega^2 + 1}$

b. $\dfrac{\omega^2 + 10}{\omega^4 + 6\omega^2 + 4}$

e. $\left[\dfrac{\sin \omega}{\omega}\right]^2$

c. $\dfrac{\omega^2 + 2\omega + 1}{\omega^6 + 10\omega^4 + 8\omega^2 + 4}$,

f. $\dfrac{\omega + 3}{\omega^3 + 3\omega^2 + 4\omega + 12}$

11-3 Consider a random amplitude pulse sequence of the form shown in Fig. 11-2 in which the pulses are rectangular with a width of $t_1/8$ and whose amplitudes are Rayleigh distributed according to

$$p(a_i) = \frac{a_i}{4}\,\epsilon^{-a_i^2/8} \qquad a_i \geq 0$$
$$\qquad\qquad = 0 \qquad\qquad a_i < 0$$

$$i = 0, \pm 1, \pm 2, \pm \cdots$$

Using the general result of Equation (11-28), write an expression for the spectral density $S_x(\omega)$ of this process.

11-4 For each of the acceptable spectral densities of Problem 11-2, write the corresponding complex frequency representation $S_x(s)$.

11-5 A stationary random process has a spectral density of

$$S_x(\omega) = \frac{\omega^2}{\omega^6 + 1}$$

Using Table 11-1, find the mean-square value of the process.

11-6 Find the autocorrelation function of the random process specified in Problem 11-5.

11-7 A stationary random process has an autocorrelation function of the form shown. Find

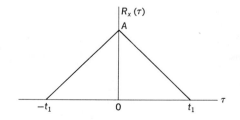

a. The spectral density of this process.
b. The mean-square value from the spectral density.

11-8 The spectral density of a stationary, band-limited, white noise process is defined to be

$$S_x(\omega) = S_0 \qquad |\omega \pm \omega_0| \leq \pi W$$
$$= 0 \qquad |\omega \pm \omega_0| > \pi W$$

Find the autocorrelation function of this process.

11-9 Let $\{x(t)\}$ be a random process having sample functions of the form shown. In this sample function the X_i are statistically independent,

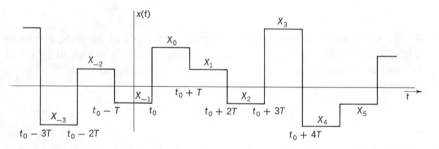

time-invariant random variables with zero means and identical probability density functions. The time t_0 is a random variable that is uniformly distributed between 0 and T and is statistically independent of the X_i. Find the spectral density of the process and sketch it.

11-10 Compute an estimate of the spectral density of the random process of Problem 10-11.

11-11 A sample function from a *white band-limited* noise process, having a bandwidth of W hertz, is sampled at intervals of $\Delta t = 1/2 W$. If the spectral density of this process is S_0, determine the covariance matrix for N samples taken from this process.

12

Response of Linear Systems to Random Inputs

12-1 Introduction

The discussion in Chapters 9 through 11 has been devoted exclusively to finding mathematical representations for random functions of time that might be used as inputs to a linear system. Having completed this not very exciting, but certainly necessary, study it is now time to consider the problems that motivated it. Briefly stated, these problems concern finding out something about the response or output of a linear system when the excitation or input is a random signal.

Before we consider random excitations it may be helpful to review briefly the procedure for nonrandom excitations. The response of a linear system to a *nonrandom* input can be determined using either time-domain or frequency-domain methods. The system is characterized either in terms of its impulse response $h(t)$ or its system function, $H(j\omega)$. The analyses based on these approaches lead to a unique relationship between the excitation and response of a system, assuming that the initial conditions are either zero or are taken into account as part of the excitation. When the system excitation is a sample function from a random process there is again a unique relationship between the excitation and the response; however, because of its random nature, we do not have an explicit representation of the excitation and, therefore, cannot obtain an explicit expression for the response. In this case we must be content with a probabilistic or statistical description of the response, just as we must use this type of description for the random excitation itself. Of these two approaches, statistical and probabilistic, the statistical approach is the most useful. In only a very limited class of problems is it possible to obtain a probabilistic description of the output based on a probabilistic description of the input, whereas in many cases of interest a statistical model of the output can be readily obtained by performing simple mathematical operations on the statistical model of the input. With the statistical method, such quantities as the mean, correlation function, and spectral density of the output can be determined. Only the statistical approach will be considered in the following sections. For information on the probability model approach the references at the end of the chapter may be consulted.

12-2 Analysis in the Time Domain

By means of the convolution integral it is possible to determine the response of a linear system to a very general excitation. In the case of time-varying systems or nonstationary random excitations, or both, the details become quite involved; therefore, these cases will not be considered here. To make the analysis more realistic we will further restrict considerations to physically realizable systems and to systems that are bounded-input/bounded-output stable. If the input time function is designated as $x(t)$, the system impulse response as $h(t)$, and the output time function as $y(t)$, as shown in Fig. 12-1, then they are related either by

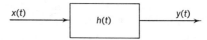

Figure 12-1 Time-domain representation of a linear system.

$$y(t) = \int_0^\infty x(t - \lambda)h(\lambda)\, d\lambda \tag{12-1}$$

or by

$$y(t) = \int_{-\infty}^t x(\lambda)\, h(t - \lambda)\, d\lambda \tag{12-2}$$

The physical realizability and stability constraints on the system are given by

$$h(t) = 0 \qquad t < 0 \tag{12-3}$$

and

$$\int_{-\infty}^{\infty} |h(t)| \, dt < \infty \tag{12-4}$$

Starting from these specifications, many important characteristics of the output of a system excited by a stationary random process can be determined.

12-3 Mean and Mean-Square Value of System Output

The most convenient form of the convolution integral for random inputs is usually

$$y(t) = \int_{0}^{\infty} x(t - \lambda)h(\lambda) \, d\lambda \tag{12-5}$$

since the limits of integration do not depend on t. Using this form, consider first the mean value of the output $y(t)$. This is[1]

$$\bar{y} = E[y(t)] = E\left[\int_{0}^{\infty} x(t - \lambda)h(\lambda) \, d\lambda\right] = \int_{0}^{\infty} E[x(t - \lambda)]h(\lambda) \, d\lambda \tag{12-6}$$

$$= \int_{0}^{\infty} \bar{x}h(\lambda) \, d\lambda = \bar{x} \int_{0}^{\infty} h(\lambda) \, d\lambda \tag{12-7}$$

when the input process is stationary. It should be recalled from earlier work in systems analysis that the *area* of the impulse response is just the *dc gain* of the system—that is, the transfer function of the system evaluated at $\omega = 0$. Hence, (12-7) simply states the obvious fact that the dc component of the output is equal to the dc component of the input times the dc gain of the system. If the input random process has zero mean, the output process will also have zero mean. If the system does not pass direct current, the output process will always have zero mean.

In order to find the mean-square value of the output we must be able to calculate the mean value of the *product* of two integrals. However, such a product may always be written as an iterated double integral if the variables of integration are kept distinct. Thus,

$$\overline{y^2} = E[y^2(t)] = E\left[\int_{0}^{\infty} x(t - \lambda_1)h(\lambda_1) \, d\lambda_1 \cdot \int_{0}^{\infty} x(t - \lambda_2)h(\lambda_2) \, d\lambda_2\right]$$

$$= E\left[\int_{0}^{\infty} d\lambda_1 \int_{0}^{\infty} x(t - \lambda_1)x(t - \lambda_2)h(\lambda_1)h(\lambda_2) \, d\lambda_2\right] \tag{12-8}$$

---

[1]The justification for moving the expectation operation inside the integral is discussed in the Appendix.

$$= \int_0^\infty d\lambda_1 \int_0^\infty E\left[x(t - \lambda_1)x(t - \lambda_2)\right] h(\lambda_1)h(\lambda_2) \, d\lambda_2 \qquad \text{(12-9)}$$

in which the subscripts on λ_1 and λ_2 have been introduced to keep the variables of integration distinct. The expected value inside the double integral is simply the autocorrelation function for the input random process; that is,

$$E\left[x(t - \lambda_1)x(t - \lambda_2)\right] = R_x(t - \lambda_1 - t + \lambda_2) = R_x(\lambda_2 - \lambda_1)$$

Hence, (12-9) becomes

$$\overline{y^2} = \int_0^\infty d\lambda_1 \int_0^\infty R_x(\lambda_2 - \lambda_1)h(\lambda_1)h(\lambda_2) \, d\lambda_2 \qquad \text{(12-10)}$$

Although (12-10) is usually not difficult to evaluate, since both $R_x(\tau)$ and $h(t)$ are likely to contain only exponentials, it is frequently very tedious to carry out the details. This is because such autocorrelation functions often have discontinuous derivatives at the origin (which in this case is $\lambda_1 = \lambda_2$) and thus the integral must be broken up into several ranges. This point will be illustrated later. At the moment, however, it is instructive to consider a much simpler situation—one in which the input is a sample function from white noise. For this case, it was shown that

$$R_x(\tau) = S_0 \delta(\tau)$$

where S_0 is the spectral density of the white noise. Hence (12-10) becomes

$$\overline{y^2} = \int_0^\infty d\lambda_1 \int_0^\infty S_0 \delta(\lambda_2 - \lambda_1)h(\lambda_1)h(\lambda_2) \, d\lambda_2 \qquad \text{(12-11)}$$

Integrating over λ_2, say, yields

$$\overline{y^2} = S_0 \int_0^\infty h^2(\lambda) \, d\lambda \qquad \text{(12-12)}$$

Hence, for this case it is the area of the *square* of the impulse response that is significant.[2]

As a means of illustrating some of these ideas with a simple example, consider the single-section, low-pass, R-C circuit shown in Fig. 12-2. The mean value of the output is, from (12-7),

$$\overline{y} = \overline{x} \int_0^\infty b\epsilon^{-b\lambda} \, d\lambda = \overline{x} b \left. \frac{\epsilon^{-b\lambda}}{-b} \right|_0^\infty = \overline{x} \qquad \text{(12-13)}$$

---

[2]It should be noted that, for some functions, this integral can diverge even when (12-4) is satisfied. This occurs, for instance, whenever $h(t)$ contains δ functions. The high-pass R-C circuit is an example of this.

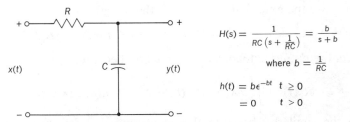

$$H(s) = \frac{1}{RC\left(s + \frac{1}{RC}\right)} = \frac{b}{s+b}$$

$$\text{where } b = \frac{1}{RC}$$

$$h(t) = be^{-bt} \quad t \geq 0$$
$$= 0 \qquad t > 0$$

Figure 12-2   Simple R-C circuit and its impulse response.

This result is obviously correct, since it is apparent by inspection that the dc gain of this circuit is unity.

Next consider the mean-square value of the output when the input is white noise. From (12-12), this is

$$\overline{y^2} = S_0 \int_0^\infty b^2 \, \epsilon^{-2b\lambda} \, d\lambda = b^2 S_0 \left. \frac{\epsilon^{-2b}}{-2b} \right|_0^\infty = \frac{bS_0}{2} \tag{12-14}$$

Note that the parameter b, which is the reciprocal of the time constant, is also related to the half-power bandwidth of the system. In particular, this bandwidth B is

$$B = \frac{1}{2\pi RC} = \frac{b}{2\pi} \text{ Hz}$$

so that (12-14) could be written as

$$\overline{y^2} = \pi B S_0 \tag{12-15}$$

It is evident from this that the mean-square value of the output of this system increases *linearly* with the bandwidth of the system. This is a typical result whenever the bandwidth of the input random process is large compared with the bandwidth of the system.

12-4   Autocorrelation Function of System Output

A problem closely related to that of finding the mean-square value is the determination of the autocorrelation function at the output of the system. By definition, this autocorrelation function is

$$R_y(\tau) = E[y(t)y(t + \tau)]$$

Following the same steps as in (12-9), except for replacing t by $t + \tau$ in one factor, the autocorrelation function may be written as

$$R_y(\tau) = \int_0^\infty d\lambda_1 \int_0^\infty E[x(t - \lambda_1)x(t + \tau - \lambda_2)]h(\lambda_1)h(\lambda_2) \, d\lambda_2 \tag{12-16}$$

In this case the expected value inside the integral is

$$E\left[x(t - \lambda_1)x(t + \tau - \lambda_2)\right] = R_x(t - \lambda_1 - t - \tau + \lambda_2) = R_x(\lambda_2 - \lambda_1 - \tau)$$

Hence, the output autocorrelation function becomes

$$R_y(\tau) = \int_0^\infty d\lambda_1 \int_0^\infty R_x(\lambda_2 - \lambda_1 - \tau)h(\lambda_1)h(\lambda_2)\,d\lambda_2 \qquad \textbf{(12-17)}$$

Note the similarity between this result and that for the mean-square value. In particular, for $\tau = 0$, this reduces exactly to (12-10), as it must.

For the special case of white noise into the system, the expression for the output autocorrelation function becomes much simpler. Let

$$R_x(\tau) = S_0\delta(\tau)$$

as before, and substitute into (12-17). Thus,

$$R_y(\tau) = \int_0^\infty d\lambda_1 \int_0^\infty S_0\delta(\lambda_2 - \lambda_1 - \tau)h(\lambda_1)h(\lambda_2)\,d\lambda_2$$

$$= S_0 \int_0^\infty h(\lambda_1)h(\lambda_1 + \tau)\,d\lambda_1$$

$$\textbf{(12-18)}$$

Hence, for the white-noise case, the output autocorrelation function is proportional to the time correlation function of the impulse response.

This point can be illustrated by means of the linear system of Fig. 12-2 and a white-noise input. Thus,

$$R_y(\tau) = S_0 \int_0^\infty (b\,\epsilon^{-b\lambda})b\epsilon^{-b(\lambda + \tau)}\,d\lambda$$

$$= b^2 S_0\,\epsilon^{-b\tau}\,\frac{\epsilon^{-2b\lambda}}{-2b}\bigg|_0^\infty = \frac{bS_0}{2}\,\epsilon^{-b\tau} \qquad \tau \geq 0$$

$$\textbf{(12-19)}$$

This result is valid only for $\tau \geq 0$. When $\tau < 0$, the range of integration must be altered because the impulse response is always zero for negative values of the argument. The situation can be made clearer by means of the two sketches shown in Fig. 12-3, which show the factors in the integrand of (12-18) for both ranges of τ. The integrand is zero, of course, when either factor is zero.

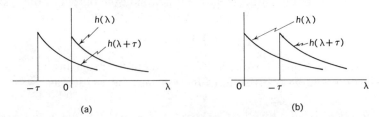

(a)   (b)

Figure 12-3 Factors in the integrand of (12-18) when the R-C circuit of Fig. 12-2 is used.

When $\tau < 0$, the integral becomes

$$R_y(\tau) = S_0 \int_{-\tau}^{\infty} (b \, \epsilon^{-b\tau}) b \epsilon^{-b(\lambda + \tau)} \, d\lambda$$

$$= b^2 S_0 \, \epsilon^{-b\tau} \left. \frac{\epsilon^{-2b\lambda}}{-2b} \right|_{-\tau}^{\infty} = \frac{bS_0}{2} \epsilon^{b\tau} \qquad \tau \leq 0 \tag{12-20}$$

From (12-19) and (12-20), the complete autocorrelation function can be written as

$$R_y(\tau) = \frac{bS_0}{2} \epsilon^{-b|\tau|} \qquad -\infty < \tau < \infty \tag{12-21}$$

It is now apparent that the calculation for $\tau < 0$ was needless. Since the autocorrelation function is an even function of τ, the complete form could have been obtained immediately from the case for $\tau > 0$. This procedure will be followed in the future.

It is desirable to consider at least one example in which the input random process is not white. In so doing, it will be possible to illustrate some of the integration problems that develop and, at the same time, use the results to infer something about the validity and usefulness of the white-noise approximation. For this purpose, assume that the input random process to the R-C circuit of Fig. 12-2 has an autocorrelation function of the form

$$R_x(\tau) = \frac{\beta S_0}{2} \epsilon^{-\beta|\tau|} \qquad -\infty < \tau < \infty \tag{12-22}$$

The coefficient $\beta S_0/2$ has been selected so that this random process has a spectral density at $\omega = 0$ of S_0; see (11-48) and Fig. 11-5(b). Thus, at low frequencies the spectral density is the same as the white-noise spectrum previously assumed.

In order to determine the appropriate ranges of integration, it is desirable to look at the autocorrelation function, $R_x(\lambda_2 - \lambda_1 - \tau)$, as a function of λ_2, for $\tau > 0$. This is shown in Fig. 12-4. Since λ_2 is always

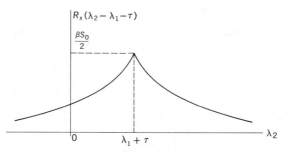

Figure 12-4 Autocorrelation function to be used in (12-17).

positive for the evaluation of (12-17), it is clear that the ranges of integration should be from 0 to $(\lambda_1 + \tau)$ and from $(\lambda_1 + \tau)$ to ∞. Hence, (12-17) may be written as

$$
\begin{aligned}
R_y(\tau) &= \int_0^\infty d\lambda_1 \int_0^{\lambda_1 + \tau} R_x(\lambda_2 - \lambda_1 - \tau) h(\lambda_1) h(\lambda_2) \, d\lambda_2 \\
&\quad + \int_0^\infty d\lambda_1 \int_{\lambda_1 + \tau}^\infty R_x(\lambda_2 - \lambda_1 - \tau) h(\lambda_1) h(\lambda_2) \, d\lambda_2 \\
&= \frac{b^2 \beta S_0}{2} \int_0^\infty \epsilon^{-(b+\beta)\lambda_1} \, d\lambda_1 \int_0^{\lambda_1 + \tau} \epsilon^{-\beta\tau} \epsilon^{-(b-\beta)\lambda_2} \, d\lambda_2 \\
&\quad + \frac{b^2 \beta S_0}{2} \int_0^\infty \epsilon^{-(b-\beta)\lambda_1} \, d\lambda_1 \int_{\lambda_1 + \tau}^\infty \epsilon^{\beta\tau} \epsilon^{-(b+\beta)\lambda_2} \, d\lambda_2 \\[6pt]
&= \frac{b^2 \beta S_0}{-2(b-\beta)} \epsilon^{-\beta\tau} \int_0^\infty \epsilon^{-(b+\beta)\lambda_1} \left[\epsilon^{-(b-\beta)(\lambda_1 + \tau)} - 1 \right] d\lambda_1 \\
&\quad - \frac{b^2 \beta S_0}{-2(b+\beta)} \epsilon^{\beta\tau} \int_0^\infty \epsilon^{-(b-\beta)\lambda_1} \epsilon^{-(b+\beta)(\lambda_1 + \tau)} \, d\lambda_1 \\
&= \frac{b^2 \beta S_0}{2(b-\beta)} \left[-\frac{\epsilon^{-b\tau}}{2b} + \frac{\epsilon^{-\beta\tau}}{b+\beta} \right] + \frac{b^2 \beta S_0}{2(b+\beta)} \left[\frac{\epsilon^{-b\tau}}{2b} \right] \\
&= \frac{b^2 \beta S_0}{2(b^2 - \beta^2)} \left[\epsilon^{-\beta\tau} - \frac{\beta}{b} \epsilon^{-b\tau} \right] \qquad \tau > 0
\end{aligned}
$$

(12-23)

From symmetry, the expression for $\tau < 0$ can be written directly. The final result is

$$
R_y(\tau) = \frac{b^2 \beta S_0}{2(b^2 - \beta^2)} \left[\epsilon^{-\beta|\tau|} - \frac{\beta}{b} \epsilon^{-b|\tau|} \right]
$$

(12-24)

In order to compare this result with the previously obtained result for white noise at the input, it is only necessary to let β approach infinity. In this case,

$$
\lim_{\beta \to \infty} R_y(\tau) = \frac{b S_0}{2} \epsilon^{-b|\tau|}
$$

(12-25)

which is exactly the same as (12-21). Of greater interest, however, is the case when β is large compared to b but still finite. This corresponds to the physical situation in which the bandwidth of the input random process is large compared to the bandwidth of the system. In order to make this comparison, write (12-24) as

$$
R_y(\tau) = \frac{b S_0}{2} \epsilon^{-b|\tau|} \left[\left(\frac{1}{1 - \dfrac{b^2}{\beta^2}} \right) \left(1 - \frac{b}{\beta} \epsilon^{-(\beta - b)|\tau|} \right) \right]
$$

(12-26)

The first factor in (12-26) is the autocorrelation function of the output when the input is white noise. The second factor is the one by which the true autocorrelation of the system output differs from the white-noise approximation. It is clear that as β becomes large compared to b, this factor approaches unity.

The point to this discussion is that there are many practical situations in which the input noise has a bandwidth that is much greater than the system bandwidth, and in these cases it is quite reasonable to use the white-noise approximation. In doing so, there is a great saving in labor without much loss in accuracy; for example, in a high-gain vacuum tube amplifier with a bandwidth of 10 MHz, the most important source of noise is shot noise in the first stage, which may have a bandwidth of 1000 MHz. Hence, the factor b/β in (12-26), assuming that this form applies will be only 0.01 and the error in using the white-noise approximation will not exceed 1 percent.

12-5 Cross-correlation between Input and Output

When a sample function from a random process is applied to the input of a linear system, the output must be related in some way to the input. Hence, they will be correlated, and the nature of the cross-correlation function is important. In fact, it will be shown very shortly that this relationship can be used to provide a practical technique for measuring the impulse response of any linear system.

One of the cross-correlation functions for input and output is defined by

$$R_{xy}(\tau) = E[x(t)y(t + \tau)] \tag{12-27}$$

which, in integral form, becomes

$$R_{xy}(\tau) = E\left[x(t) \int_0^\infty x(t + \tau - \lambda)h(\lambda)\, d\lambda\right] \tag{12-28}$$

Since $x(t)$ is not a function of λ, it may be moved inside the integral and then the expectation may be moved inside. Thus,

$$R_{xy}(\tau) = \int_0^\infty E[x(t)x(t + \tau - \lambda)]h(\lambda)\, d\lambda$$

$$= \int_0^\infty R_x(\tau - \lambda)h(\lambda)\, d\lambda \tag{12-29}$$

Hence, this cross-correlation function is just the convolution of the input autocorrelation function and the impulse response of the system.

The other cross-correlation function is

$$R_{yx}(\tau) = E[x(t + \tau)y(t)] = E\left[x(t + \tau) \int_0^\infty x(t - \lambda)h(\lambda)\, d\lambda\right]$$

$$= \int_0^\infty E[x(t + \tau)x(t - \lambda)]h(\lambda)\, d\lambda \qquad\qquad \textbf{(12-30)}$$

$$= \int_0^\infty R_x(\tau + \lambda)h(\lambda)\, d\lambda$$

Since the autocorrelation function in (12-30) is symmetrical about $\lambda = -\tau$ and the impulse response is zero for negative values of λ, this cross-correlation function will *always* be different from $R_{xy}(\tau)$. They will, however, have the same value at $\tau = 0$.

The above results become even simpler when the input to the system may be considered to be a sample function of white noise. For this case,

$$R_x(\tau) = S_0\delta(\tau)$$

and

$$R_{xy}(\tau) = \int_0^\infty S_0\delta(\tau - \lambda)h(\lambda)\, d\lambda = S_0 h(\tau) \qquad \tau \geq 0$$
$$= 0 \qquad\qquad\qquad \tau < 0 \qquad\qquad \textbf{(12-31)}$$

Likewise,

$$R_{yx}(\tau) = \int_0^\infty S_0\delta(\tau + \lambda)h(\lambda)\, d\lambda = 0 \qquad\qquad \tau > 0$$
$$= S_0 h(-\tau) \qquad \tau \leq 0 \qquad\qquad \textbf{(12-32)}$$

It is the result shown in (12-31) that leads to the procedure for measuring the impulse response, which will be discussed next.

Consider the block diagram shown in Fig. 12-5. The input signal $x(t)$

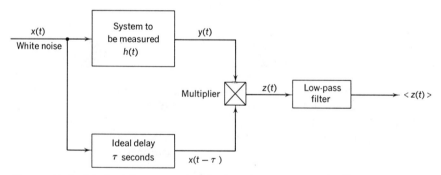

Figure 12-5   Method for measuring the impulse response of a linear system.

is a sample function from a random process whose bandwidth is large compared to the bandwidth of the system to be measured. In practice, a bandwidth ratio of 10 to 1 gives very good results. For purposes of analysis, this input will be assumed to be white.

In addition to being applied to the system under test, this input is also delayed by τ seconds. Depending upon the frequency range of $x(t)$ and the required value of τ, this delay may be a length of transmission line, a lumped-constant approximation to the transmission line, or a tape recorder with record and playback heads displaced enough to yield the desired delay. The output of the delay unit is simply $x(t - \tau)$.

The system output $y(t)$ and the delay unit output are then multiplied to form $z(t) = x(t - \tau)y(t)$, which is then passed through a low-pass filter. If the bandwidth of the low-pass filter is sufficiently small, its output will be mostly just the dc component of $z(t)$, with a small random component added to it. For an ergodic input process, $z(t)$ will be ergodic and the dc component of $z(t)$—that is, its time average—will be the same as its expected value. Thus,

$$< z(t) > \simeq E[z(t)] = E[y(t)x(t - \tau)] = R_{xy}(\tau) \tag{12-33}$$

since in the stationary case

$$E[y(t)x(t - \tau)] = E[x(t)y(t + \tau)] = R_{xy}(\tau) \tag{12-34}$$

But from (12-31), it is seen that

$$< z(t) > \simeq S_0 h(\tau) \qquad \tau \geq 0$$

Hence, the dc component at the output of the low-pass filter is proportional to the impulse response evaluated at the τ determined by the delay. If τ can be changed, then the complete impulse response of the system can be measured.

At first thought, this method of measuring the impulse response may seem like the hard way to solve an easy problem; it should be much easier to simply apply an impulse (or a reasonable approximation thereto) and observe the output. There are at least two reasons, however, why this direct procedure may not be possible or desirable. In the first place, an impulse with sufficient area to produce an observable output may also drive the system into a region of *nonlinear* operation well outside its intended operating range. Second, it may be desired to monitor the impulse response of the system continuously while it is in normal operation. Repeated applications of impulses may seriously affect this normal operation, but in the cross-correlation method the random input signal can usually be made small enough to have a negligible effect on the operation.

Some practical engineering situations in which this method has been successfully used include automatic control systems, chemical process control, and measurement of aircraft characteristics in flight. One of the more exotic applications is the continuous monitoring of the impulse response of a nuclear reactor in order to observe how close it is to being critical—that is, unstable. It is also being used to measure the dynamic response of large buildings to earth tremors or wind gusts.

12-6   Example of Time-Domain System Analysis

A simple R-C circuit responding to a random input having an exponential autocorrelation function was analyzed in Section 12-4 and was found to involve an appreciable amount of labor. Actually, systems and inputs such as these are usually handled more conveniently by the frequency-domain methods discussed later in this chapter. Hence, it seems desirable to look at some situation in which time-domain methods are easier. These situations occur when the impulse response and autocorrelation function have a simple form over a finite time interval.

The system chosen for this example is the *finite-time integrator,* whose impulse response is shown in Fig. 12-6(a). The input will be

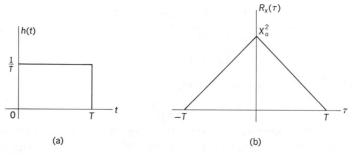

(a)   (b)

Figure 12-6   System impulse response and input autocorrelation function.
(a) Impulse response of finite-time integrator. (b) Input autocorrelation function.

assumed to have an autocorrelation function of the form shown in Fig. 12-6(b). This autocorrelation function might come from the random square-wave process discussed in Section 10-1, for example.

For the particular input specified, the output of the finite-time integrator will have zero mean, since $\bar{x}$ is zero. In the more general case, however, the mean value of the output would be, from (12-7),

$$\bar{y} = \bar{x} \int_0^T \frac{1}{T}\, dt = \bar{x} \tag{12-35}$$

Since the input process is not white, (12-10) must be used to determine the mean-square value of the output. Thus,

$$\overline{y^2} = \int_0^T d\lambda_1 \int_0^T R_x(\lambda_2 - \lambda_1)\left(\frac{1}{T}\right)^2 d\lambda_2 \tag{12-36}$$

As an aid in evaluating this integral, it is helpful to sketch the integrand as shown in Fig. 12-7 and note that the mean-square value is just the *volume* of the region indicated. Since this volume is composed of two

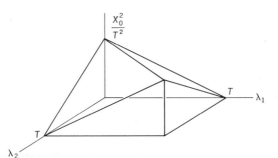

Figure 12-7   Integrand of (12-36).

right pyramids, each having a base of X_0^2/T^2 by $\sqrt{2}\,T$ and an altitude of $T/\sqrt{2}$, the volume is seen to be

$$\overline{y^2} = 2\left[\frac{1}{3}\left(\frac{X_0^2}{T^2}\right)(\sqrt{2}\,T)\left(\frac{T}{\sqrt{2}}\right)\right] = \frac{2}{3}\,X_0^2 \qquad \text{(12-37)}$$

It is also possible to obtain the autocorrelation function of the output by using (12-17). Thus,

$$R_y(\tau) = \int_0^T d\lambda_1 \int_0^T R_x(\lambda_2 - \lambda_1 - \tau)\left(\frac{1}{T}\right)^2 d\lambda_2 \qquad \text{(12-38)}$$

It is left as an exercise for the reader to show that this has the shape shown in Fig. 12-8 and is composed of segments of quadratics.

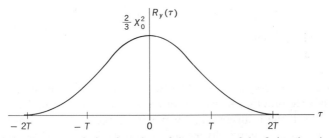

Figure 12-8   Autocorrelation function of the output of the finite-time integrator.

It may be noted that the results become even simpler when the input random process can be treated as if it were white noise. Thus, using the special case derived in (12-12), the mean-square value of the output would be

$$\overline{y^2} = S_0 \int_0^T \left(\frac{1}{T}\right)^2 d\lambda = \frac{S_0}{T} \qquad \text{(12-39)}$$

where S_0 is the spectral density of the input white noise. Furthermore, from the special case derived in (12-18), the output autocorrelation function can be sketched by inspection, as shown in Fig. 12-9, since it is just

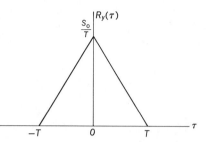

Figure 12-9 Output autocorrelation function with white-noise input.

the convolution of the system impulse response with itself. Note that this result indicates another way in which a random process having a triangular autocorrelation function might be generated.

12-7   Analysis in the Frequency Domain

The most common method of representing linear systems in the frequency domain is in terms of the system function $H(j\omega)$ or the transfer function $H(s)$, which are the Fourier and Laplace transforms, respectively, of the system impulse response. If the input to a system is $x(t)$ and the output $y(t)$, then the Fourier transforms of these quantities are related by

$$Y(j\omega) = X(j\omega)\,H(j\omega)$$ (12-40)

and the Laplace transforms are related by

$$Y(s) = X(s)H(s)$$ (12-41)

provided the transforms exist. Neither of these forms is suitable when $x(t)$ is a sample function from a stationary random process. As discussed in Section 11-1, the Fourier transform of a sample function from a stationary random process generally never exists. In the case of the one-sided Laplace transform the input-output relationship is defined only for time functions existing for $t > 0$, and such time functions can never be sample functions from a stationary random process.

One approach to this problem is to make use of the spectral density of the process and to carry out the analysis using a truncated sample function in which the limit $T \to \infty$ is not taken until after the averaging operations are carried out. This procedure is valid and will lead to correct results. There is, however, a much simpler procedure that can be used. In Chapter 11 it was shown that the spectral density of a stationary random process is the Fourier transform of the autocorrelation function of the process. Therefore, using the results we have already obtained for the correlation function of the output of a linear time-invariant system we can obtain the corresponding results for the spectral density by carrying out the required transformations. When the basic relationship has been obtained, it will be seen that there is a close analogy between computations involving nonrandom signals and those involving random signals.

12-8 Spectral Density at the System Output

The spectral density of a process is a measure of how the average power of the process is distributed with respect to frequency. No information regarding the phases of the various frequency components is contained in the spectral density. In (11-46) the relationship between the spectral density $S_x(\omega)$ and the autocorrelation function $R_x(\tau)$ for a stationary process is given as

$$S_x(\omega) = \mathscr{F}\{R_x(\tau)\} \tag{12-42}$$

Using this relationship and (12-17), which relates the output correlation function $R_y(\tau)$ to the input correlation function $R_x(\tau)$ by means of the system impulse response, we have

$$R_y(\tau) = \int_0^\infty d\lambda_1 \int_0^\infty R_x(\lambda_2 - \lambda_1 - \tau)h(\lambda_1)h(\lambda_2)\, d\lambda_2$$

$$S_y(\omega) = \mathscr{F}\{R_y(\tau)\}$$

$$= \int_{-\infty}^\infty \left[\int_0^\infty d\lambda_1 \int_0^\infty R_x(\lambda_2 - \lambda_1 - \tau)h(\lambda_1)h(\lambda_2)\, d\lambda_2\right]\epsilon^{-j\omega\tau}\, d\tau$$

Interchanging the order of integration and carrying out the indicated operations gives

$$S_y(\omega) = \int_0^\infty d\lambda_1 \int_0^\infty h(\lambda_1)h(\lambda_2)d\lambda_2 \int_{-\infty}^\infty R_x(\lambda_2 - \lambda_1 - \tau)\epsilon^{-j\omega\tau}\, d\tau$$

$$= \int_0^\infty d\lambda_1 \int_0^\infty h(\lambda_1)h(\lambda_2)S_x(\omega)\epsilon^{-js(\lambda_2-\lambda_1)}\, d\lambda_2 \tag{12-43}$$

$$= S_x(\omega)\int_0^\infty h(\lambda_1)\epsilon^{j\omega\lambda_1}d\lambda_1 \int_0^\infty h(\lambda_2)\epsilon^{-j\omega\lambda_2}\, d\lambda_2$$

$$= S_x(\omega)H(-j\omega)H(j\omega)$$

$$= S_x(\omega)|H(j\omega)|^2 \tag{12-44}$$

In arriving at (12-44) use was made of the property that $R_x(-\tau) = R_x(\tau)$.

From (12-44) it is seen that the output spectral density is related to the input spectral density by the power transfer function, $|H(j\omega)|^2$. This result can also be expressed in terms of the complex frequency s as:

$$S_y(s) = S_x(s)H(s)H(-s) \tag{12-45}$$

where $S_y(s)$ and $S_x(s)$ are obtained from $S_y(\omega)$ and $S_x(\omega)$ by substituting $-s^2 = \omega^2$, and $H(s)$ is obtained from $H(j\omega)$ by substituting $s = j\omega$. It is this form that will be used in further discussions of frequency analysis methods.

It is clear from (12-45) that the quantity $H(s)H(-s)$ plays the same role in relating input and output spectral densities as $H(s)$ does in relating input and output transforms. This similarity makes the use of frequency-domain techniques for systems with rational transfer functions very convenient when the input is a sample function from a *stationary random process*. However, contrary to some statements found in the literature, this same technique is *not* always applicable when the input process is *nonstationary*, even though the definition for the spectral density of such processes is the same as we have employed. A detailed study of this matter is beyond the scope of the present discussion but the reader would do well to question any application of (12-45) for nonstationary processes.

Since the spectral density of the system has now been obtained, it is a simple matter to determine the mean-square value of the output. This is simply

$$\overline{y^2} = \frac{1}{2\pi j} \int_{-j\infty}^{j\infty} H(s)H(-s)S_x(s)\, ds \tag{12-46}$$

and may be evaluated by either the method discussed in Section 11-4 or that discussed in the Appendix.

In order to illustrate some of the methods, consider the *R-C* circuit shown in Fig. 12-10 and assume that its input is a sample function from a white-noise process having a spectral density of S_0.

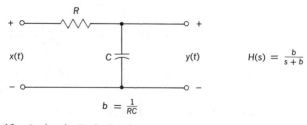

$$b = \frac{1}{RC}$$

Figure 12-10 A simple *R-C* circuit.

The spectral density at the output is simply

$$S_y(s) = \frac{b}{s+b} \cdot \frac{b}{-s+b} \cdot S_0 = \frac{-b^2 S_0}{s^2 - b^2} \tag{12-47}$$

The mean-square value of the output can be obtained by using the integral I_1, tabulated in Table 11-1, Section 11-4. In order to do this it is convenient to write (12-47) as:

$$S_y(s) = \frac{(b\sqrt{S_0})\,(b\sqrt{S_0})}{(s + b)\,(-s + b)}$$

from which it is clear that

$$c(s) = b\sqrt{S_0} = c_0$$
$$d(s) = s + b$$

Thus

$$d_0 = b$$
$$d_1 = 1$$

and

$$\overline{y^2} = I_1 = \frac{c_0^2}{2d_0 d_1} = \frac{b^2 S_0}{2b} = \frac{bS_0}{2} \tag{12-48}$$

As a slightly more complicated example, let the input spectral density be

$$S_x(s) = \frac{-\beta^2 S_0}{s^2 - \beta^2} \tag{12-49}$$

This spectral density, which corresponds to the autocorrelation function used in Section 12-4, has been selected so that its value at zero frequency is S_0. The spectral density at the output of the R-C circuit is now

$$S_y(s) = \frac{b}{s + b} \cdot \frac{b}{-s + b} \cdot \frac{-\beta^2 S_0}{s^2 - \beta^2}$$

$$= \frac{b^2 \beta^2 S_0}{(s^2 - b^2)\,(s^2 - \beta^2)} \tag{12-50}$$

The mean-square value for this output will be evaluated by using the integral I_2 tabulated in Table 11-1. Thus,

$$S_x(s) = \frac{c(s)c(-s)}{d(s)d(-s)} = \frac{(b\beta\sqrt{S_0})\,(b\beta\sqrt{S_0})}{[s^2 + (b + \beta)s + b\beta]\,[s^2 - (b + \beta)\,s + b\beta]} \tag{12-51}$$

it is clear that $n = 2$, and

$$c_0 = b\beta\sqrt{S_0}$$
$$c_1 = 0$$
$$d_0 = b\beta$$
$$d_1 = b + \beta$$
$$d_2 = 1$$

Hence,

$$\overline{y^2} = I_2 = \frac{c_0^2 d_2 + c_1^2 d_0}{2d_0 d_1 d_2} = \frac{b^2 \beta^2 S_0}{2b\beta\,(b + \beta)} = \frac{b\beta S_0}{2\,(b + \beta)} \tag{12-52}$$

since $c_1 = 0$.

It is also of interest to look once again at the results when the input random process has a bandwidth much greater than the system bandwidth; that is, when $\beta >> b$. From (12-50) it is clear that

$$S_y(s) = \frac{-b^2 S_0}{(s^2 - b^2)(1 - s^2/\beta^2)} \tag{12-53}$$

and as β becomes large this spectral density approaches that for the white-input-noise case given by (12-47). In the case of the mean-square value, (12-52) may be written as

$$\overline{y^2} = \frac{bS_0}{2(1 + b/\beta)} \tag{12-54}$$

which approaches the white-noise result of (12-48) when β is large.

Comparison of the foregoing examples with similar ones employing time-domain methods should make it evident that when the input spectral density and the system transfer function are rational, frequency-domain methods are usually simpler. In fact, the more complicated the system, the greater the advantage of such methods. When either the input spectral density or the system transfer function are not rational, this conclusion may not hold.

12-9   Cross Spectral Densities between Input and Output

The cross spectral densities between a system input and output are not widely used, but it is well to be aware of their existence. The derivation of these quantities would follow the same general pattern as shown above, but only the end results will be quoted here. Specifically, they are

$$S_{xy}(s) = H(s)S_x(s) \tag{12-55}$$

and

$$S_{yx}(s) = H(-s)S_x(s) \tag{12-56}$$

12-10   Example of Frequency-Domain Analysis

Although there are many different examples of frequency-domain analysis that might be used, the one that has been selected for discussion here involves some elements of system design as well. By means of this example, it is hoped to demonstrate that all of the concepts pertaining to the analysis of linear systems with random inputs also have application to the *design* of such systems. As a means of introducing this idea, a very simple situation has been selected so that the basic ideas do not get lost in a maze of intricate detail. As a consequence of this simplicity, the assumed spectral densities are unrealistic, but it should be made clear that more practical situations can be handled in a similar way but with greater effort.

It is assumed here that one is attempting to separate a desired random signal $x(t)$ from a background of statistically independent random noise $n(t)$. The desired signal might be, for example, the output of a vibration detector located on some critical component of a large mechanical system. The background noise, in this case, results from vibrations from other parts of the system, which are also picked up by the detector. It is desired to design a simple R-C filter that will do the best job of eliminating the unwanted noise while retaining the wanted signal.

The spectral density of the signal will be assumed to be of the form

$$S_x(\omega) = \frac{100\omega^2}{(\omega^2 + 4)(\omega^2 + 64)} \tag{12-57}$$

This is sketched in Fig. 12-11. The background noise will be assumed to

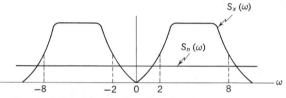

Figure 12-11 Spectral densities of signal and noise.

have a bandwidth sufficiently greater than that of the signal that it may be assumed to be "white" in comparison. Thus, let

$$S_n(\omega) = 0.25 \tag{12-58}$$

The R-C filter to be used is the one shown in Fig. 12-10; it has a transfer function of

$$H(s) = \frac{b}{s + b} \tag{12-59}$$

where the parameter $b = 1/RC$ is to be determined. This parameter is proportional to the bandwidth of the filter. The inputs and outputs are shown in Fig. 12-12. The output component $y(t)$ is the response of the

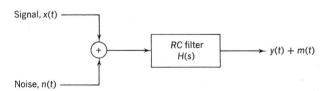

Figure 12-12 Inputs and outputs of the filter.

filter to the input signal $x(t)$ and the output $m(t)$ is the filter response to the noise $n(t)$. The only thing that can be observed at the output is the *sum* of these two responses, and it is desired to make this sum as nearly like the input signal $x(t)$ as possible. However, this sum differs from $x(t)$ in two respects. In the first place, it contains the noise $m(t)$, which is completely unrelated to the desired signal. In the second place, the filter itself alters the desired signal so that $y(t)$ is not an exact replica of $x(t)$ unless the filter bandwidth is made infinite.

Consider the output noise $m(t)$ first. It was shown in Section 12-8 that the mean-square value of the output of an R-C filter, with a white-noise input, is, by analogy to (12-48),

$$\overline{m^2} = \frac{b(0.25)}{2} = 0.125b \tag{12-60}$$

Note that this value is made small by making b small.

Next consider the output signal component $y(t)$. Since this is to be like $x(t)$, it is desirable to define a signal error function as

$$e(t) = x(t) - y(t) \tag{12-61}$$

Expressed in terms of Laplace transforms, this function can be written as

$$\begin{aligned} E(s) &= X(s) - H(s)X(s) \\ &= [1 - H(s)]X(s) \end{aligned} \tag{12-62}$$

from which it is clear that the factor $[1 - H(s)]$ can be considered to be the transfer function that relates the signal error to the input signal. Hence, from (12-46), the mean-square value of the error is

$$\overline{e^2} = \frac{1}{2\pi j} \int_{-j\infty}^{j\infty} [1 - H(s)][1 - H(-s)]S_x(s)\,ds \tag{12-63}$$

For the particular case being considered

$$1 - H(s) = 1 - \frac{b}{s + b} = \frac{s}{s + b}$$

$$S_x(s) = S_x(\omega)\big|_{s=j\omega} = \frac{-100s^2}{(s^2 - 4)(s^2 - 64)}$$

so that (12-63) becomes

$$\begin{aligned} \overline{e^2} &= \frac{1}{2\pi j} \int_{-j\infty}^{j\infty} \frac{s}{s + b} \cdot \frac{-s}{-s + b} \cdot \frac{-100s^2}{(s^2 - 4)(s^2 - 64)}\,ds \\ &= \frac{1}{2\pi j} \int_{-j\infty}^{j\infty} \frac{-100s^4}{(s^2 - b^2)(s^2 - 4)(s^2 - 64)}\,ds \end{aligned} \tag{12-64}$$

This may be evaluated, by either of the techniques mentioned previously, to yield

$$\overline{e^2} = \frac{10(5b + 8)}{(b + 2)(b + 8)} \tag{12-65}$$

Note that this is made small by making b large.

A reasonable criterion for selecting the best value of b is to use the value that minimizes the mean-square value of the total difference between the filter output and the desired output. Since the signal and noise are statistically independent and $\bar{n} = 0$, this is just the sum of the two mean-square values calculated in (12-60) and (12-65). Hence, the quantity

$$\overline{e^2} + \overline{m^2} = \frac{10(5\,b + 8)}{(b + 2)\,(b + 8)} + 0.125b \tag{12-66}$$

is to be minimized by selecting the appropriate value of b. The minimization is accomplished by differentiating (12-66) with respect to b and setting the derivative equal to zero. This operation leads to the quartic equation

$$b^4 + 20b^3 - 268b^2 - 960b + 256 = 0 \tag{12-67}$$

Since b is the reciprocal of the time constant of a physical circuit, it must be real and positive. Hence, it is possible to use synthetic division to find a real, positive root of (12-67). This leads to

$$b \simeq 11.25$$

from which the required time constant can be determined.

It is also possible to evaluate the effectiveness of this filter by substituting the optimum value of b into the expression for the total mean-square error as given by (12-66). If this is done, the result is

$$\overline{e^2} + \overline{m^2} = 2.52 + 1.40 = 3.92 \tag{12-68}$$

Since the mean-square value of the signal alone is 5.0, it is clear that a very appreciable error remains even when the best R-C filter is used. If the noise spectral density had been smaller, then the optimum value of b would have been greater and the total mean-square error would have been less.

12-11   State-Space Analysis for Random Vector Inputs

The general analysis, by state-space methods, of systems with several inputs and several outputs was discussed in Chapter 8. In particular, it was shown that a system with m input signals and p output signals could be described by a $(p \times m)$ impulse-response matrix, $\mathscr{H}(t)$, whose (i, j) elements represent the zero-state response at the ith output due to a unit impulse applied at the jth input at $t = 0$. For a general input $\mathbf{x}(t)$, the zero-state response can be expressed as

$$\mathbf{y}(t) = \int_{t_0}^{t} \mathscr{H}(t - \lambda)\, \mathbf{x}(\lambda)\, d(\lambda) \tag{12-69}$$

in which the previous lower limit of zero has been replaced by the more general t_0.

It is now of interest to consider the case in which $\mathbf{x}(t)$ is a sample function from a stationary, random vector process as discussed in Section 10-7. It was shown there that the correlation matrix for such a process could be expressed as

$$\mathbf{R}_x(\tau) = E\left[\mathbf{x}(t)\mathbf{x}^T(t + \tau)\right] = \begin{bmatrix} R_{11}(\tau) & R_{12}(\tau) & \cdots & R_{1m}(\tau) \\ R_{21}(\tau) & R_{22}(\tau) & & \\ \vdots & & & \\ R_{m1}(\tau) & \cdots & \cdots & R_{mm}(\tau) \end{bmatrix} \tag{12-70}$$

where

$$R_{ij}(\tau) = E\left[x_i(t)x_j(t + \tau)\right] \qquad i, j = 1, 2, \cdots, m \tag{12-71}$$

Since this is a stationary process the lower limit of (12-69) is taken as $t_0 = -\infty$. It is also convenient to make a change of variable by letting $t - \lambda = \lambda_1$ and $d\lambda = -d\lambda_1$. Thus, (12-69) becomes

$$\mathbf{y}(t) = \int_0^{\infty} \mathscr{H}(\lambda_1)\mathbf{x}(t - \lambda_1)\, d\lambda_1$$

One item of interest concerning the system output is the correlation matrix of $\mathbf{y}(t)$, which is defined by

$$\mathbf{R}_y(\tau) = E\left[\mathbf{y}(t)\mathbf{y}^T(t + \tau)\right]$$

This is a $(p \times p)$ matrix which can be expressed in the form of a double integral as[3]

$$\mathbf{R}_x(\tau) = E\left[\int_0^{\infty} d\lambda_1 \int_0^{\infty} \mathscr{H}(\lambda_1)\mathbf{x}(t - \lambda_1)\mathbf{x}^T(t + \tau - \lambda_2)\, \mathscr{H}^T(\lambda_2)\, d\lambda_2\right] \tag{12-72}$$

When the expectation is taken inside the integral, the result becomes

$$\mathbf{R}_y(\tau) = \int_0^{\infty} d\lambda_1 \int_0^{\infty} \mathscr{H}(\lambda_1)\mathbf{R}_x(\lambda_2 - \lambda_1 - \tau)\, \mathscr{H}^T(\lambda_2)\, d\lambda_2 \tag{12-73}$$

---

[3]This result makes use of the general relationship concerning the transpose of products; that is,

$$(AB)^T = B^T A^T$$

This general result relates the correlation matrix of the output to the correlation matrix of the input and is analogous to (12-17) for the single-input, single-output case.

It is also possible to express the cross-correlation between the input and output by a similar procedure. This can be done by defining an $(m \times p)$ cross-correlation matrix as

$$\mathbf{R}_{xy}(\tau) = E\left[\mathbf{x}(t)\mathbf{y}^T(t + \tau)\right] \tag{12-74}$$

Hence,

$$\mathbf{R}_{xy}(\tau) = E\left[\mathbf{x}(t)\int_0^\infty \mathbf{x}^T(t + \tau - \lambda_1)\mathcal{H}^T(\lambda_1)\,d\lambda_1\right]$$

$$= \int_0^\infty \mathbf{R}_x(\tau - \lambda_1)\mathcal{H}^T(\lambda_1)\,d\lambda_1 \tag{12-75}$$

A similar result can be obtained for the other cross-correlation matrix, $\mathbf{R}_{yx}(\tau)$, but will not be considered here.

A special case of considerable interest is that in which all of the components of $\mathbf{x}(t)$ are sample functions from statistically independent, jointly stationary, white-noise processes. For such a case the correlation matrix of the input becomes

$$\mathbf{R}_x(\tau) = \begin{bmatrix} S_1\delta(\tau) & 0 & 0 \cdots 0 \\ 0 & S_2\delta(\tau) & 0 \cdots 0 \\ \vdots & & \\ 0 \cdots & & S_m\delta(\tau) \end{bmatrix} = \mathbf{S}\delta(\tau) \tag{12-76}$$

where $S_1, S_2, \cdots, S_m$ are the spectral densities of the various components of $\mathbf{x}(t)$ and $\mathbf{S}$ is a diagonal matrix with these as components. That is,

$$\mathbf{S} = \begin{bmatrix} S_1 & 0 & \cdots & 0 \\ 0 & S_2 & \cdots & 0 \\ \vdots & & & \\ 0 & \cdots & \cdots & S_m \end{bmatrix}$$

The correlation matrix of the output can then be expressed as

$$\mathbf{R}_y(\tau) = \int_0^\infty d\lambda_1 \int_0^\infty \mathcal{H}(\lambda_1)\mathbf{S}\mathcal{H}^T(\lambda_2)\delta(\lambda_2 - \lambda_1 - \tau)\,d\lambda_2$$

$$= \int_0^\infty \mathcal{H}(\lambda_1)\mathbf{S}\mathcal{H}^T(\lambda_1 + \tau)\,d\lambda_1 \tag{12-77}$$

Furthermore, the cross-correlation matrix becomes

$$\mathbf{R}_{xy}(\tau) = \int_0^\infty \mathbf{S}\mathcal{H}^T(\lambda_1)\delta(\tau - \lambda_1)\,d\lambda_1$$

$$= \mathbf{S} \mathcal{H}^{T}(\tau) \quad \tau \geq 0 \tag{12-78}$$
$$= 0 \qquad\quad \tau < 0$$

Note that this cross-correlation matrix is related to the impulse-response matrix in a manner similar to that for the single-input, single-output system.

It is also possible to use frequency-domain methods of analysis by characterizing the system by a *system function* matrix, which is just the Fourier transform of the impulse-response matrix; that is,

$$\mathbf{H}(j\omega) = \int_{0}^{\infty} \mathcal{H}(t) \, \epsilon^{-j\omega t} \, dt \tag{12-79}$$

This is also a ($p \times m$) matrix. In addition, the input vector $\mathbf{x}(t)$ can be characterized by its spectral density matrix as discussed in Section 11-8; that is,

$$\mathbf{S}_{x}(\omega) = \begin{bmatrix} S_{11}(\omega) & S_{12}(\omega) & \cdots & S_{1m}(\omega) \\ S_{21}(\omega) & S_{22}(\omega) & & \\ \vdots & & & \\ S_{m1}(\omega) & \cdots & & S_{mm}(\omega) \end{bmatrix}$$

where

$$S_{ij}(\omega) = \mathcal{F}\left[R_{ij}(\tau)\right]$$

By analogy to the results for one-input, one-output systems, the spectral density matrix of the output can be expressed as

$$\mathbf{S}_{y}(\omega) = \mathbf{H}(j\omega)\mathbf{S}_{x}(\omega)\mathbf{H}^{T}(-j\omega) \tag{12-80}$$

A similar result can be expressed in terms of the complex frequency variable s instead of $j\omega$.

The discussion in this section clearly indicates that all of the results obtained for linear systems with one input and one output can be extended to the case of linear systems having m inputs and p outputs. The only problems arise from the increased amount of computation and the need to satisfy all the rules of matrix multiplication.

■ REFERENCES

There are no known references available that cover the material of Chapters 10–12 in any appreciable depth while keeping the mathematical level sufficiently low to be comprehensible to juniors in electrical engineering. The following texts will, however, provide additional insight into some aspects of the material covered here and are, for the most part, quite readable.

1. Bennett, W. R., *Electrical Noise*. New York: McGraw-Hill Book Company, Inc., 1960.

   The various sources of random signals in electrical systems are discussed in considerable detail but from an elementary mathematical point of view. Methods of analyzing noise problems are considered and the design of low noise circuits is discussed.

2. Freeman, J. J., *Principles of Noise*. New York: John Wiley & Sons, Inc., 1958.

   This book presents some of the basic principles of random-signal analysis and then describes their application to a number of specific problems.

3. Hancock, J. C., *An Introduction to the Principles of Communication Theory*. New York: McGraw-Hill Book Company, Inc., 1961.

   Chapters 3 and 4 of this text are devoted to random signals and their transmission through linear systems. In addition, there is a discussion of noise sources and of the methods for analyzing the noise performance of communication systems.

4. Papoulis, A., *Probability, Random Variables and Stochastic Processes*. New York: McGraw-Hill Book Company, Inc., 1965.

   This graduate-level text covers probability theory and stochastic processes. The treatment of random processes is quite extensive and encompasses all of the material most frequently needed for engineering analyses. The treatment starts from elementary considerations and proceeds smoothly to more advanced concepts. Much of the discussion is at a level that can be understood and appreciated by undergraduates.

5. Schwartz, M., *Information Transmission Modulation and Noise*. New York: McGraw-Hill Book Company, Inc., 1959.

   This senior-level text in communication theory contains a number of sections devoted to random signals and noise. Much useful information on modulation and information transmission is also included.

The following more advanced texts are appropriate for further study:

Bendat, J. S., *Principles and Applications of Random Noise Theory*. New York: John Wiley & Sons, Inc., 1958.

Davenport, W. D., and W. L. Root, *Random Signals and Noise*. New York: McGraw-Hill Book Company, Inc., 1958.

Laning, J. H., and R. H. Battin, *Random Processes in Automatic Control*. New York: McGraw-Hill Book Company, Inc., 1956.

Middleton, D. *Introduction to Statistical Communication Theory*. New York: McGraw-Hill Book Company, Inc., 1960.

Wozencraft, J. M., and I. M. Jacobs, *Principles of Communication Engineering*. New York: John Wiley & Sons, Inc., 1965.

■ PROBLEMS

12-1 Find the impulse response of the system shown.

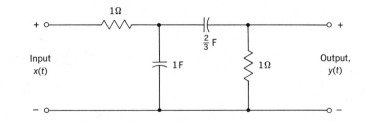

12-2 A *finite-time integrator* can be represented by the block diagram shown.

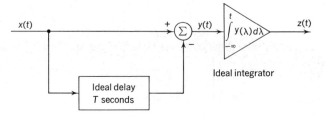

a. Find the impulse response of the system.
b. Is this a stable system?

12-3 A linear system has an impulse response of the form

$$h(t) = \frac{u(t - 1)}{t}$$

a. Sketch the impulse response.
b. Is this system physically realizable?
c. Is this system stable?

12-4 a. White noise having a spectral density of 10 volts²/hertz is applied to the input of the system shown in Problem 12-1. Using time-domain methods, find the mean-square value of the output.
    b. If the input has a mean value of 5 volts, what is the mean value of the output?

12-5 A sample function from a stationary random process is of the form

$$x(t) = A \cos (\omega_0 t + \theta)$$

where A and ω_0 are constants and θ is a random variable uniformly distributed over the interval $-\pi \leq \theta \leq \pi$. If this process is applied to the finite-time integrator of Problem 12-2 find the mean-square value of the output.

12-6   White noise having a spectral density of S_0 volts²/hertz is applied to the R-C circuit shown. Using time-domain methods, find the auto-correlation function of the output $y(t)$.

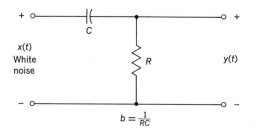

$$b = \frac{1}{RC}$$

12-7   Repeat Problem 12-6 if the input to the R-C circuit has an auto-correlation function of the form

$$R_x(\tau) = \frac{\beta S_0}{2} \epsilon^{-\beta|\tau|}$$

12-8   The process described in Problem 12-5 is applied to an R-C low-pass filter. Find the autocorrelation function of the output signal.

12-9   For the system and white-noise input of Problem 12-6, find both cross-correlation functions between input and output.

12-10   For the system shown in Problem 12-6 and the input given in Problem 12-7, find both cross-correlation functions between input and output.

12-11   A random process has sample functions of the form

$$x(t) = X_0 + n(t)$$

where X_0 is a constant and $n(t)$ is random noise having an autocorrelation function of

$$R_n(\tau) = \epsilon^{-|\tau|}$$

It is desired to estimate the value of X_0 by passing $x(t)$ through a single-section, low-pass R-C filter. If the noise at the output of the filter is to have an rms value of 1 percent of the value of X_0, and X_0 has a true value of 0.1 volt, what time constant is required in the filter?

12-12   Find the autocorrelation function of the output of the finite-time integrator discussed in Section 12-6 when the input has a triangular autocorrelation function.

12-13   Find the *power* transfer function of the system shown in Problem 12-1.

12-14   Find the *power* transfer function of the system shown in Problem 12-2.

12-15   Derive the relationship (12-44) between the input and output spectral densities using a truncated sample function. (Hint: There will be a transient term in the output resulting from the truncation. This term can be neglected, since it contains finite energy and therefore will contribute nothing to the spectral density).

12-16   Solve Problem 12-4 by using frequency-domain methods.

12-17   Find the spectral density of the output in Problem 12-6 by using frequency-domain methods.

12-18   Find the spectral density of the output in Problem 12-7 by using frequency-domain methods.

12-19   A tuned amplifier has its maximum gain of 30 dB at a frequency of 1 MHz and a half-power bandwidth of 10 kHz. The response curve has a shape equivalent to that of a single parallel R-L-C circuit. If the input to this amplifier is white noise having a spectral density of 10^{-6} volts²/hertz, find the mean-square value of the output.

12-20   Find the autocorrelation function of the output signal of an ideal bandpass filter having a center frequency of f_0, a bandwidth of W, and an input of white noise with spectral density N_0. Make a qualitative sketch of the result.

12-21   The thermal agitation noise generated by a resistance is usually assumed to be white with a spectral density of $2kTR$ volts²/hertz, where $k = 1.37 \times 10^{-23}$ watt-seconds per degree Kelvin is the Boltzmann constant, T is the absolute temperature in degrees Kelvin, and R is the resistance in ohms. Any physical resistance in the input to an amplifier is paralleled by a capacitance, so that the equivalent circuit is as shown.
a.   Calculate the mean-square value of the amplifier input noise as a function of R, C, T, and so on.
b.   Explain your result on a physical basis.

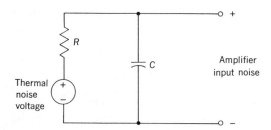

12-22 Any signal at the input of a practical amplifier is always accompanied by noise. The minimum noise theoretically possible is the thermal noise present in the resistive component of the input impedance as described in Problem 12-21. In general the amplifier will add additional noise in the process of amplifying the signal. The amount of additional noise is measured by the deterioration of signal-to-noise ratio of the signal when it is passed through the amplifier. The most common method of specifying this characteristic of an amplifier is in terms of a noise figure F, defined as

$$F = \frac{\text{input signal-to-noise power ratio}}{\text{output signal-to-noise power ratio}}$$

a. Using the foregoing definition find the overall noise figure of two cascaded amplifiers if the individual amplifiers have gains G_1 and G_2 and noise figures F_1 and F_2 respectively.
b. A particular wide-band video amplifier has a single time-constant roll-off with a half-power bandwidth of 100 MHz, a gain of 100 dB, a noise figure of 20 dB, and input and output impedances of 100 ohms. Find the rms output noise voltage when the input signal is zero.
c. Find the output signal to noise ratio for the amplifier of b when the input signal is a sine wave having an amplitude of 0.01 μV.

12-23 The noise bandwidth of a low-pass filter is defined as the bandwidth of an ideal low-pass filter having a gain equal to the zero-frequency gain of the practical filter and having an output mean-square value identical to that of the practical filter when the input to each filter is white noise.
a. Find the noise bandwidth of a single-section low-pass R-C filter in terms of its half-power bandwidth and in terms of the filter time constant.
b. Extend the foregoing definition to include bandpass filters and determine the noise bandwidth of a high-Q resonant circuit in terms of its half-power bandwidth.

12-24 In many types of optimum filtering problems it is necessary to have a circuit that will convert a specified spectral density into white noise. Find the transfer function of a physically realizable circuit that will do this for an input spectral density of

$$S_x(\omega) = \frac{10}{(\omega^2 + 1)(\omega^2 + 4)}$$

12-25 Refer to the system shown in Problem 8-30. Let the two input signals be sample functions from statistically independent, stationary *white-noise* processes having spectral densities of $S_1 = 2, S_2 = 1$.
a. Find the correlation matrix $\mathbf{R}_y(\tau)$ of the system output.
b. Find the cross-correlation matrix $\mathbf{R}_{xy}(\tau)$.

12-26 Find the spectral density matrix $\mathbf{S}_x(\omega)$ of the output of the system of Problem 12-25.

Short Mathematical Tables of Frequent Use In System Analysis

Table A-1 TRIGONOMETRIC IDENTITIES

$\sin (A \pm B) = \sin A \cos B \pm \cos A \sin B$
$\cos (A \mp B) = \cos A \cos B \mp \sin A \sin B$

$\cos A \cos B = \frac{1}{2} \left[\cos (A + B) + \cos (A - B) \right]$
$\sin A \sin B = \frac{1}{2} \left[\cos (A - B) - \cos (A + B) \right]$
$\sin A \cos B = \frac{1}{2} \left[\sin (A + B) + \sin (A - B) \right]$

$\sin A \pm \sin B = 2 \sin \frac{1}{2}(A \mp B) \cos \frac{1}{2}(A \mp B)$
$\cos A + \cos B = 2 \cos \frac{1}{2}(A + B) \cos \frac{1}{2}(A - B)$
$\cos A - \cos B = 2 \sin \frac{1}{2}(A + B) \sin \frac{1}{2}(B - A)$

$\sin 2A = 2 \sin A \cos A$
$\cos 2A = 2 \cos^2 A - 1 = 1 - 2 \sin^2 A = \cos^2 A - \sin^2 A$

$\sin \frac{1}{2}A = \sqrt{\frac{1}{2}(1 - \cos A)}$
$\cos \frac{1}{2}A = \sqrt{\frac{1}{2}(1 + \cos A)}$

$\sin^2 A = \frac{1}{2}(1 - \cos 2A)$
$\cos^2 A = \frac{1}{2}(1 + \cos 2A)$

Table A-1 *continued*

$$\sin x = \frac{\epsilon^{jx} - \epsilon^{-jx}}{2j} \qquad\qquad \cos x = \frac{\epsilon^{jx} + \epsilon^{-jx}}{2}$$

$$\epsilon^{jx} = \cos x + j \sin x$$

$$1 - \epsilon^{-jx} = 2j\epsilon^{-jx/2} \sin \frac{x}{2} \qquad\qquad 1 - \epsilon^{jx} = -2j \epsilon^{jx/2} \sin \frac{x}{2}$$

$$1 + \epsilon^{-jx} = 2\epsilon^{-jx/2} \cos \frac{x}{2} \qquad\qquad 1 + \epsilon^{jx} = 2j\epsilon^{jx/2} \cos \frac{x}{2}$$

$$A \cos (\omega t + \phi_1) + B \cos (\omega t + \phi_2) = C \cos (\omega t + \phi_3)$$

where

$$C = \sqrt{A^2 + B^2 - 2AB \cos (\phi_2 - \phi_1)}$$

$$\phi_3 = \tan^{-1}\left[\frac{A \sin \phi_1 + B \sin \phi_2}{A \cos \phi_1 + B \cos \phi_2}\right]$$

$$\sin (\omega t + \phi) = \cos (\omega t + \phi - 90°)$$

Table A-2   INDEFINITE INTEGRALS

$$\int \sin ax \, dx = -\frac{1}{a} \cos ax \qquad\qquad \int \cos ax \, dx = \frac{1}{a} \sin ax$$

$$\int \sin^2 ax \, dx = \frac{x}{2} - \frac{\sin 2ax}{4a}$$

$$\int x \sin ax \, dx = \frac{1}{a^2} (\sin ax - ax \cos ax)$$

$$\int x^2 \sin ax \, dx = \frac{1}{a^3} (2ax \sin ax + 2 \cos ax - a^2x^2 \cos ax)$$

$$\int \cos^2 ax \, dx = \frac{x}{2} + \frac{\sin 2ax}{4a}$$

$$\int x \cos ax \, dx = \frac{1}{a^2} (\cos ax + ax \sin ax)$$

$$\int x^2 \cos ax = \frac{1}{a^3} (2ax \cos ax - 2 \sin ax + a^2x^2 \sin ax)$$

$$\int \sin ax \sin bx \, dx = \frac{\sin (a - b)x}{2(a - b)} - \frac{\sin (a + b)x}{2(a + b)} \qquad a^2 \neq b^2$$

$$\int \sin ax \cos bx \, dx = -\left[\frac{\cos (a - b)x}{2(a - b)} + \frac{\cos (a + b)x}{2(a + b)}\right] \qquad a^2 \neq b^2$$

Table A-2 *continued*

$$\int \cos ax \cos bx \, dx = \frac{\sin (a - b)x}{2(a - b)} + \frac{\sin (a + b)x}{2(a + b)} \qquad a^2 \neq b^2$$

$$\int \epsilon^{ax} \, dx = \frac{1}{a} \epsilon^{ax}$$

$$\int x \, \epsilon^{ax} \, dx = \frac{\epsilon^{ax}}{a^2} (ax - 1)$$

$$\int x^2 \, \epsilon^{ax} \, dx = \frac{\epsilon^{ax}}{a^3} (a^2x^2 - 2ax + 2)$$

$$\int \epsilon^{ax} \sin bx \, dx = \frac{\epsilon^{ax}}{a^2 + b^2} (a \sin bx - b \cos bx)$$

$$\int \epsilon^{ax} \cos bx \, dx = \frac{\epsilon^{ax}}{a^2 + b^2} (a \cos bx + b \sin bx)$$

Table A-3 DEFINITE INTEGRALS

$$\int_0^\infty x^n \, \epsilon^{-ax} \, dx = \frac{n!}{a^{n+1}} = \frac{\Gamma(n + 1)}{a^{n+1}}$$

$$\int_0^\infty \epsilon^{-r^2x^2} \, dx = \frac{\sqrt{\pi}}{2r}$$

$$\int_0^\infty x \, \epsilon^{-r^2x^2} \, dx = \frac{1}{2r^2}$$

$$\int_0^\infty x^2 \, \epsilon^{-r^2x^2} \, dx = \frac{\sqrt{\pi}}{4r^3}$$

$$\int_0^\infty x^n \, \epsilon^{-r^2x^2} \, dx = \frac{\Gamma[(n + 1)/2]}{2r^{n+1}}$$

$$\int_0^\infty \frac{\sin ax}{x} \, dx = \frac{\pi}{2}, \; 0, \; -\frac{\pi}{2} \qquad \text{for } a > 0, \, a = 0, \, a < 0$$

$$\int_0^\infty \frac{\sin^2 x}{x} \, dx = \frac{\pi}{2} \qquad\qquad \int_0^\infty \frac{\sin^2 ax}{x^2} \, dx = |a| \frac{\pi}{2}$$

$$\int_0^\pi \sin^2 ax \, dx = \int_0^\pi \cos^2 ax \, dx = \frac{\pi}{2}$$

$$\int_0^\pi \sin mx \sin nx \, dx = \int_0^\pi \cos mx \cos nx \, dx = 0 \qquad (m \neq n; \\ m, n = \text{integers})$$

$$\int_0^\pi \sin mx \cos nx \, dx = \begin{cases} \dfrac{2m}{m^2 - n^2} & \text{if } m + n \text{ is odd} \\ 0 & \text{if } m + n \text{ is even} \end{cases}$$

Table A-4 $\text{sinc}(x) = \dfrac{\sin(\pi x)}{\pi x}$

x	sinc (x)	x	sinc (x)	x	sinc (x)
0.0	1.00000	1.0	0.00000	2.0	0.00000
0.1	0.98363	1.1	−0.08942	2.1	0.04684
0.2	0.93549	1.1	−0.15592	2.2	0.08504
0.3	0.85839	1.3	−0.19809	2.3	0.11196
0.4	0.75683	1.4	−0.21624	2.4	0.12614
0.5	0.63662	1.5	−0.21221	2.5	0.12732
0.6	0.50455	1.6	−0.18921	2.6	0.11644
0.7	0.36788	1.7	−0.15148	2.7	0.09538
0.8	0.23387	1.8	−0.10394	2.8	0.06682
0.9	0.10929	1.9	−0.05177	2.9	0.03392

For values of sinc (x) outside the range of x given in the table the following procedure may be used:

1. Subtract the largest integer, n, less than x from x.
2. Look up in the table below the value of $(1/\pi) \sin [\pi(x - n)]$.
3. Multiply the tabular value by $(-1)^n$ and divide by x to give sinc (x).

$(x - n)$		$\dfrac{1}{\pi} \sin \pi x$
0.0	1.0	0.000000
0.1	0.9	0.098363
0.2	0.8	0.187098
0.3	0.7	0.257518
0.4	0.6	0.302731
0.5	0.5	0.318310

Table A-5   FOURIER TRANSFORMS USING VARIABLE f

DESCRIPTION	$g(t)$	$G(f)$
Definition	$g(t) = \displaystyle\int_{-\infty}^{\infty} G(f)\, e^{j2\pi ft}\, df$	$G(f) = \displaystyle\int_{-\infty}^{\infty} g(t) e^{-j2\pi ft}\, dt$
Reversal	$g(-t)$	$G(-f)$
Symmetry	$G(t)$	$g(-f)$
Scaling	$g(at)$	$\dfrac{1}{\|a\|} G\left(\dfrac{f}{a}\right)$
Delay	$g(t - T)$	$\epsilon^{-j2\pi fT} G(f)$
Complex Conjugate	$g^{*}(t)$	$G^{*}(-f)$

Table A-5 *continued*

DESCRIPTION	$g(t)$	$G(f)$
Time Differentiation	$g'(t)$	$j2\pi f G(f)$
Frequency Differentiation	$-j2\pi t g(t)$	$G'(f)$
Time Integration	$\displaystyle\int_{-\infty}^{t} g(\lambda)\, d\lambda$	$\dfrac{1}{j2\pi f}G(f) + \dfrac{1}{2}G(0)\delta(f)$
Time Convolution	$g \star h = \displaystyle\int_{-\infty}^{\infty} g(\lambda)h(t-\lambda)\, d\lambda$	$G(f)H(f)$
Frequency Convolution	$g(t)h(t)$	$G \star H = \displaystyle\int_{-\infty}^{\infty} G(\xi)H(f-\xi)\, d\xi$
Parseval's Theorem	$\displaystyle\int_{-\infty}^{\infty} g(t)h(t)\, dt$	$\displaystyle\int_{-\infty}^{\infty} G(f)H^*(f)\, df$
Modulation	$\epsilon^{j2\pi f_0 t} g(t)$	$G(f-f_0)$
Unit impulse	$\delta(t)$	1
Unit step	$u(t)$	$\dfrac{1}{2}\delta(f) + \dfrac{1}{j2\pi f}$
Sine	$\sin 2\pi f_0 t$	$\dfrac{1}{2j}[\delta(f-f_0) - \delta(f+f_0)]$
Cosine	$\cos 2\pi f_0 t$	$\dfrac{1}{2}[\delta(f-f_0) + \delta(f+f_0)]$
$u\left(t+\dfrac{T}{2}\right) - u\left(t-\dfrac{T}{2}\right)=p_T\left(t-\dfrac{T}{2}\right)$		$T \operatorname{sinc}(Tf)$
Fourier Expansion	$\displaystyle\sum_{n=-\infty}^{\infty} \alpha_n\, \epsilon^{j2\pi f_0 t}$	$\displaystyle\sum_{n=-\infty}^{\infty} \alpha_n\, \delta(f-nf_0)$
Impulse Train	$\displaystyle\sum \delta(t-nT)$	$\dfrac{1}{T}\displaystyle\sum \delta\left(f-\dfrac{n}{T}\right)$

B
Matrices

Definitions

A rectangular array of elements having m rows and n columns is called an $(m \times n)$ matrix. A matrix is denoted symbolically by a boldface capital letter in the following manner:

$$\mathbf{A} \equiv \begin{bmatrix} a_{11} & a_{12} & \cdots\cdots & a_{1n} \\ a_{21} & a_{22} & \cdots\cdots & a_{2n} \\ \cdots & \cdots & \cdots\cdots & \cdots \\ a_{m1} & a_{m2} & \cdots\cdots & a_{mn} \end{bmatrix} \equiv [a_{jk}]$$

An $(n \times 1)$ matrix is called a *column matrix*, a *column vector*, or often times just a *vector*. Such a vector will be designated by boldface lower-case letters as follows:

$$\mathbf{a} = \begin{bmatrix} a_1 \\ a^2 \\ \vdots \\ a_n \end{bmatrix}$$

A similar notation is also used for a $(1 \times n)$ matrix, which is called a *row matrix* or *row vector*. However, in the present text, row vectors will always be designated as the transpose of a column vector (see below). Accordingly, boldface lower-case letters will always refer to column vectors.

An $(n \times n)$ matrix is called a *square matrix* of order n. A square matrix is *diagonal* if and only if $j \neq k$ implies $a_{jk} = 0$; that is, all elements not on the main diagonal (from upper left to lower right) are zero.

A *scalar* is an ordinary number. It is also sometimes identified with a matrix of order (1×1) — that is, a single element. Scalars will be denoted by ordinary (not boldface) type.

The *identity matrix* is a diagonal matrix that has all its diagonal elements equal to one. It will be denoted by $\mathbf{I}$.

The *null or zero matrix* (either square or rectangular) has all its elements equal to zero. It is denoted by $\mathbf{0}$.

The transpose, $\mathbf{A}^T$, of a matrix $\mathbf{A}$ is formed by interchanging the rows and columns of $\mathbf{A}$. For example, if

$$\mathbf{A} = \begin{bmatrix} a_{11} & a_{12} & a_{13} \\ a_{21} & a_{22} & a_{23} \end{bmatrix} \quad \text{then } \mathbf{A}^T = \begin{bmatrix} a_{11} & a_{21} \\ a_{12} & a_{22} \\ a_{13} & a_{23} \end{bmatrix}$$

From this definition it is seen that the transpose of a column vector is a row vector and vice versa.

The *determinant* of a matrix (necessarily square) is the determinant of the elements of the matrix and is accordingly a number or scalar. The determinant of $\mathbf{A}$ is denoted $|\mathbf{A}|$. For example if

$$\mathbf{A} = \begin{bmatrix} 1 & 1 & 2 \\ 2 & 1 & 1 \\ 1 & 2 & 2 \end{bmatrix} \quad \text{then } |\mathbf{A}| = \begin{vmatrix} 1 & 1 & 2 \\ 2 & 1 & 1 \\ 1 & 2 & 2 \end{vmatrix} = 3$$

A matrix (necessarily square) for which the determinant of its elements is zero is called a *singular matrix*; that is, if $|\mathbf{A}| = 0$ then $\mathbf{A}$ is a singular matrix. If $|\mathbf{A}| \neq 0$ then $\mathbf{A}$ is *nonsingular*.

The *cofactor* of the element a_{jk} of the square matrix $\mathbf{A}$ is the scalar element formed by considering the matrix as a determinant, striking out the jth row and kth column and multiplying by $(-1)^{j+k}$. For example, if

$$\mathbf{A} = \begin{bmatrix} a_{11} & a_{12} & a_{13} \\ a_{21} & a_{22} & a_{23} \\ a_{31} & a_{32} & a_{33} \end{bmatrix}$$

then

$$\text{cofactor of } a_{31} = (-1)^4 \begin{vmatrix} a_{12} & a_{13} \\ a_{22} & a_{23} \end{vmatrix} = a_{12}\, a_{23} - a_{13}\, a_{22}$$

The *adjoint matrix*, adj **A**, of a (necessarily) square matrix **A** is formed by replacing each element of **A** by its cofactor and transposing. Thus, if

$$\mathbf{A} = \begin{bmatrix} 1 & 2 & 1 \\ 0 & 1 & 1 \\ 0 & 1 & 0 \end{bmatrix}$$

$$\text{adj } \mathbf{A} = \begin{bmatrix} (-1)^2 \begin{vmatrix} 1 & 1 \\ 1 & 0 \end{vmatrix} & (-1)^3 \begin{vmatrix} 0 & 1 \\ 0 & 0 \end{vmatrix} & (-1)^4 \begin{vmatrix} 0 & 1 \\ 0 & 1 \end{vmatrix} \\ (-1)^3 \begin{vmatrix} 2 & 1 \\ 1 & 0 \end{vmatrix} & (-1)^4 \begin{vmatrix} 1 & 1 \\ 0 & 0 \end{vmatrix} & (-1)^5 \begin{vmatrix} 1 & 2 \\ 0 & 1 \end{vmatrix} \\ (-1)^4 \begin{vmatrix} 2 & 1 \\ 1 & 1 \end{vmatrix} & (-1)^5 \begin{vmatrix} 1 & 1 \\ 0 & 1 \end{vmatrix} & (-1)^6 \begin{vmatrix} 1 & 2 \\ 0 & 1 \end{vmatrix} \end{bmatrix}^T$$

$$= \begin{bmatrix} -1 & 0 & 0 \\ 1 & 0 & -1 \\ 1 & -1 & 1 \end{bmatrix}^T = \begin{bmatrix} -1 & 1 & 1 \\ 0 & 0 & -1 \\ 0 & -1 & 1 \end{bmatrix}$$

Matrix Algebra

Equality of Matrices. Two matrices **A** and **B** are equal if and only if they are of the same order and all their corresponding elements are equal; that is, **A** = **B** provided **A** and **B** are of the same order and $a_{jk} = b_{jk}$ for all j and k.

Addition and Subtraction of Matrices. In order for two matrices to be added or subtracted they must be of the same order. If **A** and **B** are of the same order then their sum, **C**, is defined as the matrix whose elements are the sums of the corresponding elements in **A** and **B**. Thus,

$$\mathbf{C} = \mathbf{A} + \mathbf{B} \qquad \text{where } c_{jk} = a_{jk} + b_{jk}$$

The subtraction of two matrices is defined similarly, thus

$$\mathbf{D} = \mathbf{A} - \mathbf{B} \qquad \text{where } d_{jk} = a_{jk} - b_{jk}$$

Scalar Multiplication. The multiplication of a matrix **A** by a scalar (ordinary number) k is called scalar multiplication and results in a new matrix, each element of which is multiplied by the scalar. Thus

$$\mathbf{B} = k\mathbf{A} = k \begin{bmatrix} a_{11} & a_{12} & \cdots & a_{1n} \\ a_{21} & a_{22} & \cdots & a_{2n} \\ \cdots\cdots\cdots\cdots\cdots \\ a_{m1} & a_{m2} & \cdots & a_{mn} \end{bmatrix} = \begin{bmatrix} ka_{11} & ka_{12} & \cdots & ka_{1n} \\ ka_{21} & ka_{22} & \cdots & ka_{2n} \\ \cdots\cdots\cdots\cdots\cdots \\ ka_{m1} & ka_{m2} & \cdots & ka_{mn} \end{bmatrix}$$

Scalar multiplication is commutative, and therefore $k\mathbf{A} = \mathbf{A}k$.

Matrix Multiplication. Two matrices can be multiplied together only when the number of columns of the first matrix is equal to the number of rows of the second. Such matrices are said to be *conformable* in that order. If two matrices are conformable, their product is defined as

$$\mathbf{AB} = \mathbf{C}$$

where
$$c_{jk} = \sum_{i=1}^{q} a_{ji}b_{ik}$$

and the orders of the matrices **A**, **B**, and **C** are $(m \times q)$, $(q \times n)$, and $(m \times n)$, respectively. The operation of matrix multiplication can be visualized as follows. To obtain the jkth element in the product matrix, take the jth row of the first matrix and the kth column of the second matrix and multiply them term by term and add the result. This is illustrated below for the product of a (4×3) matrix and a (3×2) matrix.

$$\mathbf{A} = \begin{bmatrix} 1 & 2 & 2 \\ 1 & -3 & 1 \\ 2 & 0 & 1 \\ -1 & 1 & -2 \end{bmatrix} \qquad \mathbf{B} = \begin{bmatrix} 2 & 1 \\ 1 & 1 \\ 2 & 2 \end{bmatrix}$$

$$\mathbf{AB} = \mathbf{C}$$

The product matrix **C** will be a (4×2) matrix. To find the element c_{32} of the product matrix we must multiply the elements in the third row of **A** by the elements in the second column of **B** and add

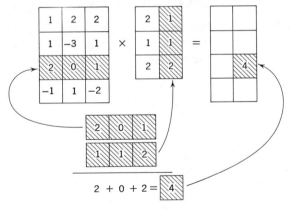

$$2 + 0 + 2 = \boxed{4}$$

The final result is as follows:

$$\begin{bmatrix} 1 & 2 & 2 \\ 1 & -3 & 1 \\ 2 & 0 & 1 \\ -1 & 1 & -2 \end{bmatrix} \times \begin{bmatrix} 2 & 1 \\ 1 & 1 \\ 2 & 2 \end{bmatrix} = \begin{bmatrix} 8 & 7 \\ 1 & 0 \\ 6 & 4 \\ -5 & -4 \end{bmatrix}$$

In general it is not possible to reverse the order of multiplication in a product. Only for an $(m \times n)$ and an $(n \times m)$ matrix would both products be defined, since otherwise the matrices would not be conformable in both orders. Over and above that, however, reversing the order of a product when possible leads, in general, to a different result. Thus

$$\mathbf{AB} \neq \mathbf{BA}$$

If two matrices do have the property that their product is independent of their order of multiplication they are said to *commute*. In particular the identity matrix $\mathbf{I}$ *commutes* with any square matrix of the same order; that is,

$$\mathbf{IA} = \mathbf{AI}$$

The product $\mathbf{AB}$ can be referred to in two ways: we may say $\mathbf{B}$ is premultiplied by $\mathbf{A}$ or that $\mathbf{A}$ is postmultiplied by $\mathbf{B}$. In the notation we are using, a vector $\mathbf{a}$ is a column matrix; therefore when a vector premultiplies a matrix $\mathbf{B}$ the product will always be in the form $\mathbf{a}^T\mathbf{B}$ in order that the matrices be conformable. When the order of multiplication is reversed the transpose is not required and the product will be $\mathbf{Ba}$. Premultiplication and postmultiplication of a matrix by a vector leads to the scalar form $\mathbf{a}^T\mathbf{Ba}$.

The Inverse Matrix. The matrix operation corresponding to division is defined in terms of the inverse matrix. For a given matrix $\mathbf{A}$, the inverse matrix $\mathbf{A}^{-1}$, when it exists, is defined by the following equation:

$$\mathbf{AA}^{-1} = \mathbf{I} = \mathbf{A}^{-1}\mathbf{A}$$

Thus any matrix multiplied by its inverse leads to the identity matrix. Only a nonsingular matrix (that is, one whose determinant does not vanish) has an inverse. The inverse of a nonsingular (necessarily square) matrix is

$$\mathbf{A}^{-1} = \frac{\text{adj } \mathbf{A}}{|\mathbf{A}|}$$

as an example consider

$$\mathbf{A} = \begin{bmatrix} a_{11} & a_{12} \\ a_{21} & a_{22} \end{bmatrix}$$

$$\text{adj } \mathbf{A} = \begin{bmatrix} a_{22} & -a_{21} \\ -a_{12} & a_{11} \end{bmatrix}^T = \begin{bmatrix} a_{22} & -a_{12} \\ -a_{21} & a_{11} \end{bmatrix}$$

$$\det \mathbf{A} = a_{11}a_{22} - a_{12}a_{21}$$

Therefore,

$$\mathbf{A}^{-1} = \frac{1}{a_{11}a_{22} - a_{12}a_{21}} \begin{bmatrix} a_{22} & -a_{12} \\ -a_{21} & a_{11} \end{bmatrix}$$

Characteristic Equation of a Matrix. A frequently occurring problem in matrix analysis is to find values of a scalar parameter λ for which there exist vectors $\mathbf{x} \neq \mathbf{0}$ that satisfy the matrix equation

$$\mathbf{Ax} = \lambda\mathbf{x}$$

where $\mathbf{A}$ is a given nth-order square matrix. Such a problem is called a characteristic value or eigenvalue problem. This equation can be rewritten by means of the identity matrix as

$$\mathbf{Ax} = \lambda\mathbf{Ix}$$
$$(\mathbf{A} - \lambda\mathbf{I})\mathbf{x} = \mathbf{0}$$

There will be a solution if and only if

$$|\mathbf{A} - \lambda\mathbf{I}| = 0$$

that is, if and only if

$$\begin{vmatrix} a_{11} - \lambda & a_{12} & \cdots & a_{1n} \\ a_{21} & a_{22} - \lambda & & \\ \vdots & \vdots & & \\ a_{n1} & a_{n2} & \cdots & a_{nn} - \lambda \end{vmatrix}$$

Either of these last two equations is called the *characteristic equation* of the matrix $\mathbf{A}$ and the expression

$$f(\lambda) = |\mathbf{A} - \lambda\mathbf{I}| = \lambda^n + \alpha_{n-1}\lambda^{n-1} + \cdots \alpha_1\lambda + \alpha_0 = 0$$

is called the *characteristic polynomial* for $\mathbf{A}$.

The roots of the characteristic equation, denoted by λ_i (where $i = 1$, $2, \cdots n$) are called the *characteristic values* or *eigenvalues* of the matrix $\mathbf{A}$. The vectors $\mathbf{x}$ that satisfy the equation $\mathbf{Ax} = \lambda\mathbf{x}$ are called *characteristic vectors* or *eigenvectors* of the matrix $\mathbf{A}$.

If there exists a nonsingular matrix $\mathbf{T}$ such that $\mathbf{B} = \mathbf{TAT}^{-1}$, the square matrices $\mathbf{A}$ and $\mathbf{B}$ are said to be *similar*. All similar matrices have the same eigenvalues and eigenvectors.

If $\mathbf{A}$ is a symmetric matrix, then all of its eigenvalues are real and the eigenvectors corresponding to different eigenvalues are orthogonal; that is, if $\mathbf{x}_j$ is the eigenvector corresponding to λ_j (where $\lambda_j \neq \lambda_k$), then

$$\mathbf{x}_j^T \mathbf{x}_k = 0$$

Cayley–Hamilton Theorem. The Cayley–Hamilton theorem states that "Every square matrix satisfies its own characteristic equation in a matrix sense." This means that if an nth-order square matrix $\mathbf{A}$ has as its characteristic equation

$$f(\lambda) = \lambda^n + \alpha_{n-1}\lambda^{n-1} + \cdots \alpha_1\lambda + \alpha_0 = 0$$

then

$$f(\mathbf{A}) = \mathbf{A}^n + \alpha_{n-1} \mathbf{A}^{n-1} + \cdots \alpha_1 \mathbf{A} + \alpha_0 \mathbf{I} = 0$$

Matrix Calculus.   If the elements of a matrix $\mathbf{A}$ are differentiable functions $a_{jk}(t)$ of a scalar parameter t, then the derivative of $\mathbf{A}$ with respect to t is defined as

$$\frac{d}{dt}\mathbf{A} = \begin{bmatrix} \dfrac{da_{11}(t)}{dt} & \dfrac{da_{12}(t)}{dt} & \cdots & \dfrac{da_{1n}(t)}{dt} \\[2mm] \dfrac{da_{21}(t)}{dt} & \dfrac{da_{22}(t)}{dt} & \cdots & \dfrac{da_{2n}(t)}{dt} \\[2mm] \vdots & \vdots & & \\[2mm] \dfrac{da_{m1}(t)}{dt} & \dfrac{da_{m2}(t)}{dt} & \cdots & \dfrac{da_{mn}(t)}{dt} \end{bmatrix}$$

Partial differentiation and integration of matrices are defined in an analogous manner.

Functions of Matrices.   The definition of a function can be extended to matrix arguments. This concept is particularly useful when the function can be expanded in a convergent power series. Such a representation takes the following form

$$g(\mathbf{A}) = \sum_{m=0}^{\infty} B_m \mathbf{A}^m \qquad \mathbf{A}^0 = \mathbf{I}$$

For example, the exponential function of the square matrix $\mathbf{A}$

$$\epsilon^{\mathbf{A}} = \mathbf{I} + \mathbf{A} + \tfrac{1}{2}\mathbf{A}^2 + \cdots$$

This series converges for all square matrices. From the Cayley–Hamilton theorem it is seen that if $\mathbf{A}$ is an nth-order matrix we can express $\mathbf{A}^n$ as a polynomial in $\mathbf{A}$ where the highest power of $\mathbf{A}$ is $n-1$. Using this relationship it is possible to systematically reduce a polynomial of any order in $\mathbf{A}$ to an equivalent expression containing no terms of power higher than $n-1$. The resulting expression will be of the form

$$g(\mathbf{A}) = \frac{\Delta_{n-1}}{\Delta} \mathbf{A}^{n-1} + \frac{\Delta_{n-2}}{\Delta} \mathbf{A}^{n-2} + \cdots \frac{\Delta_1}{\Delta} \mathbf{A} + \frac{\Delta_0}{\Delta} \mathbf{I}$$

where Δ is the determinant

$$\Delta = \begin{vmatrix} 1 & 1 & \cdots & 1 \\ \lambda_1 & \lambda_2 & \cdots & \lambda_n \\ \lambda_1^2 & \lambda_2^2 & \cdots & \lambda_n^2 \\ \vdots & \vdots & & \\ \lambda_1^{n-1} & \lambda_2^{n-1} & \cdots & \lambda_n^{n-1} \end{vmatrix}$$

and λ_1, λ_2, $\cdots$ λ_n are the eigenvalues of $\mathbf{A}$. The determinant Δ_{r-1} is derived from Δ by replacing the elements of the rth row by $g(\lambda_1)$, $g(\lambda_2)$, $\cdots$ $g(\lambda_n)$.

If the n eigenvalues of $\mathbf{A}$ are distinct then the expression for the matrix function can be written in the following alternative form:

$$g(\mathbf{A}) = \sum_{j=1}^{n} f(\lambda_j) \frac{\prod\limits_{j \neq k} (\mathbf{A} - \lambda_k \mathbf{I})}{\prod\limits_{j \neq k} (\lambda_j - \lambda_k)}$$

This is known as *Sylvester's theorem.*

Miscellaneous Matrix Relationships. It is assumed in the following that the various matrix operations are permissible; that is, matrices being multipled are conformable, matrices being inverted are nonsingular, and so on.

$(\mathbf{ABC}) = (\mathbf{AB})\mathbf{C} = \mathbf{A}(\mathbf{BC})$
$\mathbf{A}^n = \mathbf{AA} \cdots \mathbf{A}$ to n factors
If $\mathbf{D} = \mathbf{ABC}$ then $\mathbf{D}^{-1} = \mathbf{C}^{-1}\mathbf{B}^{-1}\mathbf{A}^{-1}$
$\mathbf{A}^{-n} = (\mathbf{A}^{-1})^n$
If $\mathbf{C} = \mathbf{AB}$ then $\mathbf{C}^T = (\mathbf{AB})^T = \mathbf{B}^T \mathbf{A}^T$
If $\mathbf{D} = \mathbf{ABC}$ then $\mathbf{D}^T = (\mathbf{ABC})^T = \mathbf{C}^T \mathbf{B}^T \mathbf{A}^T$

Premultiplication (postmultiplication) of $\mathbf{A}$ by the matrix obtained by replacing the 1 in the jth row (column) of the identity matrix by α multiplies all elements in the jth row (column) of $\mathbf{A}$ by α.

Premultiplication (postmultiplication) of $\mathbf{A}$ by the matrix obtained by replacing the zero in the nondiagonal element δ_{jk} of the identity matrix by 1 adds the kth row (column) of $\mathbf{A}$ to jth row (column) of $\mathbf{A}$.

Premultiplication (postmultiplication) of $\mathbf{A}$ by the permutation matrix obtained by a permutation of the rows (columns) of the identity matrix results in an identical permutation of the rows (columns) of $\mathbf{A}$.

C

Mean-Square Values
by Complex Integration

It was shown in the course of defining the spectral density that the mean-square value of the random process was proportional to the *area* of the spectral density. That is,

$$\overline{x^2} = \frac{1}{2\pi} \int_{-\infty}^{\infty} S_x(\omega)\, d\omega \qquad \text{(C-1)}$$

This integral may be difficult to evaluate as a real integral, particularly in the case of rational spectra of high order. A classical way of evaluating such an integral is to treat it as a contour integral in the plane of a complex variable. The complex frequency plane is as convenient as any other for this purpose. When expressed in this form, (C-1) becomes

$$\overline{x^2} = \frac{1}{2\pi j} \int_{-j\infty}^{j\infty} S_x(s)\, ds \qquad \text{(C-2)}$$

where

$$S_x(s) = S_x(j\omega)\big|_{\omega = -js}$$

A complete discussion of the *theory* of evaluating these integrals is beyond the scope of this book since an adequate mathematical background has not been laid. The *mechanics* of carrying out such an evaluation are relatively simple, however, and will be discussed here. The student should be aware that there are many pitfalls associated with using mathematical tools without having a thorough grasp of their theory and, hence, he is encouraged to acquire the proper theoretical understanding as soon as possible.

The following method is based on the evaluation of residues in much the same way as we have done in connection with finding inverse Laplace transforms. This method is best demonstrated by means of a simple example along with some words of explanation. Consider the rational spectral density

$$S_x(\omega) = \frac{\omega^2 + 4}{\omega^4 + 10\omega^2 + 9} = \frac{\omega^2 + 4}{(\omega^2 + 1)(\omega^2 + 9)} \qquad \text{(C-3)}$$

which, in the *s* plane, becomes

$$S_x(s) = \frac{-s^2 + 4}{(-s^2 + 1)(-s^2 + 9)} = \frac{-(s^2 - 4)}{(s^2 - 1)(s^2 - 9)}$$

$$= \frac{-(s + 2)(s - 2)}{(s + 1)(s - 1)(s + 3)(s - 3)} \qquad \text{(C-4)}$$

This spectral density can be represented by the pole-zero configuration in the *s* plane, as shown in Fig. C-1. It will be noted that the plot is sym-

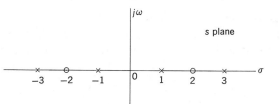

Figure C-1   Pole-zero configuration for spectral density.

metrical about the *jω* axis. This symmetry will always exist for spectral densities.

The path of integration called for by (C-2) is along the *jω* axis. A closed contour can be obtained by adding a semicircle at infinity which encloses either the left half plane or the right plane. Less difficulty with the algebraic sign is encountered if the left half plane is used, so the path shown in Fig. C-2 will be assumed from now on. In order for the integral around this closed path to be the same as the integral along the *jω* axis, it is necessary for the contribution due to the semicircle to vanish as

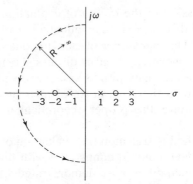

Figure C-2 Path of integration for evaluating mean-square value.

$R \to \infty$. For rational spectral densities this will be true whenever the denominator polynomial is of higher degree than the numerator polynomial (since only even powers are present).

A basic result of complex variable theory states that the value of an integral around a simple closed contour in the complex plane is equal to $2\pi j$ times the sum of the residues at the poles contained *within* that contour. Since the expression for the mean-square value (C-2) has a factor of $1/2\pi j$, and since the chosen contour completely encloses the left half plane, it follows that the mean-square value can in general be expressed as

$$\overline{x^2} = \sum (\text{residues at LHP poles}) \tag{C-5}$$

For the example being considered, the only LHP poles are at -1 and -3. The residues can be evaluated easily by multiplying $S_x(s)$ by the factor containing the pole in question and letting s assume the value of the pole. Thus,

$$K_{-1} = [(s + 1)S_x(s)]_{s=-1} = \left[\frac{-(s + 2)(s - 2)}{(s - 1)(s + 3)(s - 3)} \right]_{s=-1}$$

$$= \frac{3}{16}$$

$$K_{-3} = [(s + 3)S_x(s)]_{s=-3} = \left[\frac{-(s - 2)(s - 2)}{(s + 1)(s - 1)(s - 3)} \right]_{s=-3}$$

$$= \frac{5}{48}$$

and

$$\overline{x^2} = \frac{3}{16} + \frac{5}{48} = \frac{14}{48} = \frac{7}{24} \tag{C-6}$$

This result may be compared with that obtained in Section 11-4. Had the poles not been simple, the usual methods for evaluating residues of multiple-order poles could be employed.

■ P R O B L E M S

C-1   Repeat Problem 11-5 using the method of complex integration.

C-2   Find the mean-square value of the random process whose spectral density can be defined by the pole-zero configuration shown. A scale factor of 10 may be assumed.

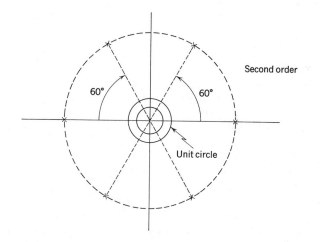

D

Interchanging Expectations and Time Integration

The problem of finding the expected value of an integral whose integrand contains a random variable arises many times. In almost all such cases it is desirable to be able to move the expectation operation inside the integral and thus simplify the integrand. Fortunately, this interchange is possible in almost all cases of practical interest and, hence, is used throughout this book with little or no comment. It is advisable, however, to be aware of the conditions under which this is possible, even though the reasons for these conditions are not understood. The conditions may be stated as follows:

If $z(t)$ is a sample function from a random process (or some function, such as the square, of the sample function) and $f(t)$ is a nonrandom time function, then

$$E\left[\int_{t_1}^{t_2} z(t) f(t)\, dt\right] = \int_{t_1}^{t_2} E\left[z(t)\right] f(t)\, dt \qquad \text{(D-1)}$$

if

(1) $\displaystyle\int_{t_1}^{t_2} E\left[|z(t)|\right] |f(t)| dt < \infty$

and

(2) $z(t)$ is bounded on the interval t_1 to t_2. Note that t_1 and t_2 may be infinite. (There is *no* requirement that $z(t)$ be from a stationary process.)

In applying this result to the analysis of linear systems the nonrandom function $f(t)$ is usually the impulse response $h(t)$. For stationary input random processes the quantity $E[|z(t)|]$ is a *constant* not dependent on time t. Hence, the stability condition of (12-4) is sufficient to satisfy condition (1). The boundedness of $z(t)$ is always satisfied by physical signals, although there are some mathematical representations that may not be bounded.

Selected Answers

■ CHAPTER 1

1-4

a. $i_c = \dfrac{2.47 \times 10^{-6} R_3 R_T - 12 \times 10^{-2}}{1.12 \times 10^{-4} R_3 R_T + 1.455 \times 10^{-2} (R_3 + R_T) + 1}$

b. $R_3 = 205 \quad \Omega \quad$ for $\quad T = 150°F$
$R_3 = 157 \quad \Omega \quad$ for $\quad T = 250°F$

c. $T_{(dropout)} = 125.6°F$

■ CHAPTER 2

2-1
a. Series resistance in inductors is important.
b. Shunt resistance of capacitance is important.
c. One must consider mutual inductances.
d. Inductance may depend on the value of the current.

2-3

a. Causal case: $y(t) = \begin{cases} 10\,[1 - \epsilon^{-t}] & t \geq 0 \\ 0 & t < 0 \end{cases}$

Noncausal: $y(t) = \begin{cases} C\epsilon^{-t} + 10\,(1 - \epsilon^{-t}) & t \geq 0 \\ C\epsilon^{-t} & t < 0 \end{cases} C \neq 0$

2-4
a. First-order; linear; time-invariant; dynamic; lumped-parameter; continuous
b. Second-order; linear; time-varying; dynamic; lumped-parameter; continuous

c. Zero-order; nonlinear; time-invariant; instantaneous; lumped-parameter; continuous

d. Second-order; nonlinear; time-invariant; dynamic; lumped-parameter; continuous

2-5

a. Invariant

b. Invariant

c. Time-varying

d. Invariant

e. Time-varying

f. Time-varying

g. Time-varying

2-6 Discrete; causal; dynamic; linear; time-invariant

2-7

a. $(LC)^2 \dfrac{d^4y}{dt^4} + 3LC \dfrac{d^2y}{dt^2} + y(t) = x(t)$

b. Fourth-order

2-8

a. $\dfrac{d^2y}{dt^2} + 2\dfrac{dy}{dt} + y(t) = \dfrac{d^2x}{dt^2} + \dfrac{dx}{dt}$, or: $\dfrac{dy}{dt} + y(t) = \dfrac{dx}{dt}$

b. Second-order

2-9 $\dot{v}_1 = v_2 \qquad \dot{v}_2 = v_3 \qquad \dot{v}_3 = v_4 \qquad \dot{v}_4 = \dfrac{-3}{LC} v_3 - \left(\dfrac{1}{LC}\right)^2 v_1 + x(t)$

where $v_1 = y \qquad v_2 = \dot{y} \qquad v_3 = \ddot{y} \qquad v_4 = \dddot{y}$

2-10 let $q = y(t) - x(t) \qquad \dot{q}(t) = -q(t) - x(t)$
$y(t) = q(t) + x(t)$

■ CHAPTER 3

3-1

a. Periodic; power

b. Nonperiodic; random; energy

c. Periodic; energy; deterministic

d. Random; energy

e. Nonperiodic; power

f. Nonperiodic; random; energy

3-2
a. $P_{av} = 25$; nonperiodic; power
b. Nonperiodic; energy; $\mathscr{E} = 10$
c. Periodic; power; period $= 1$; $P_{av} = 62.5$
d. Nonperiodic; energy; $\mathscr{E} = 9.94$
e. Almost-periodic; $P_{av} = 1$

3-3
a. No
b. True
c. True
d. True
e. False
f. True

3-4

a. $\mathscr{E}_2 = \dfrac{a^2}{|b|}\,\mathscr{E}_1$

b. $P_2 = a^2\,P_1$

3-5
a. Either energy or power

b. $\mathscr{E}_z \geq [\text{average value of } z]^2$
c. $P_z \leq \mathscr{E}_x\,P_y$

3-6
a. $[0, 1/2]$

b. $B_n = 2$

3-8

a. $I = \displaystyle\sum_{i=-\infty}^{\infty} a_i b_i$

b. $\mathscr{E} = \displaystyle\sum_{i=-\infty}^{\infty} a_i^2$

3-9 $\psi_n(t) = \dfrac{1}{\sqrt{T}}\,\phi_n\!\left(\dfrac{t}{T}\right)$

3-10

a. $\hat{f}(t) = 4\,\psi_0(t) - 2\psi_1(t) + 2\psi_2(t)$, where $\psi_n(t) = 1/2\,\phi_n\!\left(\dfrac{t}{4}\right)$

b. F.S.E. $= 0.0$

3-11 $\phi_2(t) = 6\epsilon^{-2t} - 4\epsilon^{-t}$

3-12
a. $A_1 = 4\sqrt{2}$ $A_2 = 8/7$
b. F.S.E. ≈ 0.081 percent

3-13
a. $a_1 = 3.195$ $a_2 = 0.0279$ $a_3 = -1.734$
b. $c_1 = -8.24$ $c_2 = 51.17$ $c_3 = -42.4$
c. $\mathscr{E} \approx 14.41$
d. F.S.E. = 0.0830

3-16

a. $x(t) = \begin{cases} \displaystyle\sum_{n=-\infty}^{\infty} j\frac{3}{n\pi}\, \epsilon^{jn\omega_0 t} & 0 \le t \le 1 \\ \\ 0 & \text{elsewhere} \end{cases}$

b. F.S.E. = 0.04

3-17 $x(t) = \displaystyle\sum_{n=-\infty}^{\infty} \alpha_n \epsilon^{-jn\omega_0 T}$ $\alpha_0 = \dfrac{A}{2}$ $\alpha_n = \dfrac{A}{j\pi n}$ $n = \pm 1, \pm 2, \cdots$

3-18

a. $x(t) = \dfrac{A}{2} + \dfrac{A}{2\pi} \displaystyle\sum_{n=1}^{\infty} \dfrac{1}{n} \sin\left(\dfrac{2\pi(2n-1)\,t}{T}\right)$

b. $x(t) = A$

3-19

a. $y(t) = x(t) - \dfrac{A}{2} = \displaystyle\sum_{n=-\infty}^{\infty} \dfrac{At_a}{T}\, \dfrac{\sin n\pi t_a/T}{n\pi t_a/T}\, \exp\left[j\dfrac{2\pi n}{T}\left(t - \dfrac{t_a}{2}\right)\right] - \dfrac{A}{2}$

b. $y(t) = \dfrac{At_a}{T} \displaystyle\sum_{n=-\infty}^{\infty} \dfrac{\sin n\pi t_a/T}{n\pi t_a/T}\, \exp\left[j\dfrac{2\pi nt}{T}\right]$

c. $y(t) = \displaystyle\sum_{n=-\infty}^{\infty} \dfrac{At_a}{T}\, \dfrac{\sin n\pi t_a/T}{n\pi t_a/T}\, \exp\left[j\dfrac{2\pi n}{T}\left(10t - \dfrac{t_a}{2}\right)\right]$

d. $y(t) = \displaystyle\sum_{n=-\infty}^{\infty} \dfrac{A^2 t_a}{T}\, \dfrac{\sin n\pi t_a/T}{n\pi t_a/T}\, \exp\left[j\dfrac{2\pi n}{T}\left(t - \dfrac{t_a}{2}\right)\right]$

3-22
a. $x(t) = 5r(t + 2) - 10r(t) + 5r(t - 2)$
b. $x(t) = 2u(t - 1) - 4u(t) + 2u(t - 2)$
c. $x(t) = r(t) - r(t - 1) + u(t - 1) - u(t - 2) - r(t - 2) + r(t - 3)$
d. $x(t) = 4r^2(t)\, u(-t + 1) + 4u(t - 1) - 4u(t - 2)$

3-23
a. $\mathscr{E} = \infty$ $P = \infty$ b. $\mathscr{E} = \infty$ $P = 1$

3-25

a. $\epsilon^{-\alpha t} \delta(t - t_1) = \epsilon^{-\alpha t} \delta(t - t_1)$

b. $\delta(10t - 1) = \dfrac{1}{10} \delta\left(t - \dfrac{1}{10}\right)$

e. $\delta(t - 1) \delta(2t) = 0$

f. $\cos t \, \delta(t - \pi) = \cos \pi \, \delta(t - \pi) = -\delta(t - \pi)$

g. $\displaystyle\int_{-\infty}^{t} \delta(3\lambda - 1) \, d\lambda = \dfrac{1}{3} u(t - 1/3)$

h. $\sin(t) \, \delta'(t) = \delta(t)$

3-26

a. $\cos \omega$	**d.** $37/27$
b. 0	**e.** 2
c. 12	**f.** 1
	g. $\epsilon^{-4} \delta(t - 2)$

3-27

a. $v_0(t) = 10 - 10u(t - 1) - 100 \, \delta(t - 1)$

b. $i(t) = 10^{-6} \{ 10u(t - 1) - 100 \, \delta(t - 1) \}$

3-28

a. $3\pi \, \delta(t)$	**b.** $10^6 \, \delta(t - 3)$
	c. $2 \times 10^{-6} \, \delta(t)$

■ C H A P T E R 4

4-2 $y(t) = 2[4 + 5\epsilon^{-5(t-1)}] \, u(t - 1)$

4-3

a. $f_1(t) \star f_2(t)$

4-4 250 meters

4-5 $v_0(t) = \dfrac{1}{T}[1 - \epsilon^{-t}] \quad 0 \le t \le T \quad$ for an input pulse of length T

$\qquad\quad = \dfrac{1}{T}[\epsilon^T - 1]\epsilon^{-t} \qquad t > T$

$\quad h(t) \;\; = \epsilon^{-t} u(t)$

4-6 Use the rectangular pulse with the same maximum value and whose duration is chosen to give the same energy as the nonrectangular pulse.

4-8

a. Response will be the same as in the figure except for an amplitude scale factor of 1/2.

b. The output will be approximately zero.

c. The response will be an approximate step with overshoot and ringing at the natural frequency of the system.

4-9

t	0	1	2	3	4	5	6	7	8	9	10
$f_1 \star f_2$	4.00	6.40	7.36	7.04	5.60	3.20	−0.040	−2.96	−4.64	−5.60	−6.00

t	11	12	13	14	15
$f_1 \star f_2$	−4.00	−2.40	−1.20	−0.40	0.00

4-10 $y(3) = 6.9$ $y(10) = 45.4$

4-11   a. $w(t) = \dfrac{1}{2} \epsilon^{-t/4} u(t)$ $h(t) = \dfrac{1}{2} \delta(t) - \dfrac{1}{8} \epsilon^{-t/4} u(t)$

b. $w(t) = 10 (1 - \epsilon^{-10t}) u(t)$ $h(t) = 100 \epsilon^{-10t} u(t)$

4-12 $i_i(t) = 2[u(t) - u(t - 2)]$
   $w(t) = \epsilon^{-2t} u(t)$ $h(t) = \delta(t) - 2\epsilon^{-2t} u(t)$

4-13   Pulse duration must be much longer than the system time constant.

$$y(t) = \frac{2A}{T} [t + 5 [1 - \epsilon^{-0.2t}]] \quad 0 \le t \le T/2$$

$$= \frac{2A}{T} [T - t + 5 [2 \epsilon^{-0.2(t - T/2)} - 1 - \epsilon^{-0.2t}]] \quad T/2 \le t \le T$$

$$= \frac{2A}{T} [10 \epsilon^{-0.2(t - T/2)} - 5 \epsilon^{-0.2t} - 5 \epsilon^{-0.2(t - T)}] \quad T \le t < \infty$$

4-14 $y(t) = \dfrac{5}{2\pi} [1 - \cos 2\pi t] \quad 0 \le t \le 1$

   $= 0$ elsewhere

■ C H A P T E R 5

5-1
a. Not transformable; not absolutely integrable
b. Not transformable; infinite number of maxima and minima
c. Not transformable; not absolutely integrable
d. Not transformable; not absolutely integrable

5-2 $F(j\omega) = t_0 \dfrac{\sin \dfrac{\omega t_0}{2}}{\dfrac{\omega t_0}{2}}$

Fourier series coefficients are: $\alpha_k = \dfrac{t_0}{T} \dfrac{\sin n\pi t_0/T}{n\pi t_0/T}$

As T gets larger, the spacing of the lines in the line spectrum gets smaller, but the envelope still remains the same and is determined solely by the shape of a single pulse.

5-3 $F(j\omega) = AT \dfrac{\sin^2 \omega T/2}{(\omega T/2)^2}$

5-4 Duration $= T$ $\qquad BW = \dfrac{2\pi}{T}$

5-6 **a.** $F_1(j\omega) = AT\, \epsilon^{-j(\omega T/2)} \dfrac{\sin \omega T/2}{\omega T/2}$

b. $F_2(j\omega) = 2AT \dfrac{\sin \omega T}{\omega T}$

c. $F_3(j\omega) = AT \left[\dfrac{\sin \omega T/2}{\omega T/2} \right]^2$

5-8 **a.** $X(j\omega) = 2AT \dfrac{\sin \omega T}{\omega T}$

b. $Y(j\omega) = -2jAT \dfrac{\sin^2 \omega T/2}{\omega T/2}$

c. $Z(j\omega) = \dfrac{2\alpha A}{\alpha^2 + \omega^2}$

5-9

a. $H(j\omega) = \dfrac{2}{(j\omega + 1)(j\omega + 3)}$

b. $H(j\omega) = \dfrac{j\omega + 1}{j\omega + 2}$.

c. $H(j\omega) = \dfrac{j\omega + 1}{2 - \omega^2 + j\omega}$

5-10

a. $H(j\omega) = \dfrac{1}{(j\omega + 4)(j\omega + 2)}$

b. $|H(j\omega)| = \dfrac{1}{\sqrt{(\omega^2 + 16)(\omega^2 + 4)}}$

5-11   a. $H(j\omega) = \dfrac{1}{(1 - \omega^2 R^2 C^2) + 3j\omega\, RC}$

b. $H(j\omega) = \dfrac{1}{1 - \omega^2 R^2 C^2 + 2j\omega\, RC}$

The difference is caused by loading in part a.

5-13   8

5-14 $W = 0.069$ Hz

5-15 $BW \simeq \dfrac{5}{\pi t_0}$ Hz

The bandwidth would be smaller for isoceles-triangular pulses.

5-16 $H(j\omega) = \epsilon^{-j\omega t_0}$

5-17

a. $\dfrac{3 + j\omega}{72 - \omega^2 + j18\omega}$

b. $\dfrac{(1 + j\omega)\epsilon^{-j2\omega}}{(8 - \omega^2) + 6j\omega}$

c. $\dfrac{3 + j\omega}{72 - \omega^2 + 18j\omega}\left[\epsilon^{-j2\omega/3}\right]$

d. $10\,\dfrac{1 + 2j\omega}{8 - 4\omega^2 + 12j\omega}$

5-18 $H(j\omega) = \dfrac{1 - (1 + j\omega)\epsilon^{-j\omega}}{1 + j\omega}$

5-19 $F(\alpha + j\omega)$

5-20

a. $\epsilon^{-2j(\omega - 6)} \dfrac{1 + j(\omega - 6)}{8 - (\omega - 6)^2 + 6j(\omega - 6)}$

b. $\dfrac{6j\omega\,(1 + j\omega)}{8 - \omega^2 + 6j\omega}$

c. $\dfrac{\dfrac{1}{2}\left(1 - j\dfrac{\omega}{2}\right)}{8 - \dfrac{\omega^2}{4} - 3j\omega}$

d. $j\dfrac{5}{3} \cdot \dfrac{\left[\left(8 - \dfrac{\omega^2}{9}\right) + 2j\omega\right]j/3 - (1 + j\omega/3)\left[-\dfrac{2}{9}\omega + 2j\right]}{[8 - \omega^2/9 + 2j\omega]^2}$

e. $\dfrac{5\epsilon^{-2j\omega}\,[1 - j\omega]}{8 - \omega^2 - 6j\omega}$

f. $\dfrac{1}{2} \cdot \dfrac{1 + j(\omega + 1)}{8 - (\omega + 1)^2 + 6j(\omega + 1)} + \dfrac{1}{2}\dfrac{1 + j(\omega - 1)}{8 - (\omega - 1)^2 + 6j(\omega - 1)}$

5-21

a. $\dfrac{2}{1 + \omega^2}$

b. $\dfrac{-2j\omega}{1 + \omega^2}$

c. $\dfrac{1}{(j\omega + 1)^2}$

d. $\dfrac{1}{j\omega + 1}\left[1 - \left(1 + \dfrac{1}{\epsilon}\right)\epsilon^{-j\omega}\right]$

5-22
a. $H'(j\omega) = H(j\,10\omega)$ **b.** $H'(j\omega) = H(j\omega)$

5-23 Time constant of RC filter $= \dfrac{1}{4.92\,W}$

5-24   The spectra must be narrow-band.

$$H_{LP}(j\omega) = H_{BP}[j(\omega - \omega_c)] + H_{B_P}[j(\omega + \omega_c)]$$

5-25   c. $v_0(t) \approx \begin{cases} 1 - \epsilon^{-0.157 \times 10^6 t} & 0 < t < 10^{-2} \\ (\epsilon^{0.157 \times 10^4} - 1)\,\epsilon^{-0.157 \times 10^6 t} & t > 10^{-2} \end{cases}$

gives the envelope of the system response.

5-26

a. $d^k/d\omega^k |H(j\omega)| \Big|_{\omega = 0} = 0,\ k = 1, 2, 3, \cdots$

b. $H(j\omega) = \dfrac{1}{1 - 2\omega^2 + j\omega\,(2 - \omega^2)}$

$|H(j\omega)|^2 = \dfrac{1}{1 + \omega^6}$; third order.

c.   Half-power $BW = \dfrac{1}{2\pi}$ Hz

5-27

a. $A\left(j\dfrac{\pi}{2}\right)[\delta(\omega + \omega_0) - \delta(\omega - \omega_0)] - \dfrac{A\omega_0}{\omega^2 - \omega_0^2}$

b. $\pi\delta(\omega - \omega_0) + \pi\delta(\omega + \omega_0) + (m\pi/2)\,\delta(\omega - \omega_0 + \omega_1)$
$\quad + (m\pi/2)\,\delta(\omega + \omega_0 + \omega_1) + (m\pi/2)\,\delta(\omega - \omega_1 + \omega_0)$
$\quad + (m\pi/2)\,\delta(\omega - \omega_0 - \omega_1)$

c. $a_0\,\pi\delta(\omega) + \pi \displaystyle\sum_{n=1}^{\infty} \{(a_n - jb_n)\,\delta(\omega - n\omega_0) + (a_n + jb_n)$

$\delta(\omega + n\omega_0)\}$

5-28 $\dfrac{2\pi}{T} \displaystyle\sum_{n=-\infty}^{\infty} \dfrac{j2\pi n}{1 + j(2\pi n/T)} \dfrac{\sin n\pi/2}{n\pi/2} (\epsilon^{j(n\pi/2)} - \epsilon^{-T/2}\epsilon^{-j(n\pi/2)})$

$\delta\left(\omega - \dfrac{2\pi n}{T}\right)$

5-29 $A\pi \displaystyle\sum_{n=-\infty}^{\infty} \left[\dfrac{\sin n\pi/2}{n\pi/2}\right]^2 \delta(\omega - 2\pi n/T)$

5-30

a. $\pi\delta(\omega - \omega_c) + \pi\delta(\omega + \omega_c) + \dfrac{1}{2} M[j(\omega - \omega_c)] + \dfrac{1}{2} M[j(\omega + \omega_c)]$

b. $\dfrac{T}{t_1} \displaystyle\sum_{n=-\infty}^{\infty} \dfrac{\sin [(\omega - 2\pi n/t_1)T/2]}{(\omega - 2\pi n/t_1)T/2}$

c. $-\dfrac{j}{2}\left[\dfrac{1}{j(\omega - \omega_0) + \alpha} - \dfrac{1}{j(\omega + \omega_0) + \alpha}\right]$

5-32 $f_s \min = 40$ Hz

5-33 Error power $= \dfrac{25}{32}$

$f_s > 5000$ Hz for no distortion

5-35 See Problem 4-7 for answers.

5-36 $\left|\dfrac{Y(j\omega)}{X(j\omega)}\right| = \dfrac{10}{\sqrt{\omega^2 + (1 + 10K)^2}}$

5-37

a. $\dfrac{5}{j\omega + 0.01}$ **b.** 0

5-38 **b.** The energy in the waveform is proportional to the energy in the sample values.

■ C H A P T E R 6

6-1

a. $\dfrac{1}{s}\,\epsilon^{-st_0}$

b. $\dfrac{1}{s^2}\,\epsilon^{-st_0}$

c. $\dfrac{6\epsilon^{-5s}}{s^3}\left[1 + 5s + \dfrac{25}{2}\,s^2\right]$

d. $\dfrac{5}{s}\,[1 - \epsilon^{-3s}]$

e. $\dfrac{n!}{s^{n+1}}$

f. $\dfrac{\sqrt{\pi}}{2s^{3/2}}$

g. $\dfrac{\sqrt{\pi}}{s^{1/2}}$

h. $\dfrac{1}{2}\sqrt{\dfrac{\pi}{\alpha}}\,\epsilon^{s^2/4\alpha}\,[1 - \text{erf}\,(s/2\sqrt{\alpha})]$

6-2

a. $\dfrac{10}{s}\,[1 - \epsilon^{-2s}]$

b. $\dfrac{1}{(s + \alpha)^2}$

c. $\dfrac{s}{s^2 - \beta^2}$

d. $\dfrac{s + \alpha}{(s + \alpha)^2 - \beta^2}$

6-3   a. $\dfrac{\beta}{s^2 - \beta^2}$

b. $\dfrac{\beta}{s^2 + \beta^2}$

c. $\dfrac{\epsilon^{-(s + 1)}}{(s + 1)^2}$

6-4   a. $\dfrac{2A}{T}\,\dfrac{1}{s^2}\,[1 - \epsilon^{sT/2}]^2$

b. $\dfrac{10}{s^2 + 4}\,[\epsilon^{-(\pi/2)s} - \epsilon^{-(3\pi/2)s}]$

c. $\dfrac{1}{s}\,[2 - 3\epsilon^{-s} + \epsilon^{-3s}]$

6-5 $\dfrac{s}{s + \alpha}$

6-6

a. $\dfrac{s}{(s + \alpha)^2}$

b. $\dfrac{s^2}{(s + \alpha)^2}$

c. $\dfrac{1}{s(s + \alpha)^2}$

6-8 $f(t) : s^n F(s) - s^{n-1} f^{(0)} (0^-) - s^{n-2} f^{(1)} (0^-) \cdots - s f^{(n-2)} (0^-)$
$- f^{(n-1)} (0^-) \; f(t) \, u(t) : s^n \, F(s)$

6-9 $\dfrac{\left(s - \dfrac{1}{2}\right)^n}{\left(s + \dfrac{1}{2}\right)^{n+1}}$

6-10

a. $\epsilon^{\alpha t_0} \left\{ \dfrac{\omega_0 \cos \theta_0}{(s + \alpha)^2 + \omega_0^2} + \dfrac{(s + \alpha) \sin \theta_0}{(s + \alpha)^2 + \omega_0^2} \right\}$

b. $\dfrac{(s + \alpha)^2 - \omega_0^2}{[(s + \alpha)^2 + \omega_0^2]^2}$

c. $\dfrac{\omega_0}{(s + \alpha)(s^2 + \omega_0^2)}$

6-11 **a.** $F(s) = T \dfrac{\sinh s T/2}{s T/2} \epsilon^{-sT/2} + T \dfrac{\sinh s T/2}{s T/2} \epsilon^{-(5/2)sT}$

b. $2 \epsilon^{-5s/2T} \dfrac{\sinh (5s/2T)}{s^2 + (2\pi/T)^2}$

6-14 **a.** $F_2(s) = \dfrac{F_1(s)}{s}$

b. $F_2(s) = \dfrac{\epsilon^{as} - 1}{s} \cdot F_1(s)$

c. $T \epsilon^{-sT} \dfrac{\sinh^2 (sT/2)}{(sT/2)^2}$

6-15 **a.** $\dfrac{2\pi}{s^2 + (2\pi)^2} \dfrac{[1 - \epsilon^{-s/2}]}{[1 - \epsilon^{-s/2}]}$

b. $\dfrac{2\pi}{s^2 + (2\pi)^2} \dfrac{[1 - \epsilon^{-1s/2}]}{[1 - \epsilon^{-1s/2}]}$

6-16

a. $T \dfrac{\sinh s T/2}{s T/2} \qquad -\infty < \operatorname{Re} s < \infty$

b. $\dfrac{a}{s} - 1/s^2 \qquad \operatorname{Re} s < 0$

c. $\dfrac{\alpha - s}{(\alpha - s)^2 + \omega_0^{\,2}} + \dfrac{(\alpha + s)}{(\alpha + s)^2 + \omega_0^{\,2}}$ $-\alpha < \mathrm{Re}\, s < \alpha$

d. $\sqrt{\pi/\alpha}\, \epsilon^{s^2/4\alpha}$ $-\infty < \mathrm{Re}\, s < \infty$

6-17

a. $\dfrac{1}{(s + \alpha)^2} - \dfrac{1}{(s - \alpha)^2}$

b. $-\alpha < \mathrm{Re}\, s < \alpha$

c. $\dfrac{1}{(\alpha - \beta + s)^2} - \dfrac{1}{(\alpha + \beta - s)^2}$ $-(\alpha - \beta) < \mathrm{Re}\, s < \alpha + \beta$

6-18

a. $2\pi j\, \delta(s)$ $\mathrm{Re}\, s = 0$

b. $j\pi\, [\delta(s - j\omega_0) + \delta(s + j\omega_0)]$ $\mathrm{Re}\, s = 0$

■ CHAPTER 7

7-1

a. $\left[\dfrac{4}{3}\, \epsilon^{-4t} - \dfrac{1}{3}\, \epsilon^{-t} \right] u(t)$

b. $\delta'(t) + 2\, [\epsilon^{-2t} - 2\epsilon^{-4t}]\, u(t)$

c. $\dfrac{1}{2}\, [1 + \epsilon^{-2t}]\, u(t)$

d. $u(t - 2)\, [\epsilon^{-(t-2)} - (t - 2)\epsilon^{-2(t-2)} - \epsilon^{-2(t-2)}]$

e. $\left[5\epsilon^{-2t} \cos 3t - \dfrac{22}{3}\, \epsilon^{-2t} \sin 3t \right] u(t)$

f. $\dfrac{1}{3} \left[\dfrac{3}{2}t - 9/4 + 9/4\, \epsilon^{-2t/3} \right] u(t) - \dfrac{1}{3} \left[\dfrac{3}{2}(t - 4) - \dfrac{9}{4} \right.$

$\left. + 9/4\, \epsilon^{-2(t-4)/3} \right] u(t - 4)$

7-2

a. $\delta(t) + 3\, [\epsilon^{-t} - \epsilon^{-2t}]\, u(t)$

b. $\delta(t - T) + \cos(t - T)\, u(t - T)$

c. $\dfrac{1}{3} \sin 3(t - 1)\, u(t - 1) + [1 + \cos 3t]\, u(t)$

d. $\left[-\dfrac{1}{2} \epsilon^{-t} + \dfrac{1}{2} \cos t + \dfrac{1}{2} \sin t \right] u(t)$

e. $\left[\dfrac{1}{2} \sin t - \dfrac{1}{2} t \cos t + \cos 2t \right] u(t)$

f. $\left[-t \epsilon^{-2t} + \epsilon^{-t} \cos 3t \right] u(t)$

7-3

c. $\mathcal{L}^{-1}\{F(s)\} = \displaystyle\sum_{k=1}^{n} \dfrac{P(\alpha_k)}{Q'(\alpha_k)} \epsilon^{-\alpha_k t} u(t)$

7-4

a. $x(t) = \cos 2t \, u(t)$

b. $y(0) = 2 \quad y'(0) = 3 - 2\epsilon^{-1}$

7-5

a. $2\left[\dfrac{t^3}{6} + 1 + \epsilon^{-t} \right] u(t)$

b. $x(t) = 2\left[\epsilon^{-2t} - \epsilon^{-3t} \right] u(t) \quad y(t) = \epsilon^{-3t} u(t)$

7-6 ϵ^{-t}

7-7 $t\, u(t) - (t-1)\, u(t-1) + (t-2)\, u(t-2) + \cdots$

7-8 $\left[1 - \epsilon^{-2t} \right] u(t)$

7-9

b. $I(s) = \dfrac{5}{s} + \dfrac{5/3}{s+0.2} - \dfrac{10/3}{s+5}$

c. $i(t) = \left[5 + \dfrac{5}{3} \epsilon^{-0.2t} - \dfrac{10}{3} \epsilon^{-5t} \right] u(t)$

7-10

a. $50 \left[1 - \epsilon^{-2t} \right] u(t)$
b. $25 \left[1 - \epsilon^{-2(t-200)} \right] u(t-200)$

7-11 $i_1(t) = \dfrac{1}{8} p_1(t) + \dfrac{1}{8} \epsilon^{-(1/2)t} u(t) - \dfrac{1}{8} \epsilon^{1/2(t-1)} u(t-1)$

7-12 $v_2(t) = [15\,\epsilon^{-t/3} - 5\epsilon^{-3t}]\,u(t)$

7-13

a. $\dfrac{1}{(s+1)(s+3)}$

b. $\dfrac{1}{s^2 + 3s + 1}$

c. $\dfrac{1}{s^2 + 4s + 3}$

d. $\dfrac{1}{s^2 + 3s + 1}$

7-14

a. $\dfrac{10}{s^2 + s + 10K}$

b. $K = 0$
Step: $10\,[t - 1 + \epsilon^{-t}]\,u(t)$

Ramp: $10\left[\dfrac{1}{2}t^2 - t + 1 - \epsilon^{-t}\right]u(t)$

$K = \dfrac{1}{8}$:

Step: $8\left[1 - \epsilon^{-(1/2)t}\cos t - \dfrac{1}{2}\epsilon^{-(1/2)t}\sin t\right]u(t)$

Ramp: $\left[8t - \dfrac{32}{5} + \dfrac{32}{5}\epsilon^{-1/2t}\cos t - \dfrac{24}{5}\epsilon^{-1/2t}\sin t\right]u(t)$

7-15

a. $K^n \displaystyle\sum_{k=0}^{n-1}\binom{n-1}{k}\dfrac{(-\alpha)^{n-k-1}}{(n-k-1)\,!}\,t^{n-k-1}\,\epsilon^{-\alpha t}\,u(t)$

b.   One-stage: $\epsilon^{-t}u(t)$
Two-stage: $(1 - t)\epsilon^{-t}\,u(t)$

c. $\left.\dfrac{dv_0{}^{(n)}}{dt}\right|_{t-0^+} = -n$

d.   No

7-16 $R_1 C_1 = R_2 C_2$ is a reasonable choice.

7-17
a. $t_R = 10^{-6} = 2.2 \, RC$
b. $3.1 \times 10^{-7} \quad 2.05 \times 10^{-7}$
Peaking is limited by overshoot.
c. 400 kHz; 1.3 MHz (with critical damping)

7-19
a. $1.245 \, \epsilon^{-t} u(t) - 2 \, \epsilon^{-(t-1/2)} u\left(t - \dfrac{1}{2}\right) + 0.755 \, \epsilon^{-(t-1)} u(t - 1)$ for one period.
b. $1.245 \, \epsilon^{-(t-3)} u(t - 3) - 2 \, \epsilon^{-(t-3.5)} u(t - 3.5)$
$+ 0.755^{-(t-4)} u(t - 4) - 0.245 \, \epsilon^{-t} \quad 3 \leq t \leq 4$

7-20
a. $[1 - \epsilon^{-\alpha t}] \sin(\omega_0 t + \phi) \, u(t) \quad \alpha = 3.14 \times 10^4 \quad \omega_0 = 2\pi \times 10^6$
b. $\omega_0 [1 - \epsilon^{-\alpha t}] \sin(\omega_0 t + \phi) u(t) \quad \phi = \tan^{-1} \dfrac{2\omega_0}{\alpha}$

7-21 $\quad u(t) [\sin \omega_0 t - 0.85 \, \epsilon^{-0.38 \times 10^5 t} \sin \omega_0 t$
$+ 0.171 \, \epsilon^{-0.262 t} \sin \omega_0 t] - u(t - 10^{-6}) [\sin \omega_0 (t - 10^{-6})$
$- 0.85 \, \epsilon^{-0.38 \times 10^5 (t - 10^{-6})} \times \sin \omega_0 (t - 10^{-6})$
$+ 0.171 \, \epsilon^{-0.262 \times 10^5 (t - 10^{-6})} \times \sin \omega_0 (t - 10^{-6})]$

7-22
a. $\dfrac{j\omega}{(j\omega + 8)^2}$

b. $3\pi \, \delta(\omega) + \dfrac{-\omega^2 + 9}{j\omega \, (-\omega^2 + 4j\omega + 3)}$

c. $\dfrac{j\omega + 3}{(j\omega + 4)(-\omega^2 + 9)} + \dfrac{\pi}{50} [\delta(\omega + 3) + \delta(\omega - 3)] + j\dfrac{7\pi}{50}$
$\cdot [\delta(\omega + 3) - \delta(\omega - 3)]$

d. $\dfrac{1}{j\omega \, (-\omega^2 + 9)} + \dfrac{1}{9} \pi\delta(\omega) - \dfrac{\pi}{18} [\delta(\omega - 3) + \delta(\omega + 3)]$

7-23
a. $5/2 \, \epsilon^{-2|t|}$
b. $-\epsilon^{2t} \cos 3t \, u(-t)$
c. $te^{-4t} u(t) + t \, \epsilon^{4t} u(-t)$

7-24 $A\left[(1 - \epsilon^{-t})\, u(t) - \dfrac{1}{5}\left[\epsilon^t - \cos 2t + 2\sin 2t\right] u(-t)\right]$

7-25 $\left[-\dfrac{2}{9}\,\epsilon^{-t} + \dfrac{6}{5}\,\epsilon^{-3t} - 8/9\,\epsilon^{-4t}\right] u(t) + \dfrac{12}{15}\,\epsilon^{2t}\, u(-t)$

7-26
a. $v_0(t) = 0.145\,\epsilon^{-188t}\sin 2\pi\,(186)t$
b. $v_0(t) = 0.555\,\epsilon^{-188t}\sin 2\pi\,(49)t$
c. As R_0 gets smaller the output is reduced, but the system is better damped.

■ C H A P T E R 8

8-3 $h(t) = 200\left[\epsilon^{-t} - \epsilon^{-2t}\right] u(t)$

8-5 a. $H(s) = H_3(s)\left[H_1(s) - H_2(s)\right]$
b. $H(s) = 1 - H_2(s) + H_1(s)H_2(s)$
c. $H(s) = 3\,H_1(s)\,H_2(s) - H_1(s) - H_2(s)$

8-6
a. $h^{-1}(t) = 10\left[\delta'(t) + 2\,\delta(t)\right]$
b. Causal

8-8 $H(s) = \dfrac{1}{s^2 + s + 1}$

$H(s) = \dfrac{1}{2}\dfrac{s + 1}{s^2 + 3s + 1}$

$H(s) = \dfrac{s}{s + 1}$

8-9 $y'''(t) + 6y''(t) + 11\,y'(t) + 6y(t) = x(t)$

8-11 $\dot{q}_1(t) = -2q_1(t) + 2q_2(t)$
$\dot{q}_2(t) = -q_2(t) + 3x(t)$
$\dot{q}_3(t) = -3q_3(t) + 4x(t)$

$y(t) = q_1(t) - \dfrac{1}{2}\,q_3(t)$

8-12
a. $\dot{q}_1(t) = -\dfrac{1}{1000}\,q_1(t) + \dfrac{1}{1000}\,x_1(t)$

$$\dot{q}_2(t) = -1000\, q_2(t) + x_2(t)$$
$$y_1(t) = q_1(t) - 1000\, q_2(t)$$

8-13

a. $\mathbf{q}(t) = \begin{bmatrix} q_1 \\ q_2 \end{bmatrix}$ $\mathbf{x}(t) = \begin{bmatrix} x_1 \\ x_2 \end{bmatrix}$ $\mathbf{y}(t) = [\, y_1(t)\,]$

$$\mathbf{A} = \begin{bmatrix} -\dfrac{1}{1000} & 0 \\ 0 & -1000 \end{bmatrix} \quad \mathbf{B} = \begin{bmatrix} \dfrac{1}{1000} & 0 \\ 0 & 1 \end{bmatrix}$$

$$\mathbf{C} = [\, 1 \quad -1000\,] \qquad \mathbf{D} = [\, 0 \quad 0\,]$$

$$\frac{d\mathbf{q}}{dt} = \mathbf{A}\, \mathbf{q}(t) + \mathbf{B}\, \mathbf{x}(t)$$

$$\mathbf{y}(t) = \mathbf{C}\, \mathbf{q}(t)$$

8-14 $\dot{q}_1 = -2q_1 + 2q_2$
$$\dot{q}_2 = -q_2 + x_1$$
$$y_1 = 10q_1$$

$$\mathbf{A} = \begin{bmatrix} -2 & 2 \\ 0 & -1 \end{bmatrix} \quad \mathbf{B} = \begin{bmatrix} 0 \\ 1 \end{bmatrix} \quad \mathbf{C} = [\, 10, \quad 0\,] \quad \mathbf{D} = [\, 0\,]$$

$$\frac{d\mathbf{q}}{dt} = \mathbf{A}\, \mathbf{q} + \mathbf{B}\, \mathbf{x}$$

$$\mathbf{y} = \mathbf{C}\, \mathbf{q}$$

8-15 $\mathbf{q} = \begin{bmatrix} \mathbf{q}_1 \\ \mathbf{q}_2 \end{bmatrix}$ $\mathbf{x} = \begin{bmatrix} \mathbf{x} \\ 0 \end{bmatrix}$

$$\mathbf{C} = [\, \mathbf{C}_2, 0\,] \quad \mathbf{z} = \mathbf{C}\, \mathbf{q}$$

$$\mathbf{A} = \begin{bmatrix} \mathbf{A}_1 & 0 \\ \mathbf{B}_2\mathbf{C}_1 & \mathbf{A}_2 \end{bmatrix} \quad \mathbf{B} = [\, \mathbf{B}_1, 0\,]$$

$$\frac{d\mathbf{y}}{dt} = \mathbf{A}\, \mathbf{q} + \mathbf{B}\, \mathbf{x}$$

8-16 $\mathbf{q}_1 = \mathbf{A}_1\mathbf{q}_1 + \mathbf{B}_1\mathbf{x}$
$$\mathbf{q}_2 = \mathbf{A}_2\mathbf{q}_2 + \mathbf{B}_2\mathbf{x}$$

$$\mathbf{q} = \begin{bmatrix} \mathbf{q}_1 \\ \mathbf{q}_2 \end{bmatrix} \quad \mathbf{A} = \begin{bmatrix} \mathbf{A}_1 & 0 \\ 0 & \mathbf{A}_2 \end{bmatrix} \quad \mathbf{B} = \begin{bmatrix} \mathbf{B}_1 \\ \mathbf{B}_2 \end{bmatrix}$$

$$\mathbf{C} = [\mathbf{C}_1, \mathbf{C}_2]$$
$$\dot{\mathbf{q}} = \mathbf{A}\mathbf{q} + \mathbf{B}\mathbf{x}$$
$$\mathbf{z} = \mathbf{C}\mathbf{q}$$

8-17 $\dot{q}_1 = -2q_1 + 2x_1 + 3x_2$
$\dot{q}_2 = -3q_2 - 2x_1 + 3x_2$
$y_1 = 4q_1$ $y_2 = 4q_1 - 2q_2$

$$\mathbf{A} = \begin{bmatrix} -2 & 0 \\ 0 & -3 \end{bmatrix} \quad \mathbf{B} = \begin{bmatrix} 2 & 3 \\ -2 & 3 \end{bmatrix} \quad \mathbf{C} = \begin{bmatrix} 4 & 0 \\ 4 & -2 \end{bmatrix}$$

8-19

a.
$$\mathbf{q}(t_0) = \begin{bmatrix} \dfrac{R_1}{R_1 + R_2 + R_3} V \\[2ex] -\dfrac{1}{R_1 + R_2 + R_3} V \\[2ex] \dfrac{R_1 + R_2}{R_1 + R_2 + R_3} V \end{bmatrix}$$

b. No

8-21

a.
$$\mathbf{A} = \begin{bmatrix} -\alpha & 1 \\ 0 & -\alpha \end{bmatrix}$$

b.
$$\begin{bmatrix} 10\,\epsilon^{-\alpha t} - 5t\,\epsilon^{-\alpha t} \\ -5\,\epsilon^{-\alpha t} \end{bmatrix} \quad t \geq t_0$$

8-22 $\begin{bmatrix} 10 - 5(t - t_0) + 2\epsilon^{\alpha} - 2(t - t_0)\,\epsilon^{\alpha} \\ -5 - 2\epsilon^{\alpha} \end{bmatrix} \epsilon^{-\alpha(t - t_0)} \quad t \geq t_0$

8-23
$$\begin{bmatrix} \dfrac{1}{\epsilon^t} & \cdot & \cdot & \cdot & 0 & \cdot & \cdot \\ & \cdot & & & & & \\ & & \cdot & & & & \\ & & & \dfrac{1}{\epsilon^t} & \cdot & & \\ & & & & \cdot & & \\ \cdot & \cdot & \cdot & 0 & \cdot & \cdot & \dfrac{1}{\epsilon^t} \end{bmatrix} \quad (n \times n)$$

8-24

b.

$$\begin{bmatrix} \epsilon^{-\alpha_1 t} & \cdot & \cdot & & \cdot & \cdot & \cdot & 0 \\ \cdot & & & & & & & \\ & \cdot & & & & & & \\ & & \epsilon^{-\alpha_2 t} & & & & & \\ & & & \cdot & & & & \\ & & & & \cdot & & & \\ & & & & & \cdot & & \\ \cdot & 0 & \cdot & & \cdot & \cdot & \cdot & \epsilon^{-\alpha_n t} \end{bmatrix} \quad (n \times n)$$

8-25 $\phi_{11}(t) = \epsilon^{-t}$

$\phi_{12}(t) = \epsilon^{-t} - \epsilon^{-2t}$

$\phi_{13}(t) = \dfrac{1}{2}\epsilon^{-t} - \epsilon^{-2t} + \dfrac{1}{2}\epsilon^{-3t}$

$\phi_{21}(t) = 0$

$\phi_{22}(t) = \epsilon^{-2t}$

$\phi_{23}(t) = \epsilon^{-2t} - \epsilon^{-3t}$

$\phi_{31}(t) = 0$

$\phi_{32}(t) = 0$

$\phi_{33}(t) = \epsilon^{-3t}$

8-26 $\begin{bmatrix} \epsilon^{-t/1000} & 0 \\ 0 & \epsilon^{-1000t} \end{bmatrix}$

8-27 $\begin{bmatrix} \epsilon^{-4(t-t_0)} & 6(\epsilon^{-3(t-t_0)} - \epsilon^{-4(t-t_0)}) \\ 0 & \epsilon^{-3(t-t_0)} \end{bmatrix}$

8-29

a. $\left[\dfrac{\epsilon^{-t/1000}}{1000} - 1000\,\epsilon^{-1000t} \right]$

b. $y(t) = 10^{-6}\,\epsilon^{-t/1000} - 5000\,\epsilon^{-1000t}$

8-30

a. $\begin{bmatrix} \epsilon^{-t} & 0 \\ \epsilon^{-t} - \epsilon^{-2t} & \epsilon^{-2t} \end{bmatrix}$

b. $y_1(t) = (1 - \epsilon^{-t})\,u(t)$

$y_2(t) = \dfrac{1}{2}\left[1 - 2\epsilon^{-t} + \epsilon^{-2t} \right] u(t) + \dfrac{1}{2}\left[1 - \epsilon^{-2(t-1/2)} \right] u\left(t - \dfrac{1}{2} \right)$

8-31 Same answer as 8-24.

8-32 Same answer as 8-25.

8-33 $\left[\dfrac{6}{s+3} - \dfrac{6}{s+4} \right]$

8-34

a.
$$\begin{bmatrix} \dfrac{1}{s+1} & 0 \\[3mm] \dfrac{1}{s+1} & -\dfrac{1}{s+2} & \dfrac{1}{s+2} \end{bmatrix}$$

b.   Answer same as 8-30 b.

8-35   Many possibilities.

8-37

a. $\mathbf{A}(t) = [\,-a(t)\,]$

b. $C(t) \left[\exp \left(-\displaystyle\int_{t_0}^{t} a(\lambda)\, d\lambda \right) \right] b(t_0)$

8-38 $\begin{bmatrix} \left(\dfrac{t}{t_0}\right) \epsilon^{(t-t_0)} & 0 \\[4mm] 0 & \left(\dfrac{t}{t_0}\right)^2 \end{bmatrix}$

■ CHAPTER 9

9-1
a.   1/6

b.   1/2
c.   2/3

9-2
a.   1/36

b.   1/6
c.   1/2

9-3
a.   3/10
b.   7/50

c.   0
d.   3/10

9-4
a.   0.025

b.   0.0744

9-5
a. 5/16

b. 5/32
c. 1/32

9-6
b. 1/8

c. No
d. (O, E); discrete

9-7
a. 9/10

b. 1/2
c. 2/10

9-8
a. $A = b$

b. 0.632
c. $(1 - \epsilon^{-x}) u(x)$

9-9
a. 10

b. 200
c. 100

9-10   a. $\dfrac{1}{\sqrt{2\pi}} \, \epsilon^{-\frac{1}{2}(x-2)^2}$

b. $p(0) = 0.0540 \quad p(2) = 0.3989$
c. 0.9773
d. 0.6826

9-11
b. $k = 1$,
Note: $p_y(y) = 1 - |y|$

c. 1/2
d. $2x = p_x(x)$

9-12
a. No

b. 0

9-13
a. Continuous; nondeterministic; stationary; ergodic
b. Continuous; nondeterministic; nonstationary; nonergodic
c. Discrete; nondeterministic; stationary; nonergodic
d. Discrete; nondeterministic; nonstationary; nonergodic
e. Continuous; deterministic; nonstationary; nonergodic
f. Continuous; deterministic; stationary; nonergodic

9-14
a. Discrete; deterministic; stationary; ergodic

b. $p_x(x) = \dfrac{7}{8} \delta(x) + \dfrac{1}{8} \delta(x - A)$

c. $\frac{1}{8} A$

d. $\overline{X^2} = \frac{1}{8} A^2$ $\sigma_x^2 = \frac{7}{64} A^2$

e. $<X> = \frac{A}{8}$ $<X^2> = \frac{A^2}{8}$

9-15

a. X_{av} is a random variable

b. $\overline{X}_{av} = \frac{1}{T} \int_0^T \bar{x} \, dt = \bar{x}$

c. $\overline{X}_{av} = \overline{X}$

■ C H A P T E R 10

10-1

a.
$$R_x(\tau) = \begin{cases} \dfrac{X_0^2}{t_a} [b - |\tau|] & |\tau| \le b \\ \\ 0 & |\tau| > b \end{cases}$$

b. $\mathscr{R}_x(\tau) = R_x(\tau)$
c. Yes

d. $\overline{X^2} = \dfrac{b X_0^2}{t_a}$

10-2

b. $\overline{X^2} = 100$
c. They are uncorrelated
d. Negatively correlated (i.e., likely to have different signs)
e. $\overline{X} = 0$

10-3
a. 125

b. 10
c. 25

10-4
a. 0
b. Those with period 1 second
c. 1/4

10-5

a. $\hat{\rho}_{xy} = \dfrac{R_{xy}(\tau)}{\sigma_y^{\,2}}$

b. $|\rho_{xy}| \leq \dfrac{\sigma_x}{\sigma_y}$

10-6

a. $R_{xy}(\tau) = -1/2\ AB\ \sin \omega_0 t$
   $R_{yx}(\tau) = 1/2\ AB\ \sin \omega_0 t$

b. $x(t)$ and $y(t)$ are orthogonal waveforms

10-9

a. $R_z(\tau) = R_x(\tau) + R_y(\tau) - R_{yx}(\tau) - R_{xy}(\tau)$

b. $R_w(\tau) = R_x(\tau) + R_y(\tau) + R_{xy}(\tau) + R_{yx}(\tau)$

c. $R_{zw}(\tau) = R_x(\tau) - R_y(\tau)$

d. $R_{wz}(\tau) = R_x(\tau) - R_y(\tau)$

10-10

a.
$$R_y(\tau) = \begin{cases} \dfrac{X_0^2}{2}\left[\dfrac{b - |\tau|}{t_a}\right) & |\tau| < b \\[3mm] \dfrac{X_0^2}{4}\left[\dfrac{b - |\tau - Nt_a|}{t_a}\right] & |\tau - Nt_a| < b \quad N = \pm 1, \pm 2, \ldots \end{cases}$$

b. $R_{yx}(\tau) = R_{xy}(\tau) = \dfrac{X_0^2}{2} \cdot \dfrac{b - |\tau|}{t_a} \quad |\tau| < b$

$\phantom{R_{yx}(\tau)} = 0 \qquad\qquad |\tau| > b$

10-13

$R_{x_1}(\tau) = R_x(\tau) + R_y(\tau)$
$R_{x_1 x_2}(\tau) = R_x(\tau) - R_y(\tau)$
$R_{x_1 x_3}(\tau) = 2R_x(\tau)$
$R_{x_2 x_1}(\tau) = R_x(\tau) - R_y(\tau)$
$R_{x_2}(\tau) = R_x(\tau) + R_y(\tau)$
$R_{x_2 x_3}(\tau) = 2R_x(\tau)$
$R_{x_3 x_1}(\tau) = 2R_x(\tau)$
$R_{x_3 x_2}(\tau) = 2R_x(\tau)$
$R_{x_3}(\tau) = 4R_x(\tau)$

10-14

a.
$$\Lambda_z = 10 \begin{bmatrix} 1 & \epsilon^{-0.5} & \epsilon^{-1.0} \\ \epsilon^{-0.5} & 1 & \epsilon^{-0.5} \\ \epsilon^{-1.0} & \epsilon^{-0.5} & 1 \end{bmatrix}$$

b. $(\Lambda_z)_{ij} = 10\ \epsilon^{-0.5|i-j|}$

■ CHAPTER 11

11-1

a. $G(f) = \lim\limits_{T \to \infty} \dfrac{E\left[|X_T(j2\pi f)|^2\right]}{T}$

b. $G(f) = 2\,S_x\,(\omega = 2\pi f)\ \ f \geq 0$

c. $G_x(f) = \dfrac{20\,(2\pi f)^2}{(2\pi f)^4 + 2(2\pi f)^2 + 4}\ \ f \geq 0$

$\qquad = \qquad\qquad 0 \qquad\qquad f < 0$

d. $G_x(f) = 2\left\{X_0^{\,2}\,\delta(f) + \dfrac{1}{4}X_1^{\,2}\,[\delta(f - f_1) + \delta(f + f_1)]\right\}$

11-2
a. Not valid; can be negative
b. Valid
c. Not valid; not even
d. Not valid; not real
e. Valid
f. Valid

11-3 $S_x(\omega) = |F(j\omega)|^2\left[\dfrac{8 - 2\pi}{t_1} + \dfrac{(2\pi)^2}{t_1}\sum\limits_{n=-\infty}^{\infty}\delta\left(\omega - \dfrac{2\pi n}{t_1}\right)\right]$

$\qquad = \left(\dfrac{t_1}{8}\right)^2\left[\dfrac{\sin \omega t_1/16}{\omega t_1/16}\right]^2\left[\dfrac{8 - 2\pi}{t_1} + \dfrac{(2\pi)^2}{t_1}\sum\limits_{n=-\infty}^{\infty}\delta\left(\omega - \dfrac{2\pi n}{t_1}\right)\right]$

11-4

b. $\dfrac{-s^2 + 10}{s^4 - 6s^2 + 4}$

e. $\left[\dfrac{\sinh s}{s}\right]^2$

f. $\dfrac{-1}{s^2 + 4}$

11-5 $\overline{x^2} = 1/6$

11-6 $\dfrac{1}{3}\,\epsilon^{-(1/2)|\tau|}\cos\dfrac{\sqrt{3}}{2}\,\tau - \dfrac{1}{6}\,\epsilon^{-|\tau|}$

11-7

a. $S_x(\omega) = At_1 \left[\dfrac{\sin \omega t_1/2}{\omega t_1/2} \right]^2$

b. $\overline{x^2} = \dfrac{1}{2\pi} \displaystyle\int_{-\infty}^{\infty} S_x(\omega)\, d\omega = A$

11-8 $R_x(\tau) = \dfrac{S_0}{\pi\tau} \left[\sin (\omega_0 + \pi W)\tau - \sin (\omega_0 - \pi W)\tau \right]$

11-9 $S_x(\omega) = \sigma_x^2\, T \left[\dfrac{\sin \omega T/2}{\omega T/2} \right]^2$

11-11 $R_x(\tau) = 2\, S_0 W\, \dfrac{\sin 2\pi W\tau}{2\pi W\tau}$

$R_x\left(\dfrac{k}{2W} \right) = \begin{cases} 2W\, S_0 & k = 0 \\ 0 & k \neq 0 \end{cases}$

$\Lambda_x = 2\, W\, S_0\, \mathbf{I}_n$; $\mathbf{I}_n$ is an identity matrix of order n.

■ C H A P T E R   1 2

12-1 $\dfrac{1}{5} \left[6\, \epsilon^{-3t} - \epsilon^{-(1/2)t} \right] u(t)$

12-2
a. $u(t) - u(t - T)$ **b.** Stable

12-3
b. Realizable   **c.** Unstable

12-4

a. $\dfrac{10}{7}$ **b.** 0

12-5 $\overline{y^2} = \dfrac{A}{\omega_0^2} \sin^2 \omega_0 T$

12-6 $R_y(\tau) = S_0\, \delta(\tau) - \dfrac{S_0}{2}\, b\epsilon^{-b|\tau|}$

12-7 $R_y(\tau) = \dfrac{\beta^2 S_0}{2(b^2 - \beta^2)} \left[b\epsilon^{-b|\tau|} - \beta\epsilon^{-\beta|\tau|} \right]$

12-8 $R_y(\tau) = \dfrac{A}{2} \dfrac{b^2}{b^2 + \omega_0^2} \epsilon^{-2b|\tau|} \cos \omega_0 \tau$

12-9 $R_{xy}(\tau) = S_0 \left[\delta(\tau) - b\epsilon^{-b\tau} u(\tau) \right]$
$R_{yx}(\tau) = S_0 \left[\delta(\tau) - b\epsilon^{b\tau} u(-\tau) \right]$

12-10

$R_{xy}(\tau) = \begin{cases} \dfrac{\beta S_0}{2} \left[\dfrac{(\beta + 2b)\,\epsilon^{-\beta\tau} - 2b\beta\epsilon^{-b\tau}}{\beta^2 - b^2} \right] & \tau > 0 \\[4mm] \dfrac{\beta S_0}{2} \left[\dfrac{\beta}{b + \beta} \right] \epsilon^{\beta\tau} & \tau < 0 \end{cases}$

$R_{yx}(\tau) = \begin{cases} \dfrac{\beta S_0}{2} \left[\dfrac{\beta}{b + \beta} \right] \epsilon^{-\beta\tau} & \tau > 0 \\[4mm] \dfrac{\beta S_0}{2} \left[\dfrac{(\beta + 2b)\,\epsilon^{+\beta\tau} - 2b\,\beta\,\epsilon^{b\tau}}{\beta^2 - b^2} \right] & \tau < 0 \end{cases}$

12-11 If y_2 is the output due to noise, $\overline{y_2^2} = \dfrac{b}{1 + b}$ where

$h(t) = b\epsilon^{-bt} u(t)$. Then $b \approx 10^{-6}$ for (y_2) rms $= 0.01 X_0$

12-13 $|H(j\omega)|^2 = \dfrac{4\omega^2}{4\omega^4 + 37\omega^2 + 9}$

12-14 $|H(j\omega)|^2 = T^2 \left[\dfrac{\sin \omega T/2}{\omega T/2} \right]^2$

12-16 $\overline{y^2} = 10/7$

12-17 $S_y(\omega) = S_0 \dfrac{\omega^2}{\omega^2 + b^2}$

12-18 $S_y(\omega) = \dfrac{\beta^2 S_0 \omega^2}{(\omega^2 + b^2)(\omega^2 + \beta^2)}$

12-19 $\overline{y^2} = 5 \times 10^{-4}$ v²

12-20 $R_y(\tau) = 2 N_0 W \dfrac{\sin \pi W \tau}{\pi W \tau} \cdot \cos \omega_0 \tau$

12-21

a. KT/C

b. The result does not depend on R, because as R changes, the dependence of the noise spectral density on R is cancelled by the dependence of the circuit bandwidth on R.

12-22

a. $F = F_1 + \dfrac{F_2 - 1}{G_1}$

b. *rms* output noise = 1.60 V

c. Output SNR = -67.14 dB

12-23

a. $W_{eq} = \dfrac{1}{4RC}$

b. $W_{eq} = \dfrac{1}{2RC}$

12-24 $\quad H(s) = \sqrt{s_0/10}\,(s + 1)\,(s + 2)$

12-25

a. For $\tau > 0$:

$$\mathbf{R}_y(\tau) = \begin{bmatrix} \epsilon^{-\tau} & \epsilon^{-\tau} - \dfrac{2}{3}\epsilon^{-2\tau} \\[3mm] \dfrac{1}{3}\epsilon^{-\tau} & \dfrac{1}{3}\epsilon^{-\tau} + \dfrac{1}{2}\epsilon^{-2\tau} \end{bmatrix}$$

b. for $\tau < 0$:

$$\mathbf{R}_y(\tau) = \begin{bmatrix} \epsilon^{\tau} & \dfrac{1}{3}\,\epsilon^{\tau} \\[3mm] \epsilon^{\tau} - \dfrac{2}{3}\,\epsilon^{2\tau} & \dfrac{1}{3}\,\epsilon^{\tau} + \dfrac{1}{12}\,\epsilon^{2\tau} \end{bmatrix}$$

12-26

$$\mathbf{S}_x(\omega) = \begin{bmatrix} \dfrac{2}{1 + \omega^2} & \dfrac{2}{1 + \omega^2} - \dfrac{2}{(2 + \omega^2) + j\omega} \\[4mm] \dfrac{2}{1 + \omega^2} - \dfrac{2}{(2 + \omega^2) - j\omega} & \dfrac{1}{4 + \omega^2} \end{bmatrix}$$

Index

Index